621·892

Solid Lubricants
and
Self-Lubricating
Solids

Solid Lubricants and Self-Lubricating Solids

FRANCIS J. CLAUSS

Lockheed Missiles and Space Company
Sunnyvale, California

ACADEMIC PRESS   **1972**   New York and London

ACADEMIC PRESS, INC.
111 Fifth Avenue, New York, New York 10003

United Kingdom Edition published by
ACADEMIC PRESS, INC. (LONDON) LTD.
24/28 Oval Road, London NW1

LIBRARY OF CONGRESS CATALOG CARD NUMBER: 70-137615

PRINTED IN THE UNITED STATES OF AMERICA

DEDICATION

To my friends and colleagues in the aerospace and lubrication industries with whom I have had the pleasure and good fortune to participate in some very exciting applications of lubricants

Contents

Preface   xi

1. **FRICTION AND LUBRICATION**

   A. Friction . . . . A.   1
   B. Mechanisms of Friction . . . . B.   2
   C. Lubrication . . . . C. 12
   References 13

2. **LOW-FRICTION INORGANIC SOLIDS**

   A. Advantages and Disadvantages 15
   B. Useful Forms 18
   C. Crystal Structure 18
   D. Effects of Temperature and Atmosphere 23
   E. Bonded Films 24
   F. Testing 30
   References 41

3. **GRAPHITE**

   A. Occurrence and Production 42
   B. Crystal Structure 43
   C. Lubricity and Lubrication Mechanism 45
   D. Graphite Dispersions 50
   E. Bonded Films 54
   F. Carbon-Graphite Bodies 56
   G. Impregnated Carbon-Graphite 64

H.   Metal-Graphite Composites 65

I.   Carbon Brushes for Electrical Applications 67

References 73

4.   MOLYBDENUM DISULFIDE

A.   Occurrence and Properties 75

B.   Crystal Structure 75

C.   Lubrication Properties 80

D.   Dry Powders and Dispersions 90

E.   Bonded Films 97

F.   Films from Chemical Formation *in Situ* 105

G.   Solids Impregnated with MoS_2 107

H.   Oils and Greases with MoS_2 as an Additive 108

References 112

5.   MISCELLANEOUS INORGANIC COMPOUNDS

A.   Dichalcogenides 113

B.   Lead Compounds 120

C.   Fluorides 125

D.   Boron Nitride 128

References 129

6.   SOFT METALS

A.   General Characteristics 130

B.   Thin Films of Soft Metals 131

References 137

7.   PLASTICS: GENERAL

A.   Advantages 139

B.   Disadvantages 141

C.   General Comparison 142

D.   Bearing Design 146

8.   NYLON

A.   Unmodified Nylon 164

B.   Filled Molded Nylon 179

C.   Sintered Nylon 189

Reference 194

9. **FLUOROCARBONS**

A.   Properties and Characteristics of Fluorocarbons 195
B.   Filled or Reinforced Fluorocarbons 206
C.   Sheet, Tape, and Laminates 213
D.   Fluorocarbon Coatings 214
E.   Woven Products 222
F.   Powders 224
G.   Porous Compacts Impregnated with Fluorocarbons 227
H.   Greases 229
I.   Applications 229
References 237

10. **MISCELLANEOUS THERMOPLASTICS**

A.   Polyimides 239
B.   Acetals 244
C.   Polycarbonates 245
D.   Ultrahigh Molecular Weight Polyethylene 245

11. **PHENOLICS** 246
Reference 251

Index 253

Preface

Although relatively unknown or ignored in the past, solid lubricants have recently attained major importance. Their increasing use is due to the advanced requirements of modern technology, which imposes demands beyond the practical limits of oils and greases; to improved economics, which make solid lubricants less expensive than oils and greases for many applications; and to improvements in the materials and processes used in solid lubrication.

As an example of the increasing use of solid lubricants to meet critical operating conditions, McConnell* has noted that there are over 1000 applications of solid-film lubricants in the RS-70 aircraft, whereas such applications are almost nonexistent in even so recent an advanced aircraft as the X-15. Further, in the cost-conscious automotive industry, solid lubricants are replacing oils and greases in many applications and helping to make guaranteed service warranties possible. Since 1963 both the American Society for Testing and Materials and the American Society for Lubricating Engineers have formed special committees on solid lubricants in order to disseminate information and encourage their wider use. Yet, as one observer has quipped, "In the use of solid lubricants, we have only scratched the surface."

For purposes of discussion, solid lubricants have been divided into two main groups—inorganic and organic. The first group includes graphite, molybdenum disulfide, oxides, fluorides, soft metals, and others. The second group includes Teflon, Nylon, and other plastics which, while some may object to their classification as solid lubricants, at least are

---

* B. D. McConnell, Air Force Materials Laboratory solid film lubrication research. *Proc. USAF–SWRI Aerospace Bearing Conf., September 1964* (P. M. Ku, ed.), pp. 47–55.

used as self-lubricating solids. Most of the materials discussed are not new, but in each group new materials have been added to the old ones, and operating conditions have been extended.

An introductory chapter precedes the chapters on specific materials in order to acquaint the reader with some basic facts about friction and lubrication.

This book gives a reasonably concise treatment of solid lubricants and their applications. Much information from recent research has been reviewed and interpreted for the benefit of designers and operating engineers, who do not usually have the time to search out, assimilate, and evaluate such information themselves. Although it does not provide an exhaustive review of the technical literature, the book does discuss those properties and behavior that are important to most applications and that can assist in selecting the proper lubricant for a specific job. The text has been held to a minimum, and numerous figures and tables have been used to present data concisely. Useful design procedures have been summarized, and typical applications are illustrated by photographs.

It is a pleasure to acknowledge my indebtedness to my many friends and associates in the solid-lubricant field who have contributed technical data and photographs of applications.

Acknowledgment should be made of two important books which have contributed to the development of the field and have been most valuable professional reference works. One is a monograph by Dr. E. R. Braithwaite entitled, "Solid Lubricants and Surfaces" (Pergamon, Oxford, 1964) and the other edited by Dr. Braithwaite, "Lubrication and Lubricants" (Elsevier, Amsterdam, 1967).* Both books continue to be timely and most useful.

* "Lubrificazione e Lubrificanti Tribologia." Tecniche Nuove, Milan, 1969.

Solid Lubricants and Self-Lubricating Solids

Chapter 1

Friction
and
Lubrication

Friction is the resistance to sliding one solid over another, and lubrication is a means of reducing friction, usually by interposing a fluid between the sliding surfaces. Although these concepts are commonly recognized, the basic mechanisms of friction and lubrication are not widely understood. This chapter summarizes some fundamental facts about these two phenomena and serves as an introduction to lubrication by solids [1a, b].

A. FRICTION

The gross mechanical features of friction are summarized in four classical laws, which have been only slightly modified by research during the past 30 years. These four laws are

1. *Frictional resistance is proportional to the normal load across the sliding surfaces.* This relationship is expressed mathematically as

$$F = \mu N \tag{1}$$

where F is the frictional force or the force resisting sliding, N is the load acting normal to the surfaces, and μ is a proportionality constant known as the coefficient of friction. If the frictional force F is that necessary to initiate sliding, μ_s is the *static* coefficient of friction; if F is the force to maintain sliding at a constant velocity, μ_k is the *kinetic* coefficient of friction.

2. *Frictional resistance is independent of the apparent (or projected)*

area of contact. It is, however, proportional to the actual or true area of contact, as discussed below.

3. *Frictional resistance is independent of the velocity of sliding, at least as a first approximation.* Actually, the frictional resistance does vary slightly with velocity, but it is nearly constant over a wide range of velocities, so long as frictional heating is not significant.

4. *The coefficient of friction depends on the materials in contact.* Solids that are effective lubricants can provide values as low as 0.02 for the coefficient of friction, whereas some metal combinations have values over 1.0.

B. MECHANISMS OF FRICTION

Even the smoothest practical surfaces are rough on a microscopic scale. Early workers thought that friction was due to interlocking between the surface irregularities, and that the frictional work was the energy dissipated in raising one set of surface roughnesses over the other. They believed that the function of a lubricating film was to fill in the "valleys" and form smooth surfaces, so that there would be no irregularities that could interlock.

Modern theories interpret friction as due to two concurrent actions, namely shearing welded junctions that are formed between points of metal-to-metal contact and ploughing out surfaces of the softer material by the harder material's riding over it. For hard metals in contact with one another, the ploughing term is relatively small, and friction is largely due to shearing the welded junctions.

Three important points in the adhesion theory of friction and wear (or the welded junction theory) are: (1) The area of true contact is only a small fraction of the apparent contact area. (2) High localized temperatures are generated at the points of contact by frictional heating. (3) The two surfaces interact with each other.

Area of True Contact

When clean metal surfaces are placed together, they touch only where their asperities or high spots meet, and their real area of contact is much smaller than the apparent area. The greater the force pressing the surfaces together, the more the asperities are crushed down and suffer plastic deformation. This action increases both the number and size of the contact points that support the load, so that the true area of contact increases. The true contact area can be calculated from the yield strength of the material and the pressure acting normal to the surfaces. For example, if two flat surfaces of hard steel with a yield strength of 150,000 psi are pressed together under a pressure of 15 psi, they would have a true contact area of only 0.01% (i.e., 15/150,000) of the apparent contact area. It would require a pressure of 15,000 psi to raise the true contact area to 10% of the apparent contact area.

Surface Temperature of Rubbing Solids

When solids slide over one another, high surface temperatures are generated even under moderate conditions of load and speed. The high temperatures are confined to very thin surface layers at the contacting points, and they are of very brief duration. For example, for a constantan cylinder sliding on a steel surface under a load of 4.1 lb and a sliding speed of 120 in./sec, temperature flashes of 1000° C (1832° F) were measured that lasted for less than 10^{-4} sec [1].

Surface temperatures produced by frictional heating increase with the sliding speed and the load. The poorer the thermal conductivity of the materials, the higher are the temperatures that are generated. Even under the most severe conditions, however, surface temperatures cannot generally exceed the melting point of the bodies.

Local heating has an important effect on a number of surface phenomena, including the abrasion and seizure of metals, the deterioration of lubricating films, volatilization and decomposition of oils and other surface films, "frictional welding," and the initiation of chemical reactions and chemical decomposition under friction and impact.

Interaction of Surfaces

Sliding is not a smooth, continuous process. It usually proceeds in a series of starts and stops. Friction rises to a maximum during the "stick" and falls rapidly during the "slip," and there are corresponding changes in the area of contact and the surface temperature. Under the intense pressure acting at the summits of the surface irregularities, localized adhesion or welding takes place between the metal surfaces. These junctions must be sheared if the surfaces are to slide past one another, and the force required to shear the junctions is proportional to the product of the shear strength of the junctions and the area of real contact.

The formation of welded junctions is strongly affected by physically or chemically adsorbed gas films, such as oxides, that are present on even the cleanest metal surfaces in the normal air atmosphere. These films prevent bare metal-to-metal contact and interfere with the formation of strong welded junctions, so that the coefficient of friction is less than when bare metal-to-metal contact is obtained. This fact has been demonstrated by a series of laboratory experiments, beginning with the classic studies of Bowden and Tabor at Cambridge about 30 years ago and continuing to the present time.

Figure 1 shows the equipment used in the first of these studies [2].

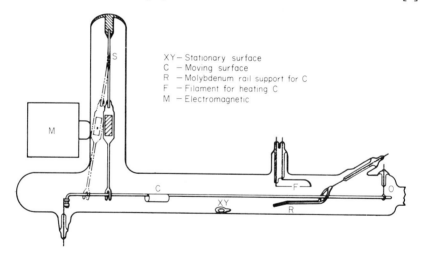

Figure 1. Apparatus for measuring friction between outgassed metal surfaces.

The method consisted essentially of propelling a metal cylinder C along a wire XY and photographically estimating its deceleration. From the resulting data, the frictional force between the two surfaces could be calculated.

The cylinder was propelled by the spring S, which was released by the electromagnet M. The lower surface XY was degassed by passing a heating current through it, and the cylinder C was degassed by lifting it off the lower surface with the molybdenum rail support R and heating it by electron bombardment from the filament F. The entire apparatus, except for the electromagnet, was encased in a silica envelope 0 which was connected to a vacuum system.

Both metals were kept at a temperature just below that at which excessive evaporation might occur during the final stages of degassing. During the friction measurements, the pressure in the envelope was maintained below 10^{-6} Torr, and, except when otherwise stated, the friction was measured immediately after the degassed surfaces had cooled to room temperature.

Figure 2 presents the main results for nickel on tungsten and copper on copper. Parts (a) and (c) show that the coefficient of friction was initially about 0.5 for the two combinations in air. After degassing in vacuum and cooling to room temperature, the coefficients increased by a factor of about 10. When the clean surfaces were allowed to stand at room temperature in a vacuum of 10^{-5}–10^{-6} Torr, the coefficients of friction

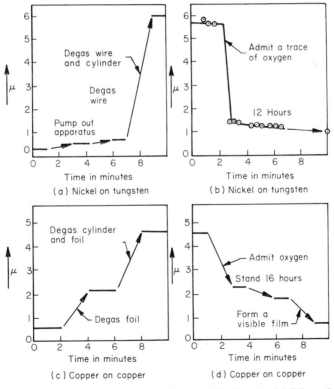

Figure 2. Effects of surface films on coefficient of friction. (a), (c) Effect of removing adsorbed film of oxygen and other contaminants from metal surfaces. (b), (d) Effect of adding a trace of oxygen to clean outgassed metals.

steadily decreased, presumably because of gradual recontamination of the surfaces by residual gases in the apparatus. Parts (b) and (d) show that when a trace of oxygen was deliberately admitted, there was a sudden large reduction in friction, followed by a slower reduction that continued with time. On the other hand, admitting pure hydrogen or nitrogen had little effect on the friction of the clean surfaces.

In later experiments with somewhat different equipment [3], the coefficients of friction of metal surfaces degassed in a vacuum readily reached values of 9 and, in some cases, large-scale seizure occurred on contact. The friction was too high to be measured, and the surfaces could be separated only by prying them apart. Admitting air or a trace of oxygen reduced the friction, but hydrogen had no measurable effect.

Although degassing in vacuum was used in these experiments in order to produce clean surfaces, one should not be misled into believing that metals cannot cold weld together in the normal environment. Cold welding is experienced whenever contact pressures are high enough to break through oxide or oil films on metal surfaces or when continued sliding causes the films to be scrubbed off. Such conditions are common in conventional applications. The laboratory experiments in high vacuum are simply an expedient means for preparing and maintaining clean surfaces while measurements can be made on them.

Later research has attempted to develop a satisfactory theory of the mechanism by which adhesion occurs between metals. These studies make it clear that the mechanism is a complex one that involves the physical metallurgy of the bodies and the physics and chemistry of their surfaces. This is illustrated by the items listed in Table 1, which includes (1) some of the elements of metal and surface behavior that have been found important in cold welding, and (2) some of the external environments, or service conditions, that affect cold welding through their influence on the behavior of the metals and their surfaces.

Many of the items listed in Table 1 are, of course, interrelated and are not mutually exclusive. Some of them are repetitions, in which the same factor may be considered with a slight change in view or emphasis. Although a complete discussion of these items, and the theories of adhesion and cold welding that have been developed around them, would be too lengthy to present here, a few remarks are presented in the following paragraphs to illustrate their significance.

The items 1–3 in the list have been reduced to the general "rule of thumb" to avoid contact between like metals, which has often been used by design engineers as a guide for selecting materials for parts that slide

TABLE 1.   Factors Involved in Friction and Adhesion of Solids

---

Metal and surface behavior

---

1. Specific metals and metal combinations
2. Metallurgical relations and alloying tendencies of the mating metals
3. Crystal structure and crystallographic orientation at the surfaces
4. Annealing behavior (i.e., recovery, recrystallization, and grain growth of the strained metals)
5. Sintering behavior
6. Strain-hardening characteristics
7. Microstructural stability
8. Diffusion rates and the effects of stress and temperature on them
9. Melting and recrystallization temperatures
10. Vapor pressures of the metals
11. Modulus of elasticity
12. Thermal conductivity
13. Hardness and yield strength of the metals
14. Reactivity of surfaces and wear debris with the surrounding atmosphere to form oxides, nitrides, etc.
15. Surface cleanliness
16. Stability of surface oxides, nitrides, etc.
17. Cohesive strength and ductility of surface oxides, nitrides, etc.
18. Spalling of surface layers under cyclic stressing
19. Adhesion of monolayers and thicker surface films to the metal substrate
20. Dissociation pressure of surface oxides, nitrides, etc.
21. Abrasiveness of wear debris
22. Surface roughness
23. Surface energy and surface tension

External environment or service conditions

---

24. Atmospheric pressure (or vacuum)
25. Atmospheric composition
26. Ambient temperature
27. Type of motion (e.g., rolling, reciprocating, and twisting)
28. Relative velocity of motion
29. Contact load or pressure
30. Hertzian stresses
31. Time duration
32. Passage of electrical current across the interface

---

over one another. This dictum has a sound theoretical basis, and it might otherwise be stated in metallurgical terms as: *Avoid combinations of metals that tend to alloy or dissolve into one another, since these combinations tend to have high friction and wear.* The importance of the metallurgical relations is illustrated by the following results, which indicate combinations of metals that either did or did not adhere to one another when they were brought together in ultrahigh vacuum after carefully cleaning their surfaces (Keller [4]; see also Roach *et al.* [5] and Coffin [6] for similar results and discussion):

Adhesion occurred	No adhesion occurred
Fe–Al	Cu–Mo
Cu–Ag	Ag–Mo
Ni–Cu	Ag–Fe
Ni–Mo	Ag–Ni

All of the metal combinations for which adhesion occurred form solid solutions and/or intermediate alloy phases, whereas those for which no adhesion occurred have extremely limited solid solubility in one another.

Metallurgical principles are well enough advanced to predict alloying behavior of metals from their basic atomic and crystallographic properties. For example, two metals tend to form solid solutions alloys when the following conditions are satisfied: (1) the atoms of both metals are approximately the same size (extensive solubility is favored when the atomic diameters of both metals are within 15% of each other); (2) both metals have the same crystal structure (e.g., both are face-centered cubic, as with copper and silver); and (3) both metals have similar chemical reactivities (i.e., they are on the same side of the periodic table), so that they have a minimal tendency to interact and form intermediate phases. Such items as 1–3 in Table 1, then, provide one set of considerations for anticipating friction and wear.

While items 1–3 emphasize material relations that are favorable or unfavorable for cold welding, items 4–10 place the emphasis more on the atomic rearrangements that occur when metal surfaces are placed into intimate contact and that result in forming welded junctions. From a metallurgical point of view, the fact that the contacting metal asperities are in a stress–strain condition (as a result of the load) and at an elevated temperature (as a result of frictional heating), places this behavior in the general area of high-temperature metallurgy. An important part of the high-temperature behavior of metals is the annealing that occurs when a strained metal is heated, which in turn can be divided into the more or less distinct stages of recovery, recrystallization, and grain growth. The relation between this behavior and cold welding is pointed out in a recent theory of metal adhesion [7], which is based on the recrystallization and recovery of strain-hardened metals.

Closely allied to the recovery–recrystallization concept of metal adhesion is the concept of sintering of powder metallurgy compacts, by which compacted powders are welded together at temperatures well below their melting points. Asperities on metal surfaces can be analyzed by procedures similar to those that are used to analyze the sintering of powders. Table 2 compares the temperatures for adhesion between clean, "de-

TABLE 2. Relation of Melting Temperature and Minimum Sintering Temperature to the Temperature at Which the Adhesion between Two Clean, "Denuded" Metal Surfaces Begins To Increase Rapidly[a]

Metal	Temp. for onset of adhesion, T_1 (°K)	Minimum temp. for sintering, T_2 (°K)	Melting temp., T_m (°K)	T_1/T_m	T_2/T_m
Platinum	880	770	2046	0.43	0.38
Nickel	780	920	1728	0.45	0.53
Gold	520	520	1315	0.40	0.40
Silver	480	450	1233	0.40	0.36
Lead	~300	470	600	0.50	0.78
Indium	<300	—	429	<0.7	—

[a] F. P. Bowden and G. W. Rowe, The adhesion of clean metals. *Proc. Roy. Soc. Ser. A* **233**, 429–442 (1956).

nuded" metal surfaces with the minimum sintering temperatures and melting points of several metals [8]. The temperature for the onset of adhesion (T_1) was measured as the temperature at which adhesion first became appreciable when the solid metals were heated in vacuum, and the minimum sintering temperature (T_2) was measured as the temperature at which a solid rod first became difficult to move in a box of powdered metal when heated in an atmosphere of hydrogen [9]. The minimum temperatures for adhesion and sintering are seen to be similar, though the accuracy of measurement is not great in either case, and both are roughly one-half of the absolute melting points of the metals. Other experiments indicate that there is a one-to-one correspondence between coefficients of friction and coefficients of adhesion [10].

Both annealing and sintering are, in turn, largely influenced by other factors, such as items 6–10 in Table 1.

As pointed out earlier, localized temperatures generated by sliding surfaces can reach the melting point of the metal. Under such conditions, localized fusion welding might occur, and it would not be surprising to find that the coefficients of adhesion correlate with melting points. Such a correlation has, in fact, been obtained [4, 10], in which adhesion increases as melting point decreases. The correlation is particularly interesting in that the data points for different metals define three distinct curves rather than one, thereby indicating the importance of other factors. The coefficients of adhesion for most metals fall along a central curve that represents the normal behavior. Noble metals that do not form stable oxides (e.g., Au, Pd, and Pt) show greater adhesion than expected from their melting points, whereas metals that crystallize in a close-packed hexagonal structure (e.g., Be, Cd, Zn, and Mg) have lower adhesion than normal. Thus, the "normal" behavior defined by the central curve of this correlation is modified by the reactivity of the metal with the atmosphere and by the metal's crystal structure.

Since recrystallization and melting temperatures of metals also correlate with each other, the correlation between adhesion and melting temperature also implies a correlation between adhesion and recrystallization temperature. Both recrystallization and melting temperatures are, in turn, measures of the effect of temperature on atomic mobility, whereby the atoms of a metal can rearrange themselves into a condition of more nearly perfect crystallinity by processes that take place without melting (i.e., recovery and recrystallization) or with melting (i.e., fusion and resolidification).

High thermal conductivity (item 12) increases the rate of heat dissipation from the sliding interface into the bulk of the substrate, and it thereby decreases the interface temperature and reduces wear.

Items 13–23 deal with the ability of metal surfaces to come into intimate contact with one another, which is a necessary first condition if they are to cold weld together. The hardness and yield strength of the metals (item 13) are important in that, together with the applied load and the amount of sliding, they govern the true area of contact and the ability of the substrate to provide a nonyielding support for the surface films. The area of true contact between two metals is given by the equation

$$A = N/P \tag{2}$$

where A is the area of true contact, N is the contact force normal to the surface, and P is the yield or flow pressure of the softer metal. The frictional force F is then given by the relation

$$F = sA \tag{3}$$

where s is the average shear strength of the junctions. Combining Equations (2) and (3), one obtains

$$F = sN/P \tag{4}$$

or, defining the coefficient of friction μ in the usual way

$$\mu = F/N = s/P \tag{5}$$

Equation (5), of course, is a rearrangement of Equation (1), which is a statement of the first law of friction. It also provides a means for estimating the coefficient of friction from intrinsic material properties rather than from the external forces.

Surface oxide films are more brittle than metals, and they are likely to crack and expose bare metal if the metal is too soft and fails to provide uniform support under load. Thus, the hardness and yield strength also influence the true contact area through their effect on the integrity of the surface films.

Items 14–20 deal with the presence, nature, and stability of surface films on metals. In the sense that these surface films reduce the friction and cold welding that would otherwise occur with truly clean surfaces, as illustrated in the experiments described earlier, the surface films are lubricating films, and the entire art of lubrication can be said to be an attempt to improve upon the lubricating films that nature otherwise provides in the normal air atmosphere. The presence and nature of these films will depend upon the reactivity of the surfaces with the surrounding atmosphere to form oxides, nitrides, or other compounds that are held by chemical bonds or to form physically adsorbed gas films that are held by weaker van der Waals-type forces. The ability of the films to remain on the surfaces during sliding friction (item 16) depends on their mechanical strength and their ability to deform without cracking when the substrate below them is deformed (items 17 and 18), on the adhesion of the film to the substrate (items 18 and 19), and on their thermal stability (item 20).

Wear debris that is abrasive (item 21) can act as a grinding compound to accelerate wear and reexpose fresh metal. Smooth surfaces (item 22) do not heat up as rapidly as rough surfaces, and they can generally support heavier loads with less wear.

Research also indicates that friction is related to the work of adhesion and surface free energies of the contacting materials (item 23). High coefficients of friction occur for metals with high ratios of the work of adhesion to hardness [11].

The last group of items in Table 1 (24–32) are the external environments or service conditions under which the metal combinations must operate. These environments affect the degree of cold welding principally by their effects on the intimacy of contact between the mating metals and on the temperatures of the metal surfaces and asperities. Most of these effects are fairly obvious from the preceding discussion. The effect of atmospheric pressure (or vacuum) on the rate at which contaminating films form on freshly cleaned surfaces has already been discussed. The type of motion is important in its effect on the rupture and removal of surface films (easier under reciprocating sliding than rolling) and the exclusion of atmospheric contaminants from freshly exposed surfaces (exclusion is more complete with twisting than with rolling or reciprocating sliding). High sliding velocities can generate frictional heating and increase surface temperature; this, in turn, can modify the material properties as well as accelerate oxidation and its effects. Items 29 and 30 are important in that they determine the true contact area and the extent to which surface films are ruptured. The passage of an electric current results in heating and may also introduce polarity effects with certain types of contaminating films.

The foregoing discussion emphasizes that although there are many diverse factors involved in friction and wear, there is a sound theoretical basis for understanding and anticipating many of their effects and, in some cases, for establishing quantitative correlations. Although imperfect, theory provides some useful guidelines for minimizing friction and wear in service, even in the absence of lubrication.

C. LUBRICATION

The most effective way to reduce friction and wear is to separate the two sliding surfaces by means of a viscous fluid, such as a film of oil or gas. This ideal situation is known as *hydrodynamic lubrication*. It provides coefficients of friction on the order of 0.003, or less, depending on the sliding velocity, load, and the viscosity of the fluid. It eliminates wear entirely, since the solids do not touch or collide with each other. Gyroscope bearings are one example where the ideal conditions of hydrodynamic lubrication are substantially achieved.

Ideal conditions of hydrodynamic lubrication can rarely be maintained in practice. Starting, stopping, misalignment, heavy loads, and other service conditions can cause the fluid film to be squeezed out, or allow the surface asperities to break through the film, so that the two solids are pressed into contact with one another. Ideal hydrodynamic lubrication then ends, and *boundary lubrication*, or lubrication by solids, begins.

As preceding paragraphs point out, truly clean metal surfaces have no lubricity at all; in fact, they tend to weld together. The general task of lubrication by solids is to prevent contact between clean metal surfaces by interposing low shear strength solid films rather than viscous fluid films.

As emphasized in the preceding discussion, practically all metals have natural lubricants on their surfaces in the form of oxide layers. These oxide films reduce friction and prevent metals from welding together. For example, oxide layers on steel provide coeffcients of friction on the order of 0.50. However, the coefficients rise steadily during sliding as the oxide films are removed, and ultimately the steel surfaces seize or weld together. The practical goal of boundary lubrication is to improve upon the films provided by nature, that is, to provide alternate solid films or surfaces that have lower friction and better wear.

The succeeding chapters discuss the solids that are largely being used today for reducing friction and wear. There are also brief discussions of some newer materials that have so far received only limited use in special applications. Both inorganic and organic solids are discussed, and specific materials are grouped according to this general classification; thus, Chapters 2–6 discuss inorganic solid lubricants, and Chapters 7–11 discuss the organic ones.

REFERENCES

1a. E. R. Braithwaite, "Solid Lubricants and Surfaces." Pergamon, Oxford, 1964.
1b. E. R. Braithwaite, ed., "Lubrication and Lubricants." Elsevier, Amsterdam, 1967. "Lubrificazione e Lubrificanti Tribologia." Tecniche Nuove, Milan, 1969.
1. F. P. Bowden and D. Tabor, "The Friction and Lubrication of Solids." Oxford Univ. Press, London and New York, 1954.

2. F. P. Bowden and T. P. Hughes, The friction of clean metals and the influence of adsorbed gases: The temperature coefficient of friction. *Proc. Roy. Soc. Ser. A* **172**, 263 (1939).

3. F. P. Bowden and J. E. Young, Friction and adhesion of clean metals. *Nature (London)* **164**, 1089 (1949).

4. D. V. Keller, Adhesion between solid metals. *Wear* **6**, 353 (1963).

5. A. E. Roach, C. L. Goodzeit, and R. P. Hunnicutt, Scoring characteristics of thirty-eight different elemental metals in high speed sliding contact with steel. *Trans. ASME* **78**, 1659 (1956).

6. L. F. Coffin, Jr., A study of the sliding of metals, with particular reference to atmosphere. *Lubric. Eng.* **12**, 50–59 (1956).

7. F. P. Ling, On the mechanism of metal adhesion. *Aerospace Bearing Conf., San Antonio, Texas, March* 1964.

8. F. P. Bowden and G. W. Rowe, The adhesion of clean metals. *Proc. Roy. Soc. Ser. A* **233**, 429–442 (1956).

9. R. C. Smith, *J. Chem. Soc.* **123**, 2088 (1923).

10. M. E. Sikorski, Correlation of the coefficients of adhesion with various physical and mechanical properties of metals. *J. Basic Eng.* **85**, 279 (1963).

11. E. Rabinowicz, Influence of surface energy on friction and wear phenomena. *J. Appl. Phys.* **32**, 1440 (1961).

Chapter 2

Low-Friction
Inorganic
Solids

Typical inorganic solid lubricants include the element carbon in its graphitic form, lamellar compounds such as molybdenum disulfide (MoS_2), and soft metals such as silver. These materials reduce friction and wear by interposing between the rubbing surfaces a thin, adherent layer of material that shears easily and prevents direct contact between the substrate materials.

A. ADVANTAGES AND DISADVANTAGES

These solids can be particularly advantageous under the following conditions (typical applications are given in parentheses):

1. *Loads are high.* Extreme pressures squeeze fluid lubricants out from between mating surfaces, causing high friction and wear. With lamellar solids, shearing takes place more easily when loads are high (exactly the reverse of hydrodynamic lubrication), so that lamellar solids are well suited to extreme pressure lubrication (e.g., heavy machining, wire drawing through dies).

2. *Speeds are low.* At low sliding velocities, the asperities on mating surfaces tend to penetrate hydrodynamic films provided by fluid lubricants, so that stick-slip action and coldwelding occur (e.g., machine ways).

3. *Operating temperatures are extreme.* Oils thin out at elevated temperatures, and the lower viscosity reduces the load-carrying capacity of their hydrodynamic films; in addition, oils and greases suffer thermal de-

composition and oxidation at elevated temperatures. At low temperatures, oils become extremely viscous and eventually solid. Solid lubricants have better thermal stability and do not become viscous at low temperatures or thin out at elevated temperatures, so that they provide a wider service range, from $-400°$ to $+2000°$ F (e.g., oven chains and sprockets, turbojet bearings, and cryogenic pump bearings).

4. *Environment may wash away oils and greases.* Where parts must operate immersed in liquids or exposed to rain, solid lubricants have the advantage of not being washed away (e.g., outdoor drive chains, parts in immersion pumps).

5. *Environments are dirty or abrasive.* The tacky surfaces of oils and greases collect dust particles, so that they act more as a grinding compound than a lubricant. Solid lubricants are often superior in dusty applications, where complete sealing is impractical (e.g., exposed gearing in equipment for mining, road construction, and farming).

6. *Cleanliness is important.* Since solid lubricants do not gather abrasive dust and dirt, they are useful where cleanliness is important (e.g., food packaging and processing equipment; office and business machines).

7. *Fretting is likely.* Vibration in many machine joints can cause fretting-type wear, even though there is no apparent motion between the parts. Solid lubricants remain effective under such conditions (e.g., splined drives in aircraft engines; splines, arbors, and keyways; sleeve bearings in unbalanced automatic tools).

8. *Maintenance may be inadequate or unreliable.* One may not wish to rely on mechanisms to pump or recirculate lubricating oils (e.g., aircraft and missile applications) or rely on human maintenance, where parts or lubrication schedules can be overlooked (e.g., domestic appliances, sewing machines, office mimeograph equipment, and fishing reels).

9. *Parts are inaccessible after assembly or operation.* In complex equipment where relubrication by oils or greases is not feasible, solid lubricants can often provide permanent, in-place lubrication (e.g., locks, flexible shafts, buried mechanisms in business machines, hinges and pivots in aerodynamic linkages, hermetically sealed units, and nuclear power plant equipment).

10. *Design must be simplified.* Designs can often be simplified, with resultant savings in weight, size, and cost, by eliminating machined oil passages, oil cups and other reservoirs, filters, and recirculating pumps (e.g., machinery and aerospace equipment).

11. *Intermittent action involves long periods of part disuse or storage.* Oils and greases can dry out or migrate away during long idle periods. By contrast, solid lubricants retain their lubricity and are immediately available when called upon to operate after prolonged storage (e.g., safety-release mechanisms and missile defense systems).

12. *Equipment must be sterilized.* Solid lubricants are not degraded by exposure to high temperatures for sterilization (e.g., food processing equipment and planetary exploration systems).

13. *Assembly of parts is difficult.* Solid lubricants prevent galling and seizing during press-fitting or assembling close-fitting parts, and bolts are more easily torqued to the proper tension. Disassembly is also easier (e.g., various machine parts).

14. *Lubricant must be compatible with nonmetallic substrates.* Wood, paper, glass, rubber, and plastics can all be lubricated with solid lubricants. Solid film lubricants can also act as wood sealants and protective coatings for wood and rubber products (e.g., rubber gaskets, O-rings, and protective seals).

15. *Electrical conductivity or insulation is necessary.* Graphite is an excellent conductor of electricity, as well as an effective solid lubricant (e.g., electrical switch plates and variable resistors). Bonded films of other inorganic solids provide excellent electrical insulation.

16. *Nuclear radiation would decompose other lubricants.* The radiation stability of most of the solid lubricants is many orders of magnitude greater than that of oils and greases (e.g., equipment for nuclear power sources).

17. *Reaction with the surroundings must be avoided.* Strong acids or bases, fuels, solvents, and liquid oxygen are reactive with oils and greases, whereas solid lubricants are available that are inert to such environments (e.g., aerospace propulsion systems).

On the debit side, solid lubricants do not cool. Unlike oils, solid lubricants cannot carry away any heat generated during operation. Also, although the coefficients of friction provided by solid lubricants are low (typically on the order of 0.04–0.25), they are not as low as those provided by hydrodynamic films (typically on the order of 0.001–0.003). However, the coefficients of friction provided by solid lubricants can be lower than those provided by oils operating under conditions of boundary lubrication. They have finite wear lives, and replenishment of lubricant is more difficult.

B. USEFUL FORMS

Table 1 lists the forms in which inorganic solid lubricants are most commonly used. It is also possible to dissolve certain compounds in a liquid and deposit them by thermochemical reaction with a metal surface. Extreme pressure (EP) additives to oils and greases that deposit compounds of chlorine, sulfur, and phosphorous are examples of this type of compound. However, these compounds are outside the scope of this book.

TABLE 1.   Useful Forms of Low-Friction, Inorganic Solid Lubricants

Form	Comments
Loose powder	Simplest and oldest form of application, but usually not as effective as the other forms and not generally used because of the difficulty in handling by the consumer
Powder dispersed in volatile carriers	Easily applied; useful for assembling parts with close fits
Powder dispersed in liquids, oils, and greases	Most commonly used form, both in industrial applications (e.g., metalworking) and consumer products
Powder bonded to the surfaces of parts by various types of adhesives	A commonly used form; provides longer lived films than provided by loose powders or powders dispersed in volatile carriers
Powder dispersed or impregnated into solid bodies	Used in "self-lubricating" bearings and similar parts
As bulk solids	Graphite brushes for electrical contacts are best example
Films formed by chemical treatments or reaction with a metal surface	Not commonly used

C. CRYSTAL STRUCTURE

Part of the explanation for the slipperiness and lubricating qualities of solid lubricants lies in their crystal structure. Graphite and the inorganic sompounds that are most useful as solid lubricants have crystal structures in which the atoms are closely packed together on widely spaced planes, giving rise to their classification as "lamellar solids." The interatomic forces that hold such structures together are strong between atoms that lie in the same plane, but weak between atoms that lie in adjacent planes. As a result, the planes can slide over one another with relative ease and without breaking down or being penetrated by surface asperities.

Electron diffraction studies show that lamellar solids tend to form oriented layers when rubbed, so that the platelike crystallites lie flat on a surface with favorable orientation for shearing. Although the exact mechanisms by which the lamellar solids provide lubrication is still unsettled, it appears most probable that the single crystals of the lamellar solids shear by cleavage initiated at an edge. Edge forces and intercrystalline adhesion also appear to be involved in the sliding mechanism.

Not all lamellar solids are effective lubricants. Table 2 presents friction and wear data for a number of inorganic solids that have lamellar types of crystal structures.* For comparison purposes, data are also included for SAE 60 mineral oil and for three compounds that have low shear strength but do not have lamellar types of crystal structures (i.e., AgCN, CuCl, and AgI). The solids that were the most effective lubricants, giving the lowest coefficients of friction and wear, were the lamellar solids MoS_2, graphite, zinc stearate, $CdCl_2$, PbI_2, $CoCl_2$, and WS_2. Lamellar solids that were less effective were $AgSO_4$ and HgI_2, and lamellar solids that were ineffective included Na_2SO_4, $Ba(OH)_2$, TiS_2, BN, and others. The ability of the solids to form films that adhered strongly to the rubbing surfaces was important in reducing friction and wear.

Table 3 lists similar results from another study. Graphite, MoS_2, and WS_2 again appear to be the most effective lubricants of the inorganic solids studied.

From these and similar studies [1–5], the inorganic solids that appear to offer the best general lubricating performance are graphite and the heavy metal dichalcogenides. The latter group includes the disulfides and diselenides of molybdenum and tungsten (i.e., MoS_2, WS_2, $MoSe_2$, and WSe_2). Certain monoxides and sulfides, such as those of lead (PbO and PbS), calcium fluoride (CaF_2), and films of soft metals such as silver appear useful at elevated temperatures or other special conditions.

---

* Data quoted throughout this book for the coefficients of friction and wear are for general orientation and guidance only. The amount of friction and wear can vary with the manner of application and testing, such as the mating metal combinations, substrate hardness, surface roughness, sliding velocity, loads, temperature, humidity, etc. Service tests should be conducted where performance is critical.

TABLE 2. Friction and Wear of Various Solids[a]

Material[b]	Purity	Affinity for water	Coefficient of friction		Wear area (sq in.)	Observed effect of solid on specimens
			1-min sliding	30-min sliding		
Effective lubricants						
MoS_2	Possibly slight oxide present	Insoluble	0.017	0.047	0.0016	None
CdI_2	Chemically pure	Soluble	0.04	0.06	0.0023	None
$CdCl_2$	Chemically pure	Soluble	0.03	0.07	0.0019	None
WS_2	Unknown	Insoluble	0.05	0.08	0.0018	None
Ag_2SO_4	Chemically pure	Slightly soluble	0.14	0.14	Nil	None
PbI_2	Chemically pure	Slightly soluble	0.28	0.28	0.0018	None
Graphite	Purified commercial lubricant small particle size	Absorbs water	0.06	0.11	0.0034	None
$Zn(C_{18}H_{35}O_2)_2$	Chemically pure	Insoluble	0.07	0.11	0.0032	None
$CoCl_2$	Prepared by dehydration	Soluble	0.04	0.10	0.0020	Slight rusting
HgI_2	Chemically pure	Very slightly soluble	0.18	0.18	0.0021	Appreciable corrosion
$CuBr_2$	—	Deliquescent	0.04	0.06	0.0021	Considerable rusting
AgI	Chemically pure	Insoluble	0.19	0.25	0.0033	None
SAE 60	—	—	0.13	0.108	0.0020	—

Ineffective lubricants

NiCl$_2$	Prepared by dehydration	Deliquescent	0.03	0.10–0.15	0.0024	Rusting
Ca(OH)$_2$	Chemically pure	Slightly soluble	0.18	0.2–0.25	0.0026	None
Mo(OH)$_2$	Chemically pure	Soluble	0.32	F^c	—	None
TiS$_2$	Unknown	Hydrolysis	0.20	F	—	—
I$_2$	—	—	0.15	0.30	—	—
HgCl$_2$	Chemically pure	Soluble	0.32	0.38	—	Appreciable corrosion
PbCl$_2$	Chemically pure	Slightly soluble	0.31	0.45	0.0029	None
AgCN	Unknown	Insoluble	0.02	—	0.0036	—
CuCl	Chemically pure	Slightly soluble	0.38	0.37	0.0039	Slight rusting
Na$_2$SO$_4$	Chemically pure	Soluble	0.36	F	—	None
Fe$_3$O$_4$	Chemically pure	Insoluble	F	—	—	None
BN	Technical grade	Insoluble	F	—	—	None
NiO	Chemically pure	Insoluble	F	—	—	None
Mica	Technical grade	Insoluble	F	—	—	None
Talc	Unknown	Insoluble	F	—	—	None

[a] M. B. Peterson and R. L. Johnson, *NACA Tech. Note* NACA TN **3334** (1954).

[b] *Test conditions*: three hemispherical sliders of 1095 steel, Rockwell B-97 hardness, ground to 0.1875-in. radius, riding under a 40-lb. load on a disk of 1020 steel, Rockwell A-50 hardness, with a vapor-blasted surface. All materials except graphite were tested in dry air with a dewpoint below —60° F; graphite was tested in moist air.

[c] F, failed to lubricate.

TABLE 3. Coefficients of Friction for Four Types of Solid Lubricants[a]

| Classification | Solid lubricant | Coefficient of friction | | Stick-slip action |
		Kinetic	Static	
None	Steel on steel (dry)	0.40	0.40 to 0.80	
Layer-lattice inorganics	Molybdenum disulfide:			
	natural	0.050	0.053	no
	synthetic	0.091	0.106	no
	paste-concentrate	0.093	0.096	no
	Tungsten disulfide	0.090	0.098	no
	Titanium disulfide	0.25	—	yes
	Tellurium disulfide	0.25	—	yes
	Selenium disulfide	0.25	—	yes
	Graphite:			
	natural	0.25	—	no
	colloidal (22% in H_2O)	0.100	—	no
	Boron nitride	0.25	—	yes
	Barium hydroxide	0.151	0.163	no
	Lead chloride	0.191	0.214	no
	Mica	0.25	—	yes
	Silver iodide	0.231	0.245	yes
	Talc	0.25	—	yes
Other inorganics	Borax	0.210	0.226	no
	Kaolin	0.25	—	yes
	Rottenstone	0.189	0.195	no
	Lead oxide, zinc oxide	0.25	—	yes
	Vermiculite	0.160	0.167	no
Chemical conversion layers	Iron–manganese–phosphate layer	0.213	0.218	no
	Iron–manganese–phosphate layer with molybdenum disulfide rubbed on top	0.067	0.074	no
	Sulfide melt (570° C) "Sulfinuz"	0.242	—	no
Organics	Spermaceti wax (43–49° C)	0.048	0.062	no
	Beeswax (60–63° C)	0.050	0.055	no
	Bayberry wax (44–49° C)	0.054	0.070	no
	Synthetic wax (comm. average) (93–96° C)	0.061	0.062	no

TABLE 3 (*Continued*)

Classification	Solid lubricant	Coefficient of friction		Stick-slip action
		Kinetic	Static	
Organics (continued)	Polyethylene glycol (high MW) (53–56° C)	0.077	0.078	no
	Hydrogenated tallow glyceride (59–63° C)	0.082	—	no
	Candelilla wax (67–70° C)	0.099	0.113	no
	Paraffin (49–77° C)	0.104	0.112	yes
	Montan wax (78–90° C)	0.108	0.120	yes
	Carnauba wax (83–86° C)	0.143	0.169	no
	Diethylene glycol stearate (54–59° C)	0.083	0.089	no
	Calcium stearate (157–163° C)	0.107	0.113	no
	Aluminium stearate (129–160° C)	0.114	0.119	no
	Sodium stearate (198–210° C)	0.164	0.192	yes
	Lithium-12-hydroxy stearate (210–215° C)	0.211	0.218	no

[a] A. Sonntag, Lubrication by solids as a design parameter. *Electro-Technol.* (*New York*) **66**, 108–115 (1960).

D. EFFECTS OF TEMPERATURE AND ATMOSPHERE

The lubricity of lamellar solids varies with the operating conditions, and these circumstances largely determine the choice of one solid lubricant over another for a specific application. A favorable crystal structure does not in itself appear sufficient for providing easy shear, and adsorbed materials may be needed. For example, moisture or some other condensable vapor must be present in order for graphite to lubricate. Moreover, as the data in Table 4 indicate, graphite provides a lower coefficient of friction in moist air than in dry air or vacuum, whereas MoS_2 behaves oppositely, and the friction of other solid lubricants is indifferent to the presence or absence of moisture.

The effects of temperature on the friction of several solid lubricants are shown in Figure 1. As temperature increases, the coefficients of friction generally remain near their values at room temperature or decrease

TABLE 4.   Effect of Atmospheric Moisture on the Coefficient of Friction
of Various Solids[a]

Lubricant	Coefficient of friction, f		
	Dry air[b]	Moist air[c] after dry air	Dry air after moist air
Molybdenum disulfide:			
powder	0.06	0.20	0.06
bonded film on disk	0.09	0.22	0.09
bonded film on slider and disk	0.26	0.34	0.31
Lead iodide powder	0.27	0.29	0.27
Cadmium iodide powder	0.08	0.19	0.07
Graphite powder	Fails	0.16[d]	0.19
Zinc stearate	0.06–0.09	0.06–0.09	0.06–0.09

[a] M. B. Peterson and R. L. Johnson, Factors influencing the friction and wear with solid lubricants. *Lubric. Eng.* **11**, 325–330 (1955).

[b] Dry air is air with less than 6% relative humidity.

[c] Moist air is air with 85% relative humidity.

[d] When graphite was run first in moist air, the coefficient of friction was 0.06–0.10.

slightly until the temperature reaches some level, above which there is a gradual rise in friction. Temperature effects are usually associated with such changes as the driving off of volatile matter and the onset of oxidation. Some of the changes are reversible on cooling, and the exact temperatures at which the solids become ineffective vary with the manner in which they are used.

E. BONDED FILMS

Rubbing powders of solid lubricants on the surfaces to be lubricated is the simplest and oldest form of application, and it is very effective for the assembly of close tolerance parts. But unless they are bonded to the substrate, the powders are soon brushed away and lubrication is lost. Some solids have the ability to self-bond to metal surfaces, apparently due to their chemical reactivity or to the presence of loosely bound electrons.

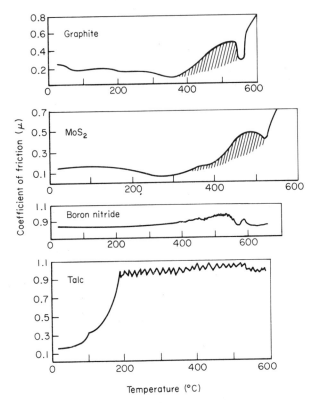

Figure 1. Effects of temperature on coefficients of friction of various solids. *Test conditions*: Solids were tested as powders between sliding surfaces of steel. [R. F. Deacon and J. F. Goodman, Lubrication by lamellar solids. *Proc. Roy. Soc. Ser. A.* **243**, 464–482 (1958)].

Examples of lamellar solids that are capable of some degree of self-bonding to metals include graphite and molybdenum disulfide [5a]. In the case of MoS_2 on steel, strong metal-to-sulfur bonds are thought to form between the MoS_2 particles and the steel surface. Examples of lamellar solids that do not bond well to metal surfaces include boron nitride, talc, and mica, and none of these are very effective lubricants.

To extend their wear lives and achieve other advantages (e.g., to serve as protective coatings), lamellar solids are bonded to surfaces by various adhesives, such as the following: (1) air-drying thermoplastic resins, such as acrylics; (2) thermosetting resins, such as alkyds, phenolics, epoxies, and silicones; (3) inorganic binders and ceramics, such as silicates, phosphates, and borates; (4) metal matrix bonds.

TABLE 5. Some General Characteristics of Binders for Solid Film Lubricants

Type of binder	Curing	Advantages	Disadvantages
Thermoplastic resin	Air	Can be applied by the user to parts already installed in a machine Can be applied to parts that cannot withstand a high-temperature cure Can be applied to parts that are too large to be cured in an oven Applicable to all metals and most nonmetals Can be applied by spraying, dipping, or tumbling	Wear life, corrosion protection to base metal, and resistance to fluid attack are all less than for oven-cured films
Thermosetting resin	Oven	Better corrosion resistance than air-curing films Better wear life than air-curing films Better resistance to fluid attack than air-curing films Better high-temperature stability than air-curing films	Surface preparation, coating, and curing are all critical and should be done by a specialist for best performance Limited to materials that can withstand elevated temperatures without softening, distorting, or otherwise deteriorating
Inorganic adhesives	Oven or furnace	Better corrosion resistance than air-curing films Better wear life than air-curing films Better high-temperature stability than resin-bonded films Good resistance to nuclear radiation	May require higher curing temperatures than with thermosetting resins May be sensitive to moisture absorption unless cured properly Surface preparation, coating, are all critical and should be done by a specialist for best performance
Metal matrix	Proprietary	Better wear life than air-curing films Good high-temperature capability and resistance to nuclear radiation	Requires special processing

Acrylic resins provide flexible films with good adhesion to plastics and elastomers. Alkyd resins are relatively inexpensive, they cure at low temperatures (from room temperature to 350° F), and they are easy to handle. Phenolics have good surface adhesion and are harder than the alkyds, but they require higher curing temperatures, on the order of 300°–400° F. Epoxies have excellent adhesion and solvent resistance, but they are softer than phenolics. Modified epoxy-phenolics combine the good properties of both resins. Silicones can operate at higher temperatures, but they are softer and have relatively poor adhesion. Inorganic binders and ceramics are useful at the highest service temperatures. Table 5 summarizes some of the general advantages and disadvantages of the different types of binders.

Bonding is influenced by the substrate's surface condition, and surface pretreatment is almost as important as the binder itself in determining performance. This is illustrated by the data cited in Table 6. Note that the phosphate treatment, applied here to steel specimens, provided the

TABLE 6. Effect of Surface Pretreatment on Wear Life and Coefficient of Friction of Bonded Solid Film Lubricants[a]

Surface preparation on test specimen prior to coating with lubricant[b]	Film type A (matrix bonded)		Film type B (resin bonded)	
	Wear life (ft × 10^3)	Coefficient of friction	Wear life (ft × 10^3)	Coefficient of friction
Oxidized at 600° F for 45 min	7.2	0.017	0.27	0.10
Cleaned with ethyl alcohol	12.1	0.017	0.17	0.39
Cleaned with ethyl alcohol and alkaline cleaner	12.7	0.014	0.17	0.40
Grit-blasted with 120-mesh steel shot	14.0	0.015	3.2	0.08
Etched in chromic acid	15.3	0.013	0.15	0.30
Manganese–iron phosphate treatment	86.8	0.016	20.1	0.02

[a] B. Stupp, Effect of surface preparation on wear life of solid lubricant films. *Proc. Air Force, Navy, Industry Lubricants Conf.*, WADC TR 59-244, pp. 187–334. Wright-Patterson Air Force Base, Ohio, 1959.

[b] *Test conditions.* Equipment: Hohman A–6 tester. Test specimen: Timken test cup, AISI 4620 steel, Rockwell C-58–61 hardness. Rubbing blocks: steel, straight-faced, Rockwell C-60 hardness. Load on each block: 410 lb. Surface speed: 175 fpm. Coating thickness: 0.0003–0.0005 in., as measured with Magna-gage.

longest wear life together with low friction. Compared to specimens that were coated after cleaning with ethyl alcohol, pretreatment by phosphating improved wear life by as much as two orders of magnitude.

Table 7 indicates recommended pretreatments for various substrates. The first step in any pretreatment is degreasing and removing any corrosion films; this is usually done by immersion in perchloroethylene or

TABLE 7. Surface Pretreatments for Applying Solid Film Lubricants

Metal substrate	Pretreatment[a]
Steels (except stainless)	Phosphate coat per MIL-C-12968, type A. (This is occasionally preceded by roughening the surface by grit- or sand-blasting)
Stainless steels, chrome plate, and nickel plate	Roughen by grit- or sand-blasting or by liquid honing per MIL-C-490A-II, type 1
Aluminum and aluminum alloys	Anodize per AN-QQ-696 or occasionally chromate per MIL-C-5541 (Alodine 1200 or Iridite 14-2)
Copper and copper alloys	Roughen by grit- or sand-blasting; then usually, but not always, apply Ebonol C or Iridite 7 conversion coat or indium flash
Cadmium or zinc plate	Phosphate coat per MIL-C-12968, type B
Magnesium and magnesium alloys	Roughen by grit- or sand-blasting, then dichromate per MIL-M-3171, type 3
Titanium and titanium alloys	Roughen by vapor- or grit-blasting or by etching with nitric-hydrofluoric acid mixture; sometimes use fluorophosphate coat over roughened surface

[a] Pretreatments listed here should be preceded by degreasing and removing corrosion films, as by immersion in perchloroethylene or trichloroethylene.

Grit- or sand-blasting should be done dry with 120 mesh Nevada hard sand (silica); vapor-blasting or honing is generally done with a very hard grit such as alundum of 300 mesh, suspended in water.

trichloroethylene, as per MIL-T-7003. Subsequent steps involve roughening the surface and/or forming some type of conversion coating to promote adhesion. Following these pretreatments and inspection, the films are applied and cured.

Phosphate treatment on steels forms a surface deposit of iron and manganese phosphate that improves the bond to the lubricating film.

The wear life is affected by the thickness and crystal structure of the phosphate coating, and phosphating conditions must be controlled to secure optimum results and eliminate variability in performance. Bath temperature should be held to within 5° or 6° F of the optimum. Bath composition, especially acid strength, and time of treatment also affect the thickness of the phosphate coating. Low bath temperature and low acid strength cannot be compensated for by increasing the treatment time. Treatment times of 15 min at about 205° F with an acid strength of 7–8 points are typical, but optimum conditions for a particular steel and film must be determined by trial and error. For service above 600° F, grit- or vapor-blasting are often preferable to phosphating.

Friction coefficients generally improve when bonded films are run-in or burnished, and the minimum values remain fairly constant with further operation, until they increase abruptly at failure. Burnishing prior to operation is often advisable in order to remove any loose particles that may slough off or be easily dislodged.

Increasing the temperature initially reduces the coefficient of friction of bonded films. The coefficient passes through a minimum that extends over a wide temperature range, and then rises abruptly at failure. Decomposition products from resinous binders at the higher temperatures can improve the lubricating properties until complete failure of the binders occurs. Resin with high curing temperatures generally have higher service temperatures than those that are cured at low temperatures. The failure temperatures vary, but under comparable *short*-time conditions failure temperatures can be on the order of 800° F for alkyd resins, 900°–950° F for epoxy and phenolic resins, and 1100°–1200° F for silicone resins [6]. The maximum service temperatures for *continuous* use are, of course, lower than these values, but the relative ranking of the resins would be as indicated by the short-time results.

Increasing the sliding velocity reduces the coefficient of friction slightly, probably because of the higher temperature generated by frictional heating. Wear life generally decreases as speed is increased.

A hard substrate generally provides a lower coefficient of friction and longer wear life than a soft one. This is probably because the hard substrate provides a firmer support, thereby minimizing both the true contact area and the tendency of the coating to spall or crack as a result of repeated flexing.

Because only a very thin layer of lubricant is required, on the order of 0.3–0.5 mils (0.0003–0.0005 in.), the cost of the material itself is minor. The major costs are the labor for preparing the surfaces and for actually applying the films. Bonded films can be applied by brushing, spraying, dipping, or tumbling, either by hand or in automatic equipment. For large batches of small parts, tumbling is usually the cheapest method. It is usually preferable to coat the entire part, even areas that do not require lubrication, rather than to attempt elaborate masking.

F. TESTING

Service is the ultimate test, but service tests can be prolonged, expensive, and difficult to control, and premature failures in service can be disastrous. Low-cost laboratory tests are therefore conducted to obtain preliminary estimates of a lubricant's potential and to provide a means for production quality control.

Although one cannot predict service performance accurately from laboratory tests alone, good estimates can be made from a combination of service records for a reference lubricant plus comparative laboratory data on the two lubricants. Test conditions should simulate the actual service conditions as closely as practical. Using very heavy loads or other extreme conditions to accelerate testing and cause rapid failure can be pushed to unrealistic limits, so that laboratory results are no longer valid for real service.

Laboratory equipment should provide means for accurately controlling and reproducing operating conditions over the wide ranges of load, speed, temperature, and other factors that may be encountered in service. Table 8 and Figures 2–9 summarize the basic characteristics of some commercially available testing machines [7–9]. These machines are those most commonly used, and they are representative of the more popular principles of operation. They generally measure the coefficients of friction, wear lives, and load-carrying capacities of the lubricants at different loads and sliding speeds. Line contact is most common, although some of the testers employ point or area contact. As wear progresses, of course, point or line contact may spread into area contact. Some of the commercial testers can be used at elevated temperatures as well as ambient. Many other specialized testers have been developed to evaluate lubricants at elevated temperatures, in vacuum or in atmospheres other than air, or under conditions that simulate actual service more exactly.

The *Shell four-ball tester* (Figure 2) has three contacting balls that are held in a fixed position below a fourth ball. The fourth ball is rotated

TABLE 8. Characteristics of Some Commercial Lubricant Testers

Test machine	Specimen geometry	Type of contact	Measurement					Maximum load (lb)	Maximum sliding speed		Temp. (°F)
			Static friction	Kinetic friction	Wear life	Wear	Load capacity		(rpm)	(fpm)	
Shell four-ball	Four 0.50-in. diam balls	Point	—	X	—	X	X	4000	1800	—	Ambient
Reichert	Crossed cylinders	Point	—	X	—	X	—	130	900	—	Ambient
Timken	Block against 1.94 in.-OD rotating bearing race	Line	X	X	—	X	X	1000	800	400	Ambient
Alpha LFW-1	Block against 1.375 in.-OD rotating bearing race	Line	X	X	X	X	X	630	200	72	Ambient
Falex	0.25-in. diam pin rotating against V-blocks	Line	—	X	X	X	X	4500	750	50	Ambient
Hohman A-6	Ring rotating against two flat blocks	Line	X	X	X	X	X	600	200	200	−60−+1600
Alpha LFW-3	Annular ring rotating against one flat block	Area	X	X	X	X	—	5000	325	52	Ambient to +1200
Alpha LFW-4	Pin and bushing with various interference fits	Area	X	X	—	—	—	Depends on fit	—	—	Ambient
Almen–Wieland	0.25 in. diam pin and conforming bearing shells	Area	—	X	X	X	—	4400	600	40	Ambient

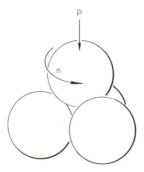

Figure 2. Shell four-ball tester. Test specimens, $\frac{1}{2}$-in. diam balls; speed, 1500 rpm with 50-cycle current; load, variable up to 12 kg. Procedure: (a) seizure load, 1-min test at increasing load to seizure; (b) weld load, 1-min test at increasing load to welding; (c) Hertz load, calculation from measured wear at various loads. Machine will test oils, dispersions, greases, and pastes. (Courtesy of Dow Corning Corp., Trumbull, Connecticut.)

under an applied load against the other three balls at a constant speed. The cup holding the lubricant encloses the four-ball assembly, so that the balls form an equilateral tetrahedron. After a period of operation, a circular scar is worn in the three stationary balls, and the bearing pressure is calculated by dividing the oblique force on the balls by the area of the

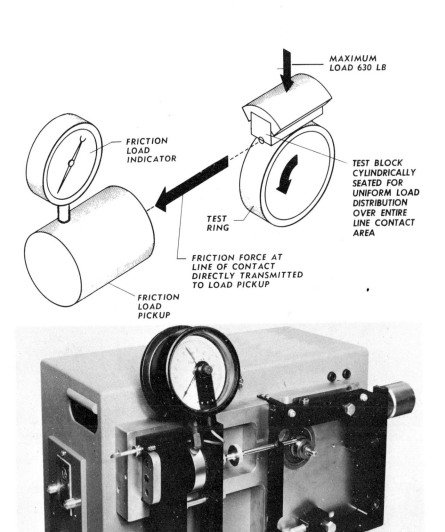

Figure 3. Alpha lubricant tester model LFW-1. Test specimens, test block and 1⅜-in. diam Timken bearing outer race; speed, 12.5, 35, 72, 120, and 197 rpm; load, 30–630 lb. Procedure: (a) step load to 630 lb, measure friction and wear at constant speed; (b) same as (a) with oscillating motion. Machine will test oils, dispersions, greases, and bonded solid lubricants. (Courtesy of Dow Corning Corp., Trumbull, Connecticut.)

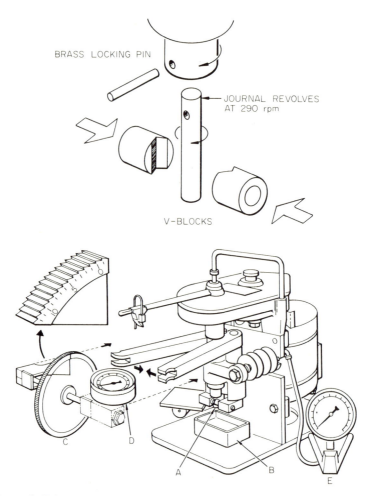

Figure 4. Falex tester. Test specimens, $\frac{1}{4}$-in. diam pin and $\frac{1}{2}$-in. diam V-blocks; speed, 290 rpm (can be readily changed to 390 and 750 rpm); load, variable up to 4500 lb. Procedure: (a) increase load on pin to failure; (b) friction and wear on specimens at constant load. Machine will test oils, dispersions, greases, bonded solid lubricants. A is V-block and journal, B oil cup, C ratchet-wheel loader, D load gage, and E torque gage.

scar. The frictional force is calculated from the torque on the arm of the specimen holder containing the three stationary balls. Wear is plotted against load by making a series of 10-sec runs at successively higher loads until the four balls weld together. After each run, the wear scar diameters on each of the three lower balls are measured twice and the average scar diameter is plotted against load. The higher the load, the larger is the scar.

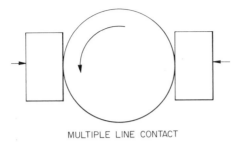

MULTIPLE LINE CONTACT

Figure 5. Hohman A-6 tester. Test specimens, 0.1875 to 1.5-in. diam rings and flat blocks; speed, 200 fpm; load, 600 lb. Machine will test solid lubricants, oils, greases, pastes, and molten metals at room and elevated temperatures. (Courtesy of Hohman Plating & Mfg. Inc., Dayton, Ohio.)

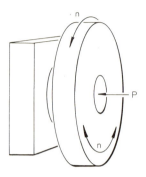

Figure 6. Alpha lubricant tester model LFW-3. Test specimens: annular ring contacting flat block. Speed: undirectional, variable from 9 to 325 rpm; oscillatory: 0°–120°, variable from 6 to 120 cpm; 0°–60°, variable from 6 to 227 cpm. Load: infinitely variable from 0 to 5000 lb. Procedure: measure friction and wear in air and other environments at temperatures to 1200° F. Machine will test pastes, bonded solid lubricants, oils, and dispersions. (Courtesy of Dow Corning Corp., Trumbull, Connecticut.)

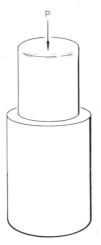

Figure 7. Alpha lubricant tester model LFW-4. Test specimens: pin and bushing. Speed: normally 0.6-in./min, variable up to 2-in./min. Load: variable up to yield point of specimen material; various press-fit interferences available. Procedure: measure static and kinetic coefficient of friction: determine seizure and stick-slip behavior. Machine will test powders, oils, greases, pastes, dispersions, and bonded solid lubricants. (Courtesy of Dow Corning Corp., Trumbull, Connecticut.)

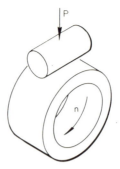

Figure 8. Reichert wear tester. Test specimens, crossed cylinders; spead, fixed 900 rpm; load, step loading up to 230 lb; procedure, measure wear life after a predetermined length of sliding. Machine will test oils, dispersions, greases, pastes, and bonded solid lubricants.

The Shell four-ball tester is easy to operate, and the tests are relatively short. Very high contact pressures are possible, with a range up to millions of pounds per square inch. The high contact pressures make the test somewhat unrealistic, and there is only a limited correlation between four-ball tests and actual service. Nevertheless, the four-ball tester gives a good indication of the load-carrying capacity of lubricants, and it is widely used.

The *Alpha LFW*-1 *tester* (Figure 3) and the *Timken tester* are among the most widely used testers for solid lubricants. Both testers use a single stationary block loaded against a rotating ring. Tests are normally performed under single-line contact, although a conforming block may also be used for area contact. The major difference between the two testers is in the loading system. Both use dead-weight loading. The Timken tester uses a lever system with knife-edge pivots to transmit and multiply the

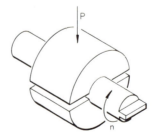

Figure 9. Almen–Wieland tester. Test specimens, $\frac{1}{4}$-in. diam pin and conforming bearing shells; speed, 200 rpm; load, variable up to 4400 lb. Procedure: (a) increase load on pin to failure; (b) friction and wear of specimens at constant load. Machine will test oils, dispersions, greases, pastes, and bonded solid lubricants.

load. The Alpha LFW-1 tester has a compound lever system in which all bearings have been replaced by flexure pivots, so that there are no bearing surfaces subjected to wear. One test piece is a block (0.625 in. × 0.375 in. × 0.250 in.) of steel hardened to Rockwell C-57–60 and finished to 6–12 μin., RMS. The block is drilled for inserting a thermocouple to measure frictional heating during the test. The block is held stationary against the other test piece, which is a rotating ring (1.375-in. diameter) of steel hardened to Rockwell C-58–63 and finished to 15 μin., RMS. Wear is determined by measuring the width or depth of the scar on the test block or by weight loss. Both speed and load can be varied during a test. The machine may either be run for a specific number of cycles at a predetermined load and speed and the wear scar measured, or the specimens may be step-loaded until failure is indicated by a sharp rise in the coefficient of friction or in frictional heating.

For testing solid film lubricants on the Alpha LFW-1 tester in accordance with technique 46 of the Coordinating Research Council, the lubricant is coated on the outer periphery of the ring and the block is usually uncoated. The test ring rotates at 72 rpm, which gives a surface sliding speed of 25 feet per minute (fpm). An initial load of 30 lb is maintained for the first minute of testing, after which the load is increased in 90-lb increments for the next 5 min to a total of 480 lb at the end of 6 min; the loading increments are then reduced to 30 lb until a total load of 630 lb is reached at the end of 10 min. The load of 630 lb is then maintained until the test ends in failure, which is defined as an increase in the coefficient of friction above a selected value (usually 0.10).

The *Falex tester* (Figure 4) uses a "nutcracker" loading principle with a test pin rotating between two stationary blocks. The blocks are V-shaped, so that there are four lines of contact with the pin. Conforming blocks may also be used to give area contact. The blocks are mounted in two arms, which are forced together by a spring-loaded lever system. The "nutcracker" loading mechanism is free to swing about its own axis, and this provides a means for measuring frictional drag through a torque pressure gauge. The loading wheel must be tightened to maintain contact pressure as wear occurs, and this provides a periodic measurement of wear during the test. The Falex tester has been widely used to evaluate solid film lubricants at room temperature, and it has been modified for testing at cryogenic and elevated temperatures.

The *Hohman A-6 tester* (Figure 5) uses two flat, stationary blocks that are loaded against opposite sides of a rotating ring, which can vary in diameter from 0.1875 to 1.5 in. The diametrically opposed rub blocks give uniform shaft loading and eliminate misalignment due to shaft bending. As with the Alpha LFW-1, Timken, and Falex testers, line contact is initially obtained, and this spreads into area contact as wear occurs. Conforming rub blocks can be substituted for the flat ones to give area contact. The vertical geometry of the Hohman A-6 tester allows the wear specimen to be completely or partially lubricated with oils, greases, molten metals, etc. The unit can be operated with controlled atmospheres other than air and at elevated temperatures up to 1600° F.

The *Alpha LFW-3 tester* (Figure 6) uses the flat surface of a rotating annular ring to give area contact against a stationary flat surface. The apparent area of contact can be varied by changing the diameter or width of the annular ring. Bearing pressures with standard specimens vary from 400 to 20,000 psi, and this can be increased by reducing the area of contact. Speeds are infinitely variable from 1.47 to 52.3 fpm, and oscillatory motion is also possible from 6 to 227 cycles per minute (cpm). The machine is designed for testing dry or liquid lubricants in various atmospheres and at temperatures from ambient to 1200° F. The Alpha LFW-3 tester is relatively expensive, wear life tests may take two or three days, and the machine requires a more skilled operator than the other machines discussed above. However, it provides very accurate measurements of friction and wear over a broad spectrum of controlled environments.

The *Alpha LFW-4 press-fit tester* (Figure 7) is a calibrated compression machine that measures the axial force necessary to press an oversized pin into a bushing. The normal force acts in a radial direction and tends to expand the outer ring and compress the inner bushing; this force can be calculated from the material properties, the amount of interference, and the change in the bushing's outside diameter caused by inserting the pin. Dividing the axial force by the radial force gives the coefficient of friction. Stick-slip and intermittent motion are easily detected by vibration of the needle on the axial force gage. The test closely simulates press-fitting applications, is extremely simple to conduct, and is rapid. Solid film lubricants and greases are applied to both the pin and bushing for test, and liquids are tested by immersing the bushing in an oil cup. The Alpha LFW-4 press-fit tester is used primarily to screen boundary lubricants and for quality control purposes.

The *Reichert tester* (Figure 8) and the *Almen–Wieland* tester (Figure 9) are two additional testers that are less commonly used than the testers described above. Their specimen geometries and operating principles are illustrated in the figures.

REFERENCES

1. M. B. Peterson and R. L. Johnson, Factors influencing friction and wear with solid lubricants. *Lubric. Eng.* **11**, 325–330 (1955).
2. M. B. Peterson and R. L. Johnson, Friction of possible solid lubricants with various crystal structures. *NACA Tech. Note* NACA TN **3334** (1954).
3. A. Sonntag, Lubrication by solids as a design parameter. *Electro-Technol.* **66**, 108–115 (1960).
4. J. Gfaensheimer, Lubrication by solids. *Int. Lubric. Seminar, Lucerne, September* 1969.
5. E. W. Bielak, E. Kay, and E. W. Mardles, Lubrication by films of solid materials, Tech. Note Chem. 1271, Roy. Aircraft Estab. Great Britain, 1955.
5a. E. R. Braithwaite and J. Hickman, Dry-film lubrication of metals. *Metal Ind.* **104** (6), 190–192 (1964).
6. E. P. Kingsbury, Solid film lubrication at high temperatures. *Trans. ASLE* **1**, 121–123 (1958).
7. G. Kitchen and H. T. Azzam, Realistic friction testing. *Mach. Des.* **39** (1967).
8. H. T. Azzam, Friction and wear testing machines to evaluate tomorrow's lubricants. *ASLE Annu. Meeting, 23rd May* 1968, ASLE Preprint No. 68AIB-4.
9. B. C. Stupp, Effects of surface preparation on wear life of solid lubricant films. *Proc. Air Force, Navy, Industry Lubricants Conf.* WADC TR 59-244, Wright-Patterson Air Force Base, Ohio, 1959.

Chapter 3

Graphite

Graphite is the classic example of a low-friction solid. Its lubricating qualities are well known, and it is widely used to lubricate fine mechanisms.

A. OCCURRENCE AND PRODUCTION

The term "graphite" refers strictly to one of the two crystalline forms of carbon, the other crystalline form being diamond. The term "carbon" is customarily used in the industry to refer to amorphous (noncrystalline) carbon.

There are two broad classification of graphite: natural and synthetic. Natural graphite is a mineral that occurs in veins or flakes with varying degrees of crystallinity, ranging from amorphous to highly crystalline, and in purity from 80 to 90% carbon. Synthetic, or manufactured, graphite is made by heating petroleum coke to around 5000° F, and it has an average purity of 98.5% carbon. It is not a specific material, however, but is a family of materials, each member of which is essentially pure carbon but differs from the other members in the degree of crystallinity, orientation of the crystallites, pore structure, etc. Available grades range from the lowest cost, coarse-grained, relatively weak graphites to fine-grained, strong, but expensive ones. Most graphite is manufactured from petroleum coke, a refinery by-product, although any organic material that leaves a high carbon residue when heated can be used [1a].

The final step in manufacturing graphite is coverting the carbon to graphite at 2600°–3000° C (4700°–5450° F). During this process the graphite crystals that are randomly arranged in the baked carbon piece grow and rearrange in an ordered pattern of stacked parallel planes. Graphitization is accompanied by an abrupt change in the physical properties, and the final properties depend upon the highest temperature reached during graphitization (e.g., the room-temperature electrical resistivity of a piece of graphite graphitized at 2600° C is 1.2 mΩ-cm, whereas that of a piece graphitized at 3000° C is 0.9 mΩ-cm).

B. CRYSTAL STRUCTURE

The crystal structure of graphite consists of parallel layers of condensed planar C_6 rings, as shown in Figure 1. Seeley [1] compares the layers to "chicken wire," where each junction of wires represents a carbon atom:

Each carbon atom joins to three neighboring carbon atoms at 120° angles in the plane of the layer. The C–C distance is 1.415 Å* (as compared to 1.397 Å in benzene); the width of each 'benzene' ring is 2.456 Å. The joined atoms between layers are pinned by weaker van der Waals forces, thus accounting, in part, for the marked anisotropic properties of the graphite crystal.

The parallel layers are stacked in ordered spacing 3.3538 Å apart (d spacing) at room temperatures. The most common stacking is the $ABABAB\cdots$ order resulting in hexagonal structure [Figure 1a]. A small percent of the layer stacking in most natural graphites is the $ABCABCABC\cdots$ order resulting in rhombohedral structure [Figure 1b]. Grinding increases the rhombohedral structure in well-crystallized graphite, probably through pressure. Heating above 2000° C transforms rhombohedral structure to hexagonal structure, suggesting that the latter form is more stable. Impact resulting from explosion, according to reports, converts rhombohedral graphite to cubic structure — diamond.

Grinding graphite to a particle size smaller than about 0.1 μ (1000 Å) reduces the crystalite size to less than 200 Å, at which level the three-dimensional ordering is replaced by two-dimensional ordering. The weakened pinning forces permit the layers to move farther apart and assume progressively random, though parallel, positions with respect to each other. This turbostratic structure is the characteristic structure of amorphous carbon. The parallel layers are of completely random lateral ordering at 3.44 Å d spacing.

Visualize the carbon crystallite as a deck of playing cards. Each card represents a single plane of condensed benzene rings (chicken wire) with adjoining carbon atoms spaced 1.415 Å apart (C–C distance). The carbon atoms are ordered in two dimensions. Consider the deck evened at the sides and at the ends, ready for dealing, as representing graphite structure — that is, three-dimensional ordering. After the cards are dealt, played, and bunched (without evening the ends and

---

* Å is the abbreviation for angstrom unit; 1 Å = 1 × 10^{-8} cm.

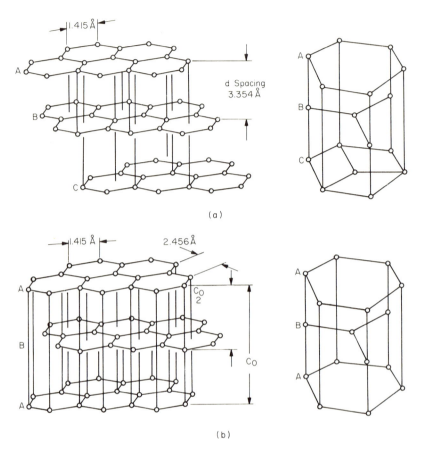

Figure 1. Crystal structure of graphite. (a) Structure of the hexagonal form of graphite; (b) Structure of the rhombohedral form of graphite. (S. B. Seeley, Natural graphite. In "Encyclopedia of Chemical Technology," 2nd ed., Vol. 4, pp. 304–335, Figs. 1 and 2. Wiley, New York, 1964.)

sides for redealing), the deck represents turbostatic structure, the structure of so-called amorphous carbon; the cards, though parallel, are without order in the third dimension of the deck.

Two other refinements complete the analogy. Graphite structure (hexagonal) requires that every other card in the ordered deck be moved laterally the same distance and that the cards be the equivalent of 3.3538 Å apart. This vertical distance between adjacent cards represents the d spacing in the crystallite structure. Turbostatic structural carbon requires that each card in the bunched deck be separated further than in the evened deck of graphite structure; the cards are a minimum of 3.44 Å apart.

[The] d spacing [is related] to the proportion of disoriented layers. Thus, the ratio of graphitic carbon to nongraphitic carbon in a specimen may readily be estimated from a measure of its mean d spacing with 3.3538 Å being completely graphitic and 3.44 Å being completely nongraphitic (turbostratic) [1, pp. 305–307].

Irradiation by high-energy neutrons can distort the crystal structure of graphite, expanding the lattice in the c-direction and compressing it in the a-direction [2]. However, the intensities for causing such changes are quite high, and there is very little probability of significant crystallographic changes during use in conventional nuclear reactors, even when the graphite is used near the reactor core.

C. LUBRICITY AND LUBRICATION MECHANISM

Table 1 lists some values for the coefficient of friction of graphite. The excellent lubricity of graphite can be appreciated by comparing the coefficients of graphite films (0.07–0.15 under sliding conditions) with those obtained on unlubricated surfaces and with mineral oil as a lubricant.

TABLE 1.   Coefficients of Friction Provided by Graphite Films[a]

Description of tester	Coefficient of friction		
	Graphite film	Unlubricated metal	Mineral oil
Three-ball slider	0.09–0.12	0.16–0.18	0.15–0.17
Plane reciprocating slider	0.15	—	—
Bowden–Leben machine	0.07–0.1	0.4	0.17–0.22
Modified Duley instrument	0.12	0.6	0.15
Rollers	0.05	—	0.07

[a] E. A. Smith, Solid lubricants. *J. Inst. Petrol.* (*London*) **42** (n. **395**), 301–347 (1956).

Figure 2 shows the effect of graphite content on the friction and wear of carbon-graphite composites. Under normal atmospheric conditions (760-mm Hg pressure), the friction and wear of amorphous carbon is significantly higher than that of either 20% graphite in amorphous carbon or

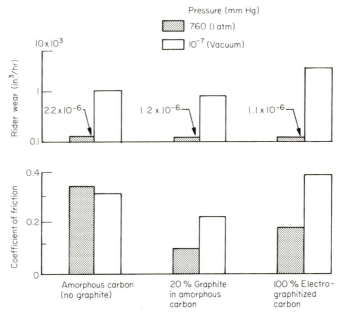

Figure 2. Effect of graphite content on the coefficient of friction and wear for carbon compositions in air and vacuum. *Test conditions:* 0.1875-in. radius hemispherical riders of carbon-graphite riding on the flat surfaces of 2.5-in. diam rotating disks of 440C stainless steel finish ground to 4–8 μin.; sliding velocity, 390 fpm; load, 1000 gm; duration of run, 1 hr [D. H. Buckley and R. L. Johnson, *Trans. ASLE* **7**, 91–100 (1964).]

100% graphitized carbon. Figure 2 also shows that at reduced pressures (i.e., under vacuum conditions), graphitic materials have about twice the friction as in air, and they wear almost 1000 times faster.

In 1928 Bragg [3] postulated that graphite's lubricity was due to its lamellar type of crystal structure, which allowed the planes of carbon atoms to slide easily over one another without disintegrating. This behavior was ascribed to the strong bonding forces between the individual carbon atoms laying *in* the planes and to the relatively weak bonding forces *between* the planes. Subsequent observations [3a] have demonstrated that the lubricity of graphite is not due to its crystal structure alone, but that it depends also upon the presence of condensable vapors, such as water (moisture). This lack of intrisic lubricity first presented a problem in the early 1940's, when it was found that the wear of carbon brushes on motors and generators on aircraft was vastly accelerated at high altitudes (above 20,000 ft). Under these conditions of rapid wear ("dusting"), the coefficient of friction of graphite increased to about 0.5, and the rate of wear increased several orders of magnitude, as illustrated in Figure 2. These problems were solved by adding barium fluoride, molybdenum disulfide, and other adjuncts (see Section I on carbon brushes).

Only a very small amount of condensable vapor is necessary to change graphite's behavior from bad to good, and some organic vapors are more effective than water vapor, as illustrated in Figure 3 [4]. Graphite wore rapidly in a "dry" vacuum in these experiments. But when a condensable vapor was introduced into the vacuum chamber, the wear rate of graphite decreased as the amount of condensable vapor increased to a critical value, at which point its wear rate decreased abruptly and could no longer be measured. For example, if water was bled into the test equipment, the

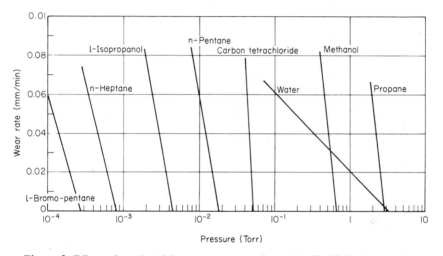

Figure 3. Effects of condensable vapors on wear of graphite. [R. H. Savage and D. L. Schaefer, *J. Appl. Phys.* **27**, 136–138 (1956).]

wear rate dropped abruptly to practically zero when the amount of water vapor reached about 3 Torr.* The wear rate decreased by a factor of about 1000 to 1 when the critical pressure was reached, and the coefficient of friction dropped from 0.8 to 0.18.

Oxygen also showed a lubricant effect similar to that of water vapor, but at pressures higher by a factor of about 100; i.e., a pressure of 200–400 Torr of oxygen was required to lower the wear rate to the level noted with 3 Torr partial pressure of water vapor. Nitrogen and carbon monoxide showed no lubricant effect, at least up to 600 Torr pressure. Ammonia

* 1 Torr is equal to 1-mm Hg.

and a number of organic materials also provided complete lubrication at pressure below 5 Torr, as indicated in Figure 3.

Increasing the rubbing speed moved the curves in Figure 3 to the right. For example, as the rubbing speed of graphite against graphite increased from 200 to 800 cm/sec, the critical amount of water vapor increased from 3 Torr to about 6 Torr.

Other studies have indicated that the critical pressure for reducing wear is less when the condensable vapor is introduced into a vacuum [5]. For example, critical pressures for water, oxygen, and carbon dioxide in nitrogen are approximately 0.65, 230, and 350 Torr, respectively,* This decrease in the values of the critical pressures is thought to be due to the lower surface temperatures at the sliding interfaces during sliding in a gas at 1 atm pressure, as compared to sliding in vacuum.

Figure 4 shows the effect of temperature on the friction of graphite in air and vacuum. Under normal atmospheric conditions graphite maintained its lubricity up to about 1000° F (538° C), at which temperature it began to oxidize rapidly and the coefficient increased abruptly. Although the coefficient for outgassed graphite in vacuum was higher than in air, there was a gradual reduction in the coefficient as temperature increased, probably due to the weakening of the intercrystalline bonds. One should recognize that in many industrial applications, as in wire drawing and forging, colloidal graphite dispersions are used successfully at temperatures well above the limiting temperature determined above for simple sliding conditions in the laboratory.

Graphite films that are "run-in" under normal atmospheric conditions can continue to lubricate effectively for an indefinite period in vacuum provided that the temperature does not exceed about 575° F. High-density graphite or graphite-carbon composites are not as sensitive to changes in the atmospheric conditions as the more porous ones, apparently because gases and absorbed surface films are not as easily desorbed.

Electron diffraction patterns have shown that graphite crystallites become oriented on rubbing so that the cleavage planes are in the plane of rubbing. Occasional wear of graphite surfaces appears due to the tilting of the crystals so that their edges are able to abrade adjacent surfaces.

Continuing research on the lubricity of graphite has uncovered a

---

* Test conditions were as follows: Load equaled 220 gm/sq cm which equaled 3.13 psi; speed equaled 10,840 in./min (2-in. diam track, 1750 rpm); ambient temperature equaled room temperature; rate of graphite brush wear in dry nitrogen equaled 1.3 mm/min.

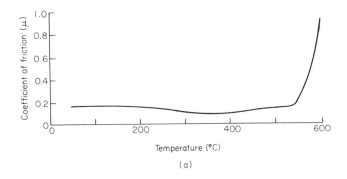

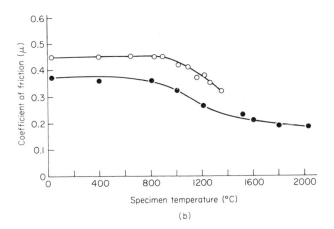

Figure 4. Effects of temperature on friction of graphite in air and vacuum. (a) Rubbed layer of graphite in air. [R. F. Deacon and J. F. Goodman, *Proc. Roy. Soc. Ser. A.* **243**, 464–482, (1958).] (b) Outgassed graphite in vacuum; ○ spectrographically standardized graphite; ● Acheson AGR graphite. [G. W. Rowe, *Wear,* **3**, 274–285 (1960).]

number of interesting facets of its behavior. Measurements indicate that the interlamellar binding strength is an order of magnitude higher in vacuum than in air, and that it is sufficiently high to remove graphite from the general category of weakly lamellar materials that are intrinsic lubricants, such as molybdenum disulfide [6]. Outgassed graphite can be considered as a polycrystalline mass linked by strong valence forces between the crystallites, which explains its high friction [7].

The role of condensable vapors has been explained as saturating the surfaces on graphite crystallites, especially the edge forces, thereby reducing the attractive forces between the crystallites and reducing the friction [6–9]. Possibly this is due to the combining of electrons from the gases with the unsatisfied π-electrons of the graphite lattice [6–10]. Or, as others have suggested, graphite's lubricity may be due to its ability to form layers or transfer films that adhere strongly to metal surfaces, and the presence of oxides or condensable gases assists this by providing an atomic link between the metal and graphite [3a, 8, 11, 12]. It has also been suggested that the vapor enters the graphite lattice and reduces the shear strength between the sheets of atoms [3a, 8]. A further explanation of graphite's lubricity, based on experimental observations of the formation of spiralled rolls of graphite on the order of 0.1–1 μ in diameter, is that rollers are formed from the graphite platelets during rubbing and that these act like roller bearings between the rubbing surfaces [6, 13].

While there is no disputing the fact that graphite is an excellent lubricant under many conditions, there is no general agreement on the mechanism by which graphite lubricates, and one is forced to agree with the conclusion universally voiced by the workers in this area that further research is necessary before we will have a complete understanding of graphite's lubricity and the role of adsorbed vapors.

D. GRAPHITE DISPERSIONS

Graphite dispersions are colloidal dispersions of fine graphite particles, ranging from about 40 μ to submicron size, in water, oil, and various solvents. The colloidal particles of graphite have an electronegative charge, which assists in stabilizing the particles in suspension and in attaching the particles to metal surfaces of opposite polarity.

Table 2 indicates the types of graphite dispersions available and typical applications. In the case of solvent carrier types, the solvent evaporates after application, leaving a film of dry graphite powder on the part. Graphite dispersions are generally easier for the user to handle and apply than dry powder.

Graphite dispersions are widely used in metalworking and other industrial operations, such as the following:

1. Metal forming and forging, including press operations, hammer operations, extrusion processes, and all other hot metal-forming and metal-shaping processes with steels, nickel, titanium, aluminum, and

TABLE 2. Graphite Dispersions[a]

Carrier	Solids content (percent)	Particle size[b]	Density (lb/gal)	Diluent	Special characteristics	Typical applications
				Solvent carrier		
S. C. solvent no. 2	50	C	10.4	Aromatic solvents	High solids for formulating uses; also desirable vaporization rate	Parting compound for gaskets and stop-off for sintering operations
Lacquer diluent naphtha	10	A	6.4	Petroleum naphtha	Small particles for very smooth surface; also very rapid vaporization	Drawing, extruding, and stretch forming of aluminum and magnesium
Isopropanal	20	B	7.4	Commercial alcohols, ketones	Rapidly evaporating carrier to produce a nonresin bonded dry film	Electrically conductive coating for printed circuits, static bleed, etc. Metalworking: die pretreatment and billet coating; as antiseizing and antigalling lubricant for press-fitting parts
Trichlor-ethylene	10	B	12.0	Trichlorethylene, chlorothene, etc.	Rapidly evaporating nonflammable carrier	Nonflammable dry-film lubricant; electrically conductive coating
Mineral spirits	10	A	7.1	Mineral spirits, Stoddard solvent, etc.	Medium evaporating carrier with low residue formulation	General design and industrial high-temperature lubricant: for conveyor chains, kiln car-wheel bearings
Mineral spirits	50	C	9.4	Mineral spirits, Stoddard solvent, etc.	Medium rate evaporation, plus high solids for formulating	General design and industrial high-temperature lubricant: for foundry-mold dressings, etc.; parting compound: for gaskets and in sintering operations, etc

TABLE 2 (*Continued*)

Carrier	Solids content (percent)	Particle size[b]	Density (lb/gal)	Diluent	Special characteristics	Typical applications
				Oil carrier		
Petroleum oil	10	A	8.2	Petroleum oil	Fine particles for low settling rate and better usage of solids	General design and industrial uses; lubricant for dies, tools, and molds for metalworking, etc.; additive for oils
Petroleum oil	40	C	9.9	Petroleum oil	High solids content for minimum formula dilution	Formulated into forging lubricants; die-casting lubricants; ingot-mold coating
Petroleum oil	37	C	10.0	None required	A unique blend of graphite with MoS_2 to promote low friction and good release	Antiseize thread lubricant
Castor oil	10	B	8.6	Castor oil, alcohols	Good for use in systems where petroleum oils or solvents must be avoided	Assembly and maintenance lubricant
				Water carrier		
Water	22	A	9.3	Water	Superior fine-particle size leading to a smooth, well-bonded film of unusual heat resistance	General design and industrial uses; lubricant for dies, tools, and molds for metalworking, etc.; electrically conductive coating

					Characteristics	Uses
Water	30	C	9.8	Water	A coarser variation of above with the same good adhesion but larger particles	Mold wash for aluminum permanent molds, ingot molds, and molds for mechanical rubber goods; stop-off coating
Water	22	B	9.3	Water	A midsize particle range lubricant with lesser binding tendencies selected for special uses	Lubricant for general metalworking and metal casting, aluminum, extruding, ferrous and nonferrous forging, and die casting; lubricant for rubber and oxygen system equipment; additive for silicone emulsions; interior wall coating for cathode-ray tubes (contains no organic binders)

Special dispersions

1,3-Butylene glycol	10	A	8.9	Glycols, water	Good for rubber systems which might be swelled by solvents or oils	Rubber lubricant; soluble-oil additive
Polyglycol (water insoluble)	10	B	8.7	Polyglycol (water insoluble)	Low residue, high-temperature resistant carrier and solid	Extreme-temperature lubricant: conveyor chains and kiln car bearings
Organic vehicle	24	C	13.4	None required	A blend of a unique carrier of low oxidizing characteristics with specially treated solid	Antiseize thread lubricant for oxygen systems

[a] Acheson Colloids Co. Port Huron, Michigan.

[b] The fineness range of the particles contained in these products has been designated arbitrarily by the letters A, B, C, and D (A representing the finest particle-size range).

other metals and alloys. Advantages include extended life of dies (often more than trebled); lower maintenance costs, due to reduced pressures and wear on equipment; better forging, due to better controlled and easier metal flow; and safer operation, due to suppression of explosion and elimination of damage to the die.

2. Die casting, such as to lubricate the plunger and dies of aluminum, magnesium, and other light alloy die-casting processes in order to extend die life, ensure easier parting, and form cleaner products.

3. Molybdenum and tungsten wire drawing to increase size reduction, permit faster drawing speed, and reduce die wear.

4. Parting agents for screws, nuts, and bolts to prevent seizure of screw threads in joints.

5. Conveyor belts for high-temperature furnaces and kilns.

6. Running-in compound to assist the smooth breaking-in of machinery.

7. Oil additive to improve lubricity under extreme conditions of heat and pressure.

8. Additive to broaching tools to extend tool life and improve the finish of broached surfaces.

9. Steel mill equipment for handling hot metal or slag, such as cropping shears, hot-mill run-out tables, slag ladles, and trolley cars carrying steel ingots to and from furnaces.

10. Bearings and gears that are overloaded or are running rough and hot.

11. Electrical conductor rails, pick-up shoes, and bus bars in order to provide lubrication and, at the same time, avoid arcing and subsequent pitting of the sliding surfaces.

12. Parting agent on glass molds.

E. BONDED FILMS

Table 3 indicates the characteristics and uses of several types of lubricating films that consist of graphite powders adhesively bonded to metal substrates. The resins most commonly used are the thermosetting resins, such as alkyd, phenolic, and epoxy types, and are baked at temperatures on the order of 300° F. Refer to Chapter 2 for a complete discussion of adhesives and processing for bonded films.

TABLE 3. Characteristics and Uses of Typical Resin-Bonded Lubricating Films of Graphite[a]

Dispersed substance	Carrier	Solids content (percent)	Particle size[b]	Density (lb/gal)	Diluent	Special characteristics	Typical applications
Colloidal graphite	Alkyd resin solution	25	A	8.0	Aromatic solvent	Provides very smooth surface for use under low-load conditions	General-purpose dry-film lubricant for business-machine parts, etc. (bake at 350° F for 10 min or 250° F for 45 min)
Colloidal graphite	Epoxy resin solution	28	B	8.2	Special epoxy resin solvent	Exhibits the excellent chemical and corrosion resistance of epoxy resins	Durable, corrosion-resistant dry-film lubricant (bake at 350° F for 1 hr)
Graphite	Alkyd resin solution	50	C	9.5	Aromatic solvent	High solids content for formulating and for higher load uses	Dry-film lubricant for rubber parts, etc.; stop-off coating (bake at 350° F for 10 min or 250° F for 45 min)
Graphite + MoS_2	Phenolic resin solution	42–56	D	9.1–10.9	Special phenolic resin solvent	A series of lubricants designed to provide balanced wear, pressure resistance, and corrosion resistance	Dry-film lubricant developed to provide a good bonded lubricating film on a variety of wear surfaces; dry-film lubricants meet extreme load and endurance requirements; excellent for aluminum lubrication. (Air dry 10 min and bake one hr at 300° F)

[a] Acheson Colloids Co. Port Huron, Michigan.

[b] The fineness range of the particles contained in these products has been designated arbitrarily by the letters A, B, C, and D (A representing the finest particle-size range).

F. CARBON-GRAPHITE BODIES

Solid carbon-graphite bodies are commonly used for mechanical applications, such as sealing rings, bearings, piston rings, and pump and valve parts. (Their use in electrical contacts and brushes is discussed later in Section I.) They combine the strength, hardness, and wear resistance of carbon with the natural lubricity and machinability of graphite.

Carbon-graphite for mechanical applications is usually either lampblack or graphite bonded with pitch. The mixtures of lampblack or graphite with pitch are compacted by molding or extrusion, and then baked at about 1055°–3000° F to convert the pitch to coke. The pitch coke-bonded lampblack consists of spherical particles of lampblack, about 0.01–0.1-μ diam, bonded together by a continuous skin of coke derived from the pitch. Pitch coke-bonded graphite consists of relatively large graphite platelets oriented in layers and surrounded by a continuous skin of coke. Parts are usually moded to shape, and then ground to finish dimensions. Both porous and nonporous bodies are produced. (Metal-impregnated and resin-impregnated porous graphite bodies are considered in Section G.) Most of the carbon-graphite seal materials contain graphitic carbon as the minor constituent (up to about 20%). Carbon made completely or largely graphitic is too soft and gives high friction and wear.

Table 4 lists properties for typical carbon-graphites that are commercially available, and Table 5 indicates the grades that are recommended for specific seal applications. Table 6 compares the properties of three grades of carbon with those of two metals and a ceramic.

The broad use of carbon-graphite bodies in mechanical applications is due to the following:

1. Better conformability and a greater elastic limit than the ceramics.
2. Outstanding resistance to thermal shock, so that it does not crack or spall when rapidly heated or cooled.
3. An elastic limit in compression that is generally five to ten times greater than the elastic limit in tension.
4. A degree of strain at the elastic limit in tension about comparable to that of cast iron.
5. Better machinability than ceramics; carbon-graphite is easily machined to close tolerances.
6. Truly elastic characteristics (i.e., it fractures at the elastic limit).

TABLE 4. Properties of Typical Carbon-Graphite for Mechanical Applications[a]

| Grades | Apparent density (gm/cm³) | Hardness | | Strength (psi) | | | Elastic modulus (psi) | Thermal conductivity (btu/hr-ft-°F) | Coefficient of thermal expansion ($\times 10^{-7}$/°F) | Max recommended temp. | Moldable (to 1% to 1 diam with 0.006-in. min. total tolerance) |
		Shore scleroscope	Rockwell E scale	Compressive	Tensile	Flexural					
CCA	1.73	90–100	105–112	38,000	7800	9,500	3,760,000	6.6	18	750° F	Yes
CCA-B	1.80	90–100	105–112	40,000	8800	10,500	3,800,000	6.6	18	350	Yes
CCA-72	1.81	90–100	105–112	40,800	8800	10,500	4,060,000	6.6	18	500	Yes
CCP	1.77	75–85	80–90	29,000	6800	8,500	3,900,000	12.0	13	750	Yes
CCP-72	1.83	75–85	80–90	33,000	7500	8,800	4,000,000	12.0	13	500	Yes
CDJ	1.75	90–100	105–112	36,000	6700	8,800	3,370,000	8.0	15	800	No
CDJ-83	1.77	90–100	105–112	36,300	6700	8,800	3,400,000	8.0	15	1200+	No
CBN	1.67	40–50	50–60	13,000	4000	4,700	1,760,000	10.0	28	750	No

[a] Data from Carbon Products Division, Union Carbide Corp., New York, New York.

TABLE 5. Recommended Grades of Carbon-Graphite for Seals and Sliding Surfaces[a]

Material sealed	Lubricating qualities of material sealed	Grades for operating Temperatures		
		To 500° F	Above 500° F (gas or vapor state)	In the cryogenic range[b] (gas–liquid state)
Water-Steam	Poor	CCP-72, CCA-72		c
Water	Poor	CCP-72	c	c
Water plus detergents	Poor	CCP-72	c	c
Gasoline	Poor–fair	CCP-72	c	c
Kerosene	Poor–fair	CCP-72	c	c
Acids	Poor–good (depending on viscosity)	CCP-72	c	c
Bases	Poor–good (depending on viscosity)	CCP-72	c	c
Petroleum lubricants	Good (SAE #20 as "normal" reference)	CCA-72, CCP-72	c	c
Synthetic lubricants	Good	CCA-72	c	c
Greases	Good except for lithium soap types	CCA-72	c	c
"Freon" 12, 22, 114	Poor	CCP-72, CCA-72	CDJ-83	c
Neutral or inert atmosphere	Poor–good[d]	CCA-72, CCP-72	CCA, CCP[e]	c

Environment	Rating			
Reducing-atmospheres	Poor–good[a]	CCA-72, CCP-72	CCA, CCP[e]	c
Air	Poor–good[a]	CCA-72, CCP-72	CCA, CCP[e]	CDJ-83, CCP-72
Various dry gas[f] environments:				
Carbon dioxide	Poor	⎧ CCA-72 / CDJ-83, CCP-72	⎧ CDJ-83,	⎧ CCA-72 / CDJ-83, CCP-72
Oxygen–argon	Poor			
Helium–hydrogen	Poor			
Nitrogen	Poor			
High vacuum	Poor	CCA-72, CCP-72, CDJ-83,	CDJ-83	CCA-72, CCP-72, CDJ-83
Liquid oxygen (LOX)	Poor	c	c	CCA-72, CCP-72, CDJ-83
Liquid hydrogen	Poor	c	c	CCP-72, CDJ-83
Liquid nitrogen tetroxide (N_2O_4)	Poor	c	c	CCA-72
Liquid nitrogen (LON)	Very poor	c	c	CCP-72, CDJ-83
Liquid halogens (Anhydrous)	Poor	c	c	CCA-72

[a] Data from Carbon Products Division, Union Carbide Corp., New York, New York.

[b] Cryogenic range specifically denotes temperatures of −162.6 to −452° F.

[c] Materials sealed do not exist at these temperatures.

[d] Depends on water content of gas and surface conditioning treat used in the carbon–graphite.

[e] Impregnant depends on temperature and operating conditions.

[f] Dry gas, gas with a dew point of −50° F or below, or gas with less than 20 ppm moisture.

TABLE 6. Comparison of Properties of Mechanical Carbon-Graphite with Those of Other Materials[a]

Properties	Carbon			Cast iron	Stainless steel (best)	Ceramic refractories
	Soft graphitized	Hard high coke	Resin or metal-impregnated			
Maximum use temp, in air (°F)	900	700	500–900	800 at 10,000 psi; 1100 (no stress)	1200 at 10,000 psi	3500
neutral or red. atm (°F)	5000	5000[b]	600–1600	800 at 10,000 psi; 1100 (no stress)	1200 at 10,000 psi	3500
Thermal cond. (btu/sq ft-hr-ft-°F)	70–86	3–3.5	3–100	27	10.8	1.7–2.7
Coefficient of thermal expansion (per °F)	1.50×10^{-6}	2.50×10^{-6}	$2.50–3.65 \times 10^{-6}$	5.9×10^{-6}	7.3×10^{-6}	4.3×10^{-6}
Tensile strain at elastic limit (in.-/in.)	0.0021	0.0016	0.0006–0.0018	0.0013–0.0029	0.0031–0.0033	0.0061
Compression strain at elastic limit (in./in.)	0.0168	0.0165	0.0084–0.0260	0.0059–0.0071	0.0031–0.0033	0.0061
Elastic modulus (1000 psi)	620	1430	1700–3223	13–21,00	27,600	52,300
Tensile strength (psi)	1300	2300	2000–3100	18–60,000	85–95,000	35,000 at room temp. 18,500 at 2000° F
Compressive strength (psi)	10,400	23,600	27–50,000	80–150,000	85–95,000	320,000
Resistance to thermal shock	Excellent	Excellent	Excellent	Fair	Excellent	Poor

[a] R. L. Hibbard, Carbon bearings and seals. *Mater. Methods* **45**, 110–114 (March 1957).
[b] Will graphitize.

7. Compressibility, which is particularly important in press- or shrink-fitted bearing sleeves, since it permits the ID* to remain constant under the external pressure of the metal housing.

8. Self-lubricating (in the presence of condensable vapors).

9. Resistant to chemical attack and corrosion; chemically inert to most acids, caustics, and solvents.

10. Dimensionally stable over a wide temperature range, so that it does not warp, creep, or crack after repeated heating and cooling.

11. Impermeable (in the nonporous types).

12. High thermal conductivity, which aids in transferring heat during fast heating or cooling.

13. Low coefficient of thermal expansion (about 1/6 that of most metals and 1/100 of plastics).

14. Not wet by or nonsticking to molten metals, glasses, or slags.

15. High strength at elevated temperatures.

16. Excellent electrical conductivity.

An average $PV^\dagger$ value of 20,000 for nonlubricated (dry) operation and 200,000 for lubricated (flooded) conditions can be used for determining the size of bearings and bushings of carbon-graphite. When carbon-graphite bearings are lubricated, the lubricant should be maintained in a flooded state. Grease is not recommended, due to lapping when moisture or grease combine with the carbon dust (detritus) worn loose from the bearing material. The wall thickness and running clearance should increase with shaft diameter, as suggested by the values given in Table 7.

Graphite has a lower thermal expansion rate than most metals. Bushings should be put into compression by pressing them into metal housings, using an interference fit that increases from 0.001 to 0.003 in. as the outside diameter of the bushing increases from 0.25 to 2.00 in. High interference fits can be used because of the high compressive strength of graphite, but press fittings with more than 0.003–0.004-in. interference should be avoided, as the stock may scale from the outside diameter of the carbon-graphite bearings or the wall may be crushed. If the temperature range causes bearings with 0.003–0.004-in. interference fit to become loose, the housing should be shrink-fitted about the bearings. In addition to securing bushings in place, shrink and interference fits aid in trans-

---

* ID means inside diameter.

† P is the pressure in pounds per square inch based on the project area (length × diam) and V is the rubbing speed of the shaft in feet per minute. (These values are recommended as conservative by the National Carbon Company).

TABLE 7. Recommended Design Practice
for Carbon-Graphite Bushings

Shaft diam (in.)	Minimum clearance (in.)	Minimum wall thickness (in.)
0.25	0.001	0.090
0.50	0.002	0.125
1.00	0.003	0.187
1.50	0.004	0.312
2.00	0.006	0.437
3.00	0.008	0.625
4.00	0.009	0.750
5.00	0.011	1.00

ferring frictional heat from the graphite bushing to the housing, from which it can be dissipated to the atmosphere and the balance of the structure.

If the liquid medium in which graphite bushings operate contains sludge, grooves should be cut into the bushing in order to trap the debris and keep it from lodging between the moving faces. These grooves will also provide a lubricant reservoir for maintaining hydrodynamic lubrication.

Mating materials should preferably have a hardness of Rockwell C-55, or better. Hardened steel, chrome-plated steel, hardenable 300 and 400 series stainless steels, and some ceramics work well against carbon. Unhardened 1040 steel is adequated for light loads and low speeds, but aluminum and brass are generally poor mating materials.

Table 8 lists some design recommendations for using mechanical carbon-graphites.

The mechanism of wear of carbon-graphite bodies is abrasion, which occurs when the asperities of the two moving surfaces touch and wear fragments are torn from the surfaces. Grooves are ploughed into the soft carbon-graphite by the harder mating material, and loose wear particles are thereby removed. A good surface finish minimizes abrasive wear.

TABLE 8.   Do's and Don'ts of Carbon Design[a]

Do

1. Mount carbon in compression. In general, carbons have about five to ten times the strength and compressibility in compression that they do in tension

2. Calculate the effect that thermal expansion will have and allow for it in your design

3. Make sure that stresses in the mounting systems are within the working limits of all materials, including the carbon

4. Estimate the amount of heat that will be generated, using known loads and speeds and a conservative coefficient of friction, such as 0.15 or 0.20, to see whether or not you need cooling

5. Consult the carbon manufacturer for his recommendations on the proper grade or grades for your application, and obtain from him any data that you may need for design purposes

Don't

1. Try to interchange carbon bushings with other types of bushings or bearings without full consideration of the factors involved

2. Run rough shafts or thrust washers against carbon. Best success is obtained with finishes better than 10 rms

3. Design a large carbon thrust bearing for operation under severe speed load conditions which require cooling without ensuring a positive flow of coolant over the running surfaces. Relatively large bearing pad areas not containing numerous small oil grooves may overheat

[a] R. L. Hibbard Carbon bearings and seals. *Mater. Methods* **45**, 110–114 (1957).

Wear rate increases with unit load, rather slowly at first and then at an increasing rate. Sliding speed has a slight effect on wear rate and generally causes the coefficient of friction to increase, apparently as a result of the higher temperature caused by the increase in frictional heating. Wear is generally proportional to the sliding distance, although a high initial wear sometimes occurs before a suitable running film has been deposited on the mating surface. Generally, the coefficient of friction decreases with sliding distance as a running film is established on the mating face. Increasing the ambient temperature generally increases both the wear and the friction.

G. IMPREGNATED CARBON-GRAPHITE

Table 9 lists properties of carbon-graphite impregnated with various fillers. One of the prime reasons for impregnation is to reduce porosity and permeability. Impregnation also improves the surface finish of machined parts, reduces friction and wear, increases strength, and retards oxidation. These improvements make it possible to operate seals and bearings at higher loads and temperatures than with conventional carbon-graphite bodies. Impregnation is usually done by saturating the carbon-graphite body in its machined state and then heating to develop the optimum properties of the impregnant.

TABLE 9. Properties of Impregnated Carbon-Graphite[a]

Properties	Conventional carbon-graphite	Carbon-graphite impregnated with:			
		Ceramic	Resin	Metal	Carbon
Apparent density (gm/cm³)	1.55–1.9	1.68–2.00	1.78–1.85	2.35–2,60	1.87
Hardness (Shore scleroscope)	20–85	40–80	60–85	45–90	—
Compressive strength (1000 psi)	3.5–30	10–27.5	20–32.5	15–42.5	9
Flexural strength (transverse) (1000 psi)	2.5–9	4.5–11	7.5–11	7–13	4.7
Tensile strength (1000 psi)	1.5–7.5	3.5–7.5	5.5–7.5	4.7–10	3.5
Temperature limit, neutral atmosphere (°F)	350–6000	1250–1500	200–500	1500	6000
oxiding atmosphere (°F)	350–900	1000–1250	200–450	500–900	—
Coefficient of thermal expansion (in./in.-°F × 10⁻⁶)	1.1–2.9	1.6–3.6	2.2–2.5	3.0–4.0	2.4
Permeability (darcies × 10⁻⁶)	100–50,000	<0.01–2000	<0.001–300	0.5–10.0	0.0002
Porosity (volume), (%)	6–25	3–18	3–10	2–5	0.7

[a] *Mater. Des. Eng.* **56** (September 1964).

H. METAL-GRAPHITE COMPOSITES

Metal Impregnated into Carbon Skeletons

In one type of metal-graphite composite, molten metal is impregnated into the pores of graphite or carbon-graphite in solid molded form. The metal increases the strength and thermal conductivity of the composite. The usual metals are babbitt, copper, bronze, cadmium, and silver. Table 10 indicates some of the typical characteristics and uses of these materials.

The metal content of these composites generally varies from 35 to 70% by weight, and the properties vary accordingly. Tensile strength varies from about 4000 to 6000 psi, compressive strength from 16,000 to 25,000 psi, and hardness from 25 to 80 scleroscope hardness. The dry coefficient of friction against polished steel shafts should be between 0.12 and 0.25, depending on the grade; when submerged in water, gasoline, or most other liquids, the coefficient should drop to one-half to one-sixth of the value for running dry.

The maximum recommended shaft speed for bushings operating under *dry* conditions is related to the total shaft load (W, in pounds) and the bushing length (L, in inches) by the relation:

$$\text{rpm}_{\text{max}} = 46,000 \times L/W$$

This formula is based on a conventional PV factor of approximately 12,000, where P is the bearing load in psi and V is the shaft surface speed in feet per minute. The formula is conservative, and for many combinations of speed and load, the calculated speed can be exceeded. For submerged bushings, the speed can be increased by a factor of 7–10 of that calculated by the above formula for dry operation.

Bushings should be operated against mating surfaces that have a finish of 4–8 μin. and a hardness of Rockwell C-50–C-55. The bushings should be installed by press-fitting them into reamed housings by means of a vise or arbor press. Running clearances should be about 0.0015 in. for shafts with diameters less than 0.50 in. and should increase progressively as the shaft size increases, to about 0.005 in. for shafts with diematers from 4 to 6 in. Larger clearances are desirable for applications where ash and coal dust are present. Bushings are available in a range of stock sizes up to about 7-in. diam. Larger sizes and special grades can also be produced to order.

TABLE 10.   Typical Characteristics and Uses of the More Commonly Used Grades of Metal-Impregnated Graphite and Carbon-Graphite[a]

Impregnant metal or alloy	Maximum use temp. (°F)		Coefficient of thermal expansion (in./in./°F)	Uses
	Oxidizing atmosphere	Nonoxidizing atmosphere or submerged		
Babbitt metal	300	300	1.1×10^{-6}	Inexpensive; medium-load and medium-speed applications, such as pump bushings, pump blades, stoker bushings, thrust washers, and rotating seal rings
Copper	700	1700	2.3×10^{-6}	High-temperature applications; high-load, slow-speed applications, such as stoker bushings, drying-oven conveyor bushings, high-temperature stirring shafts and agitators; current-carrying bushings
Bronze	600	600	1.8×10^{-6}	Specialized applications
Cadmium	250	550	1.1×10^{-6}	Specialized applications, including current-carrying bushings and electrical contacts
Silver	700	1500	2.0×10^{-6}	Current-carrying applications, such as electrical contacts and brushes; bushings in chemical solutions that attack other lubricants or metallic bushings

[a] Graphite Metallizing Corp., Yonkers, New York.

Pressed and Sintered Metal-Graphite Composites

Metal-rich composites of metals and graphite can be fabricated by powder metallurgy techniques, in which mixtures of the powders are either cold pressed and sintered in the solid state or hot pressed. The preparation of *graphite*-rich composites by powder metallurgy techniques, however, is restricted either by sweating of the molten metal from the graphite pores during sintering at temperatures above the melting point of the metal (liquid-phase sintering) or by poor strength due to inadequate bonding at sintering temperatures below the melting point of the metal (solid-phase sintering). The tendency of liquid metals to "sweat" during liquid-state sintering is due to the poor wettability of liquid metals and graphite. By adding a small amount of calcium as a calcium–silicon alloy to mixtures of graphite and iron powders, it has been possible to overcome this problem and produce strong, metal-bonded composites containing from 40 to 90% graphite by volume and with allowable PV products up to 50,000 (more than four times the PV product allowed from metal-infiltrated graphite) [14].

I. CARBON BRUSHES FOR ELECTRICAL APPLICATIONS

Carbon brushes are universally used for commutating electric power in motors and generators. Table 11 lists the grades that are most commonly supplied by one manufacturer. Although strength and current-carrying capacity of the various grades do not vary widely, the resistivity values vary as much as a factor of 150 to 1, from a low of 0.0006 Ωin. for one electrographitic grade to a high of 0.1000 Ωin. for one of the graphite grades. Table 11 also indicates typical uses of the various grades; the optimum grade for a specific application depends upon a number of factors, and the advice of the brush manufacturing companies should be sought before selecting a grade for use.

Table 12 lists the aviation-grade brushes. These incorporate additives that overcome the problem of rapid wear ("dusting") at high altitudes. Lead iodide and barium fluoride were the adjuvants most commonly used during World War II, and these often increased brush life 50 times and more by comparison with untreated types. These additives had the disadvantage of requiring sea-level "filming runs" before operation at high altitudes and were inadequate for the higher operating speeds and altitudes of post-World War II aircraft and missiles. To overcome these disadvantages, carbon brushes incorporating molybdenum disulfide were developed. These do not require sea-level "filming run-in" and are known as "quick-filming" types, since they are immediately operational (after proper seating).

Table 13 lists the characteristics of copper-graphite brushes. These

TABLE 11. Characteristics of Typical Carbon Brushes for Fractional Horsepower Applications[a]

Typical applications[b]	Grade	Spec. resistivity (Ω/in.^{3})	Carrying capacity (amp/in.^{2})	Contact drop[c]	Coef. of friction	Scleroscope hardness	Transverse strength (lb/sq. in.)	Polishing action[a]
Electrographitic grades								
A1, A3	A2C	0.0012	70	H	L	60	5000	VS
A1, A3, B1	AC4	0.0011	80	M	L	50	3000	None
A1, B1	AC18	0.0013	70	H	L	75	5500	VS
A1	F186	0.0012	70	H	L	55	2500	S
A1, B1	L1	0.0005	70	L	L	35	2500	None
A1, A3	124	0.0020	70	H	L	50	2200	S
A1	367	0.00045	80	L	L	30	3000	S
A1, A3, B1	417	0.0007	90	L	L	45	2200	VS
A1	784	0.0020	60	H	L	50	2200	VS
A1	812 Rod	0.0008	70	L	L	70	5000	S
B1	K1 Rod	0.0003	70	L	L	40	4000	S
	K10 Rod	0.00045	70	L	L	45	6000	S
Carbon graphite grades								
A2	CID	0.0018	50	H	H	70	4000	M
A2	M44A	0.0012	60	M	M	50	4000	M

A2	S10	0.0018	50	M	M	80	4500	S
A2	S11	0.0018	50	M	M	60	3500	S
A1	568	0.0027	60	H	L	65	3000	S
A1	682	0.0032	60	H	L	65	3000	S
A1	770	0.0065	60	M	L	75	3000	S
Graphite grades								
A1, A3	BP11	0.0020	60	H	L	8	4500	S
A1, A3	BP20	0.0040	50	H	L	40	7000	VS
A1, A3	BP5	0.0015	60	M	L	10	2500	VS
A1, A2, A3	T1A	0.0022	60	H	L	15	5000	S
A1, A2	X18	0.0100	50	H	M	75	5000	S
A1, A2	316	0.045	50	VH	L	40	5000	S
A1	373	0.035	50	VH	L	25	3000	None
A1	660	0.055	50	VH	L	40	5000	VS
A1	678	0.085	50	VH	L	30	2500	VS
A1, A3	687	0.045	50	VH	L	40	5000	S
A1, A2	4001	0.035	50	VH	L	25	3000	S
A1, A2	4025	0.060	50	H	L	27	2800	S
A1, A2	4026	0.079	50	H	L	25	2200	S

[a] Stackpole Carbon Co., St. Marys, Pennsylvania.

[b] A, Universal motors; A1, with undercut mica; A2, with flush mica; A3, dc motors and generators; B1, automotive alternators.

[c] H = high, M = medium, L = low, VH = very high.

[d] VS = very slight; S = slight.

TABLE 12. Characteristics of Typical Altitude-Treated Carbon Brushes[a]

Grade	Spec. resistivity (Ω/in.^{3})	Carrying capacity (amp/in.^{2})	Contact drop[b]	Coef. of friction	Scleroscope hardness	Transverse strength (lb/sq. in.)	Polishing action[c]
Electrographitic grades (altitude treated)							
43D	0.0010	70	L	L	50	2200	VS
51	0.00065	80	L	L	45	2200	VS
52	0.00065	80	L	L	45	2200	VS
57	0.0020	70	H	L	50	2000	VS
72	0.0020	70	H	L	50	2000	VS
118	0.00065	80	L	L	45	2200	VS
166	0.0006	80	L	L	55	3500	VS
199	0.0006	80	L	L	55	3500	VS
566	0.00065	80	L	L	50	3000	VS
Carbon graphite grades (altitude treated)							
423	0.0008	70	L	L	50	3500	VS
428	0.0015	70	M	L	60	3500	VS
486	0.0008	70	L	L	50	2300	VS
497	0.0008	70	L	L	50	2300	VS
555	0.0008	70	L	L	50	2800	VS
605	0.0008	70	L	L	50	2300	VS

[a] Stackpole Carbon Co., St. Marys, Pennsylvania.
[b] L = low, H = high, M = medium.
[c] VS = very slight.

TABLE 13. Characteristics of Typical Copper-Graphite Brushes[a]

Grade	Spec. Resistivity (Ω/in.^{3})	Carrying capacity (amp/in.^{2})	Contact drop[b]	Coef. of friction	Scleroscope hardness	Transverse strength (lab/sq. in.)	Polishing action[c]	Percent metal
CGL7[d]	0.00010	80	L	L	15	4,500	VS	50
R90	0.0000015	150	EL	VL	18	20,000	S	93
NS124	0.000005	150	VL	L	8	7,000	S	96
325	0.0000080	125	VL	VL	20	6,000	S	80
359	0.0000020	150	EL	VL	10	18,000	S	96
773	0.000008	125	VL	VL	15	3,000	S	80
774	0.00009	100	L	L	15	3,000	VS	50
775	0.000021	125	VL	VL	15	3,000	VS	70
793	0.00004	100	VL	VL	15	3,000	VS	65
794	0.000019	125	VL	VL	20	3,000	S	75
795	0.000006	125	VL	VL	15	3,000	S	85
5003	0.000020	125	L	VL	15	2,500	VS	50
5004	0.00003	125	VL	VL	25	4,000	VS	65
5009	0.000035	100	L	VL	20	2,500	VS	30
5011	0.00003	125	L	VL	15	1,800	VS	40
5048	0.00004	125	L	VL	20	2,000	VS	40

[a] Stackpole Carbon, St. Marys, Pennsylvania.

[b] L = low, EL = extremely low, and VL = very low.

[c] VS = very slight, S = slight.

[d] CGL7 (W9) is altitude treated.

TABLE 14. Characteristics of Typical Silver-Graphite Brushes[a]

Grade	Spec. resistivity (Ω/in.^{3})	Carrying capacity (amp/in.^{2})	Contact drop[b]	Coef. of friction[c]	Scleroscope hardness	Transverse strength (lb/sq. in.)	Polishing action[d]	Percent metal
Ground-level applications								
SG124	0.0000039	250	EL	VL	15W44	5,000	S	80
SG211	0.000045	150	EL	VL	25	3,000	VS	50
SG212	0.000005	250	EL	VL	20	5,000	S	75
SG217	0.000006	250	EL	VL	20	6,000	S	72
SG219	0.00022	100	L	VL	10	5,000	VS	40
SG505	0.000001	300	EL	VL	15	20,000	S	95
SG510	0.0000015	300	EL	VL	15	12,000	S	90
High-altitude applications								
SM340	0.0000061	250	EL	VL	15W30	4,000	S	75
SM366	0.000136	100	L	VL	15W50	3,000	VS	45
SM473	0.0000012	300	EL	VL	15T68	18,000	S	85.5
SM476	0.0000025	300	EL	VL	15T45	9,000	S	85
SM487	0.0000017	250	EL	VL	15T50	10,000	S	82.5

[a] Stackpole Carbon Co, St. Marys, Pennsylvania.
[b] EL = extremely low; L = low.
[c] VL = very low.
[d] S = slight, VS = very slight.

brushes are distinguished from the grades listed in the two preceding tables by their very low resistivities and high current-carrying capacities. They are intended for applications such as automotive starter brushes, which require low and stable resistance and the ability to carry instantaneous currents on the order of 300–500 amperes when the starter commences. In addition to copper and graphite, the brushes can contain lead and tin to help prevent excessive commutator wear.

Table 14 lists the characteristics of silver-graphite brushes. These brushes provide very low noise level, low and stable contact resistance, low friction, and high conductivity. They are useful for slip rings, commutators of low voltage generators and motors, on segmented rings, and other applications where the special requirements justify using a premium (i.e., high-cost) brush. They help suppress radio interference noise levels. Although they can be used against various contacting surfaces, the preferred mating materials are silver, coin silver, copper, bronze, and silver-plated copper and bronze, as well as gold, gold alloys, and other precious metal alloys.

REFERENCES

1a. E. R. Braithwaite, Graphite and silicon carbide. Their structure, properties, and uses. *J. Inst. Engrs. Shipbuilders (Scotland)* **442** (March 1956).

1. S. B. Seeley, Natural graphite. *In* "Encyclopedia of Chemical Technology," 2nd ed., Vol. 4, pp. 304–33. Wiley, New York, 1964.

2. E. R. Braithwaite, Graphite and molybdenum disulphide. *Nucl. Eng.* **2**, 107–110 (1957).

3. W. L. Bragg, "Introduction to Crystal Analysis," p. 64. Bell, 1928.

3a. E. R. Braithwaite, Friction and wear of graphite and molybdenum disulfide. *Sci. Lubrication (London)* **18** (5), 17–21 (1966).

4. R. H. Savage and D. L. Schaefer, Vapor lubrication of graphite sliding contacts. *J. Appl. Phys.* **27**, 136–138 (1956).

5. W. E. Campbell and R. Kozak, Studies in boundary lubrication—III. The wear of carbon brushes in dry atmospheres. *Trans. ASME* **70**, 491–497 (1948).

6. P. J. Bryant, R. L. Gutshall, and L. H. Taylor, A study of mechanisms of graphite friction and wear. *Wear* **7**, 118–126 (1964).

7. R. F. Deacon and J. F. Goodman, Lubrication by lamellar solids. *Proc. Roy. Soc. Ser A* **243**, 464–482 (1958).

8. J. W. Midgley and D. G. Teer, An investigation of the mechanism of the friction and wear of carbon. *Trans. ASME.*

9. R. H. Savage, Graphite lubrication. *J. Appl. Phys.* **19**, 1–10 (1948).

10. G. W. Rowe, Some observations on the frictional behavior of boron nitride and graphite. *Wear* **3**, 274–285 (1960).

11. E. E. Bisson, R. L. Johnson, and W. J. Anderson, Friction and lubrication with solid lubricant at temperatures to 1000° F with particular reference to graphite. *Inst. Mech. Eng. Conf. Lubric. and Wear, October* 1957, Paper 23.

12. D. H. Buckley and R. L. Johnson, Mechanism of lubrication for solid carbon materials in vacuum to 10^{-9} millimeter of mercury. *ASLE/ASME Lubric. Conf.,* October 1963.

13. W. Bollman and J. Spreadbourough, Action of graphite as a lubricant. *Nature (London)* **186**, 29–30 (1960).

14. M. Humenik, Jr., D. W. Hall, and R. L. Van Alsten, Metal bonded graphite. *ASM Metals Congr., Philadelphia, Pennsylvania, October* 1960.

Chapter 4

Molybdenum
Disulfide

Molybdenum disulfide, MoS_2,* so closely resembles graphite that the two are often confused. In many applications it is superior to graphite as a lubricant.

A. OCCURRENCE AND PROPERTIES

Table 1 summarizes the properties of MoS_2. Molybdenum disulfide is a mineral, molybdenite,[†] that occurs in thin veins in altered granite. The amount of MoS_2 in the rock is less than 1%, and the remainder consists mainly of silica, SiO_2, and other impurities. In order to be satisfactory for lubricating purposes, the MoS_2 must be purified to better than 98% purity. Some early MoS_2 powders contained as much as 15% of abrasive impurities and gave disastrous results when used as lubricants. High-purity powders have been available since the 1950's, and their excellent lubricating qualities have led to an increasing use of MoS_2.

B. CRYSTAL STRUCTURE

The crystal structure of MoS_2 is laminar, similar to graphite. It consists essentially of planes of molybdenum atoms alternating with

---

* Molybdenum disulfide is only one of a family of similar binary compounds, known chemically as chalcogenides, that have excellent lubricity. Other members of this family include WS_2, $MoSe_2$, $NbSe_2$, etc. (See Chapter 5.)

[†] Molybdenite is also the source of metallic molybdenum as well as MoS_2. It is extracted from the ore by crushing and liquid flotation. For applications other than lubrication, molybdenite is first roasted to produce molybdic oxide, which may be used in this form or further processed to other products used by chemical and metallurgical plants.

TABLE 1. Properties of Molybdenum Disulfide (MoS_2)

Property	Data
Molecular weight	160.08
Color	Blue-grey to black
Specific gravity	4.8–5.0
Melting point	Above 2700° F
Crystal structure	Hexagonal (see Figure 1)
Hardness	1–1.5, Mohs' scale; 12–60, Knoop
Thermal stability	Stable above 2000° F in vacuum or inert atmosphere; oxidizes in air
Coefficient of friction	Varies with conditions, but generally falls within the range 0.05–0.10 for av. service conditions (see Table 2)
Load-bearing capacity	Over 400,000 psi
Chemical stability	Resists attack by most acids, except aqua regia and hot conc. HCl, H_2SO_4, and HNO_3. Decomposed by F and Cl but not by dry HF. Oxidation in moist air at room temp. is slight but sufficient to give a perceptible acid value; oxidation begins slowly in dry air at about 750° F and is rapid at 1000° F; MoO_3 and SO_2 are the products of oxidation. Oxidation reaction is exothermic, with $\Delta H = -266.75$ kcal/mole. MoO_3 forms as long crystals; early reports that MoO_3 is abrasive are in error (possibly due to contamination of samples). Compatible with liquid oxygen (LOX). Attacked by alkali metals (i.e., Li, Na, K, Rb, Cs, and Fr).
Solubility	Insoluble in water, petroleum products, and synthetic lubricants
Magnetic properties	None (diamagnetic)

Electrical conductivity	Temp. (°F)	Specific resistance (Ω)
	−85	8.33
	+67	0.790
	163	0.470
	198	0.409

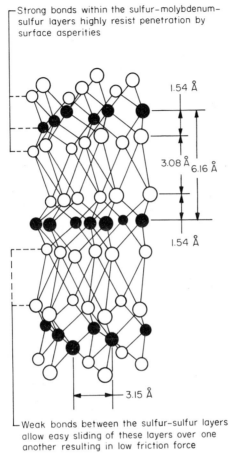

Strong bonds within the sulfur–molybdenum–sulfur layers highly resist penetration by surface asperities

1.54 Å

3.08 Å 6.16 Å

1.54 Å

3.15 Å

Weak bonds between the sulfur–sulfur layers allow easy sliding of these layers over one another resulting in low friction force

Figure 1. Crystal lattice structure of MoS_2.

planes of sulfur atoms in the sequence S : Mo : S : S : Mo : S:···, as shown in Figure 1.* The atomic arrangement in each layer is hexagonal, and each Mo atom is surrounded by a trigonal prism of S atoms at a distance of 2.41 Å. Adjacent planes of S atoms are 3.08 Å apart. Thus, the forces holding the atoms together in each group of S : Mo : S layers are relatively strong covalent bonds, whereas the forces between the adjacent planes of sulfur atoms are relatively weak van der Waal-type. As a

---

* An allotropic form of MoS_2 has been reported which has a rhombohedral unit cell. The lattice parameter of the a-axis is identical with that for the hexagonal form, but its c-axis is 1.5 times as large as the c-axis for the hexagonal form. Lubrication properties are essentially the same for both forms.

TABLE 2. Typical Experimental Measurements of the Coefficient of Friction of MoS_2

Method of applying MoS_2	Experimental conditions	Coefficient of friction
Rubbing or burnishing onto metal surface	MoS_2 film rubbed on SAE 1020 steel; speed, 40 fpm; load, 900 gm (coefficient of friction for untreated SAE 1020 steel under same conditions, 0.55)	0.05–0.095[a]
	MoS_2 pellets rubbing on MoS_2 film on stainless steel; speed, 310 cm/sec; load, 395 gm; tests run in vacuum	0.06–0.10[b]
	MoS_2 film rubbed on steel (coefficient of friction of untreated steel, about 0.8)	0.05[c]
	Tested under extreme pressure of 350,000 psi	0.025[d]
Rubbing or burnishing onto chemically treated surface	MoS_2 filled in the porous structure of the phosphated surface layer on steel	0.04–0.1[e]
Chemical formation	MoS_2 formed chemically in situ on sintered molybdenum; steel slider and 4-kg load (coefficient of friction of untreated sintered molybdenum under same conditions, 0.4–0.55)	0.06–0.10[c]
Bonding with organic binders	MoS_2 film bonded with corn syrup to SAE 1020 steel; speed, about 50 pfm; load, about 100 gm (coefficient of friction of untreated SAE 1020 steel under same conditions 0.54)	0.19[f]
	MoS_2 film bonded with corn syrup to SAE 1020 steel; speed, 400 fpm; load, 900 gm (coefficient of friction of untreated SAE 1020 steel under same conditions, 0.55)	0.20[a]
Impregnated in plastic	Low percent of MoS_2 in molded Perspex; steel slider and 4-kg load (coefficient of friction of untreated Perspex under same conditions, 0.45)	0.10–0.15[g]

1% MoS₂ in ebonite (a thermosetting plastic), spread as a thin film on a metal surface and baked; copper slider and 4-kg load (coefficient of friction of untreated ebonite under same conditions, 0.4)	0.25[g]
Microfine grade of MoS₂ in polyamide	<0.05[h]
Porous metals impregnated with MoS₂ — MoS₂ in sintered copper; steel slider and 4-kg load (coefficient of friction of untreated sintered copper alone under same conditions, 0.3–1.2)	0.13–0.2[c]
Cylinders of 10% MoS₂, 85% Ag, and 5% Cu (hot-pressed) with hemispherical ends against rotating steel disk; speed, up to 8000 fpm; load, up to 1017 gm (coefficient of friction of untreated cylinder of 95% Ag–5% Cu under same conditions, 0.26–0.29)	0.21[i]
50% MoS₂–50% bronze-tin (Sinite D-10); sliding speed, about 40 fpm (coefficient of friction of untreated hardened steel under same conditions, >0.35)	0.10[j]

[a] I.-M. Feng, Lubricating properties of molybdenum disulfide. *Lubric. Eng.* **8**, 285–289 (1952).

[b] V. R. Johnson and G. W. Vaughn, Investigation of the mechanism of MoS₂ lubrication in vacuum. *J. Appl. Phys.* **27**, 1173–1179 (1956).

[c] F. P. Bowden, Frictional properties of porous metals containing molybdenum disulphide. *Research (London)* **3**, 383–384 (1950).

[d] E. W. Bielak, E. Kay, and E. W. Maradles, Lubrication by films of solid materials. Tech. Note Chem. 1271. Roy Aircraft Establ., Great Britain, December 1955.

[e] A. A. Milne, Lubrication of steel surfaces with molybdenum disulfide. *Research (London)* **4**, 93 (1951).

[f] R. L. Johnson, D. Godfrey, and E. E. Bisson, Friction of solid films on steel at high sliding velocities. *NACA Tech. Note* NACA TN **1578** (1948).

[g] F. P. Bowden and K. V. Shooter, Frictional behavior of plastics impregnated with molybdenum disulfide. *Research (London)* **3**, 384–385 (1950).

[h] H. P. Jost, Pure molybdenum disulphide. *Sheet Metal Ind.* **33** (n. 354), 679–697 (1956).

[i] R. L. Johnson, M. A. Swikert, and E. E. Bisson, Friction and wear of hot-pressed bearing materials containing molybdenum disulfide. *NACA Tech. Note* NACA TN **2027** (1950).

[j] Data from Booker-Cooper, Inc, Los Angeles, California.

result, the adjacent planes of S atoms can slide readily over one another, and this has been though to be responsible for the low frictional resistance provided by MoS_2. At the same time, there is an immense resistance to penetration in the direction normal to the crystalline lamellae.

The structure of MoS_2 has been likened to a stack of bread in which the slices have been buttered on both sides. The bread slices represent the planes of molybdenum atoms, and the butter represents the planes of sulfur atoms. The butter portrays the action of sulfur well, since it sticks to the surface and yet slides easily. The thickness of the MoS_2 lamellae is extremely small, on the order of 1/40,000,000th of an inch, so that a "stack" only 1/1000th of an inch thick has 40,000 "slices," or cleavage planes.

Recent research suggests that this simple mechanism is not entirely correct, and that the easy shear of MoS_2 platelets is less important than edge effects in providing low friction, as discussed in Section C.

C. LUBRICATION PROPERTIES

Table 2 lists values for the coefficient of friction of MoS_2 under a variety of conditions. The list is not exhaustive, but it does illustrate typical values and the variations that are caused by different conditions. The first six values are representative for MoS_2 alone, uncontaminated by foreign materials introduced by the method of application. These values range from 0.025 to 0.10, and an average value of 0.08 covers most practical conditions. (Bonded films of MoS_2 have coefficients about twice that of MoS_2 alone.)

The coefficient of friction of MoS_2 varies with its crystallographic orientation, and it is a minimum when the cleavage planes are aligned in the plane of sliding. For example, MoS_2 specimens rubbing against a rotating steel disk gave a coefficient of 0.10 when the cleavage planes were parallel to the rubbing surface and 0.26 when perpendicular [1]. The latter value should be even higher than 0.26 because, in preparing a surface perpendicular to the cleavage plane, the cutting operation always introduces randomly oriented crystal fragments that partly cover the surface.

As a consequence of its laminar crystalline structure, MoS_2 crystals tend to be flat platelets, typically 500–1000 Å thick at the edges and 0.05–0.1 μ thick at the center, with thickness-to-diameter ratios of about

1 to 20 [2]. These platelets lie flat on the surfaces on which they are placed, and it is difficult to prepare a film with completely random orientation. Rubbing or burnishing MoS_2 increases the degree of orientation and lowers the friction coefficient slightly.

Purity

The effects of small amounts of abrasive impurities on the lubricity of MoS_2 are shown in Figure 2. These data were obtained by adding various amounts of 200-mesh silica, SiO_2, to MoS_2. When no silica was present, the amount of wear was nil. Adding 0.5% SiO_2 increased the wear area substantially and the coefficient of friction slightly.

Commercially available MoS_2 powders are generally at least 98% pure MoS_2. Table 3 indicates the typical chemical analysis of such powders, along with the particle-size distribution. The major impurity is 1.1% carbon from the oils used for flotation of the crushed ore. MoS_2 of higher purity can be produced, but there is no real gain in its properties.

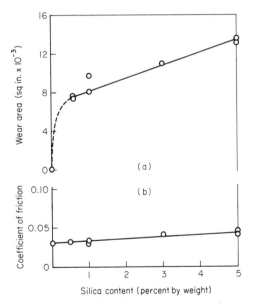

Figure 2. Effect of abrasive impurities on the friction and wear characteristics of MoS_2 powder: (a) wear, (b) friction. *Test conditions :* steel specimens in dry air; load, 4 lb; sliding velocity, 5.7 fpm; duration, 6 hr; atmosphere, dry air (6% relative humidity); room temperature. [M. B. Peterson and R. L. Johnson, Factors influencing friction and wear with solid lubricants. *Lubric. Eng.* **11**, 325–330 (1955).]

TABLE 3. Chemical Analysis and Particle-Size Distribution of Commercially Available MoS$_2$ Powder[a]

	Typical analyses (wt %)	
	Unmicronized	Micronized
MoS$_2$ (calculated)	98.0	98.0
Acid insoluble (carbon excluded)	0.40	0.40
Fe	0.13	0.13
MoO$_3$	0.05	0.20
H$_2$O (as packaged)	nil	0.15
Oil (acetone soluble)	0.03	0.20
Carbon (carbonized from oils)	1.10	1.10
Acid number (modified ASTM method D974-58T)	0.5	3.0

Coulter count, particle-size distribution			
Particle size (μ)	Unmicronized MoS$_2$ (wt. %)	Micronized MoS$_2$	
		wt. %	Total no. of particles (%)
Over 30	50		
Under 30, over 20	20		0.001 (over 20)
Under 20, over 10	17		0.002
Under 10, over 5	8	20	0.117
Under 5, over 2	3.8	47	3.880
Under 2	1.2	33	96.000
	100.0	100	100.000

Screen analysis	Unmicronized (wt. %)
On U.S. sieve no. 100 (149 μ)	0
Through 100, on 200 (74 μ)	5
Through 200, on 325 (44 μ)	20
Through 325	75
	100

	Unmicronized MoS$_2$	Micronized MoS$_2$
Fisher number	4.0	0.63

[a] J. T. McCabe, Molybdenum disulfide—its role in lubrication. *Sci. Lubric.* **15** (March 1963).

Load-Carrying Capability

Increasing the contact force between sliding surfaces reduces the coefficient of friction of MoS_2. This is illustrated by the data plotted in Figures 3–6 which were obtained with MoS_2 films applied to steel from dispersions of MoS_2 powder in water and toluene, with a paste of MoS_2 in oil, and with a MoS_2 film bonded with corn syrup. At the lowest load (13 psi), the coefficients of friction varied between 0.1 and 0.5; at the highest load (625 psi), between 0.02 and 0.05, or approximately an order of magnitude lower. (Figures 3–6 also demonstrate the benefits from using a phosphating or sulfiding treatment on steel surfaces prior to applying the MoS_2 films.)

Table 4 compares the coefficients of friction for MoS_2 with other lubricants at high contact pressures. Note that MoS_2 provides a lower coefficient than any of the other solid lubricants tested.

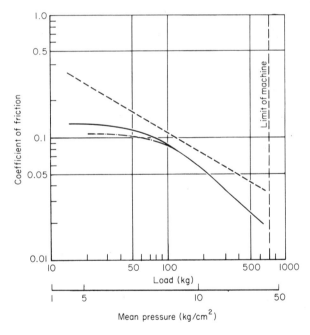

Figure 3. Variation of friction with load for surfaces lubricated with molybdenum disulfide dispersed in water, (rubbing speed, 15.5 m/min); ×, Plain mild steel; +, phosphated mild steel; ⊙, sulfided mild steel. [A. A. Milne, Experiments on the friction and endurance of various surface treatments lubricated with molybdenum disulfide. *Wear*, **1**, 92–103 (1957/1958).]

Figure 7 is another demonstration of the load-carrying capability of MoS_2. This figure shows balls of 52100 chrome steel after progressively loading to 1000 kg in Shell four-ball test. Even at the highest load, which was sufficient to extrude the top ball partially through the space between the other three balls, the load limit of the MoS_2 had still not been reached. With graphite and tungsten disulfide, the balls welded together under similar conditions; with titanium disulfide, the lubricant started to burn as the frictional heating increased. Figure 7 illustrates the excellent extreme pressure (EP) characteristics of MoS_2.

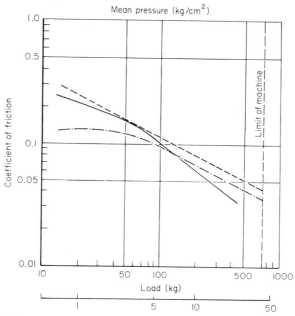

Figure 4. Variation of friction with load for surfaces lubricated with molybdenum disulfide dispersed in toluene (rubbing speed, 15.5 m/min.); ×, plain mild steel; +, phosphated mild steel; ⊙, sulfided mild steel. [A. A. Milne, Experiments on the friction and endurance of various surface treatments lubricated with molybdenum disulfide. *Wear*, **1**, 92–103 (1957/1958).]

Temperature

The effect of temperature on the coefficient of friction is shown in Figure 8. These measurements were made in air with rubbed films of MoS_2 on a platinum bar. Examination by electron diffraction indicated that there was little change in the MoS_2 films between room temperature

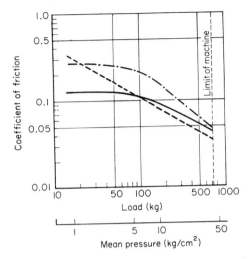

Figure 5. Variation of friction with load for surfaces lubricated with molybdenum disulfide paste (rubbing speed. 15.5 m/min); ×, plain mild steel; +, phosphated mild steel; ⊙, sulfided mild steel. [A. A. Milne, Experiments on the friction and endurance of various surface treatments lubricated with molybdenum disulfide. *Wear* **1**, 92–103 (1957/1958).]

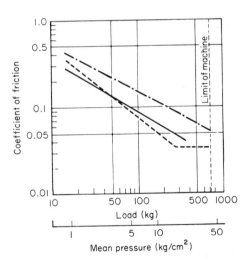

Figure 6. Variation of friction with load for surfaces lubricated with MoS$_2$ bonded with corn syrup (rubbing speed, 15.5 m/min); ×, plain mild steel; +, phosphated mild steel; ⊙, sulfided mild steel. [A. A. Milne, Experiments on the friction and endurance of various surface treatments lubricated with molybdenum disulfide. *Wear* **1**, 92–103 (1957/1958).]

TABLE 4. Coefficients of Friction of Various Lubricants
at High Contact Pressures[a]

Lubricant[b]	Coefficient of friction
Stearic acid	0.022–0.029
Molybdenum disulfide	0.032–0.033
Tungsten disulfide	0.032–0.037
Graphite	0.036–0.058
Silver sulfate	0.054–0.055
Turbine oil and 1% MoS_2	0.060–0.068
Lead iodide	0.061–0.071
Palm oil	0.063–0.075
Castor oil	0.064–0.081
Grease (zinc oxide base)	0.071–0.080
Lard oil	0.072–0.084
Grease (calcium base)	0.073–0.082
Residual	0.076–0.083
Sperm oil	0.077–0.085
Turbine oil and 1% graphite	0.081–0.105
Turbine oil and 1% stearic acid	0.087–0.096
Turbine oil	0.088–0.108
Capric acid	0.089–0.109
Turbine oil and 1% mica	0.091–0.105
Oleic acid	0.093–0.119
Machine oil	0.099–0.115
Soapstone (powdered)	0.169–0.306
Mica (powdered)	0.257–0.305

[a] J. Boyd and B. P. Robertson, The friction properties of various lubricants at high pressures. *Trans. ASME* **67**, 51–56 (1945).

[b] *Test conditions:* steel anvils of a Cr–Mo tool steel hardened to Rockwell C-63; surface finish, 2-μin. rms; rotational speed, 3.5 rad/min.; contact pressures, up to 400,000 psi; room temp.; normal air.

and 275° C (527° F). At 370° C (698° F), however, the pattern had changed to that of molybdenum trioxide, MoO_3, at the outer surface. Continued oxidation at higher temperatures caused the gradual increase in the coefficient of friction to a value of approximately 0.8 at 500° C (932° F). The MoO_3 forms as long crystals, but it does not appear to be abrasive, as had been earlier reported.* Oxidation of MoS_2 occurs first

* Earlier reports that MoO_3 is abrasive appear in error, probably due to impurities or some other side effects.

Figure 7. Shell four-ball test results showing the excellent load-carrying capability of MoS$_2$ under 1000-kg load (see text). [J. T. McCabe, Molybdenum disulfide—its role in lubrication. *Sci. Lubric.* **15**, (March 1963) Fig. 8].

on the outer surface of the films and gradually increases in depth. However, even when the fraction of MoS$_2$ remaining in the film is less than 0.1%, MoS$_2$ films still retain this lubricating property [3, 4]. Air ovens are satisfactory for baking or curing most adhesively bonded MoS$_2$ films without oxidation of the MoS$_2$.

The effect of temperature on the coefficient of friction is closely con-

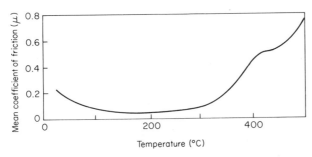

Figure 8. Effect of temperature on the friction of MoS$_2$ films heated for 30 min. in air. (MoS$_2$ films prepared by applying a few drops of an aqueous suspension of MoS$_2$ powder to a platinum bar, drying under a lamp, and removing excess lubricant by rubbing with a clean, dry cloth, then washing in a benze still. Coefficients measured with a hemispherical slider, 200-gm load, and 0.3-cm/min speed of sliding.) [R. F. Deacon and J. F. Goodman, Lubrication by Lamellar solids. *Proc. Roy. Soc. Ser. A.* **243**, 464–482 (1958).]

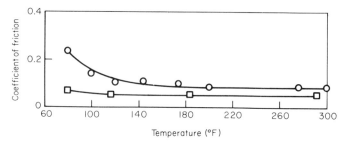

Figure 9. Effect of temperature and humidity on the friction of MoS₂ in air. Symbols: ○, room atmosphere (40–50% relative humidity); □, <6% relative humidity). *Test conditions*: 2-in, diam ring of SAE 4620 steel with Rockwell C62 hardness rotated on edge against the flat surface of a disk of SAE 1020 steel; load, 40 lb. sliding velocity, 5.7 ft/min. [M. B. Peterson and R. L. Johnson, Factors influencing friction and wear with solid lubricants. *Lubric. Engi.* **11**, 325–330 (1955).]

nected with the effect of humidity or moisture content. Thus, the fall in friction observed in Figure 8 with initially increasing temperature corresponds to the loss of volatile material, most of which is adsorbed water. This is also illustrated by the results shown in Figure 9, which shows the variation in the coefficient of friction with temperature in moist and dry air (relative humidities of 40–50% and less than 6%, respectively). The coefficient of friction in dry air is less than that in moist air, and it does not show as pronounced a drop with temperature.

Humidity

The adverse effects of humidity are further illustrated by the friction and wear of steel specimens lubricated with MoS₂ powder. As the relative humidity increased from 15 to 70%, the coefficient of friction increased from 0.05 to 0.38 and the wear in a 6-hr period increased by 200% [5].*

Drying of MoS₂ films due to frictional heating can cause a gradual reduction in the coefficient of friction with rubbing time.† As one example, the coefficient with steel specimens lubricated with MoS₂ powder decreased from 0.20 to 0.07 as the rubbing time increased to 75 min, during which time the specimen temperature increased from 22° to 50° C (72° to 122° F) [2]. Subsequent cooling back to 22° C resulted in a slight

---

* Other test conditions: Load, 40 lb; speed, 5.7 fpm; room temperature.

† The moisture content of MoS₂ powder in equilibrium with air of 60% relative humidity at room temperature is 1.1%, as determined by drying in an air oven at 120° C.

decrease in the value of the coefficient to 0.06 when the relative humidity was maintained at 0.1%; however, cooling to 22° C in a relative humidity of 60% resulted in an increase of the coefficient to 0.15. Thus, the coefficient of friction is not directly reduced by temperature itself in this range, but rather by the moisture content. The decrease in friction observed with increasing the sliding velocity or contact pressure is also probably associated with increased dryness caused by frictional heating.

Lubricity in Vacuum

Unlike graphite, MoS_2 is an effective lubricant in vacuum. In fact, MoS_2 provides a lower coefficient of friction in vacuum than in air, probably due to the removal of adsorbed water vapor, as discussed above. Typically, under conditions where the coefficient had a value of 0.20 in air, its value in vacuum was only 0.07, or about one-third of the value in air [6].

Research reported by Flom *et al.* [6] indicates that MoS_2 is an inherent lubricant, and that there is no evidence that gases or vapors are required for effective lubricity. This work disagrees with earlier work [7] which concluded that an amorphous layer of sulfur is produced during sliding with MoS_2, and that this amorphous sulfur performs a similar lubrication function for MoS_2 to that performed by water vapor for graphite. The earlier work was conducted with pressed pellets of MoS_2 riding against a stainless steel disk under the following conditions: vacuum of 10^{-6} Torr, sliding speed of 310 cm/sec, load of 395 gm, and temperatures from 25° to 60° C. When the MoS_2 surfaces were run until steady friction was obtained and then allowed to stand for a period of time (from 30 min to 16 hr), the coefficient of friction upon resumption of sliding was always higher ($\mu \approx 0.30$) than the equilibrium running value ($\mu \approx 0.07$), and then was gradually reduced to the low equilibrium value. It was thought that this was due to the evaporation of the amorphous sulfur during the periods of standing, and its subsequent regeneration when sliding was resumed. The later work of Flom *et al.* [6], which was conducted at lower pressures (vacuum $\approx 10^{-9}$ Torr), suggests that the increased friction on the resumption of sliding was actually due to contamination by residual gases in the vacuum system during the holding periods.

The low friction of MoS_2 appears to be due primarily to low adhesion between individual crystallites rather than to easy cleavage within individual crystallites (although some easy cleavage may occur) [7a]. The active edges of MoS_2 crystallites react readily with oxygen, and it is probably impossible to remove this oxide layer at temperatures below the decomposition temperature of MoS_2 in vacuum. This would account for the fact that MoS_2, unlike graphite, maintains low friction after outgassing at elevated temperatures. As water is removed, the edge oxide film becomes less hydrated, and there is less adhesion due to hydrogen bonding between the crystallites. An alternate hypothesis for the deleterious effect of moisture is that it prevents the MoS_2 from forming adherent films on steel surfaces [5]. Again, corrosive acids formed by reaction of moisture with MoS_2 can also increase wear.

Radiation Stability

The lubricity of MoS_2 is not damaged by radiation [7b], and MoS_2 has, in fact, been used effectively in nuclear power stations under conditions where conventional oils and greases are decomposed into "glues." If MoS_2 is used in the form of a bonded film, however, the bonding agent will eventually be the limiting factor that determines the film's radiation resistance.

Useful Forms

Table 5 lists the forms in which MoS_2 is used as a lubricant, and typical service applications. The various forms are discussed in Sections D through H.

D. DRY POWDERS AND DISPERSIONS

Molybdenum disulfide is often used in the form of dry powder, usually to facilitate assembly of parts or to provide lifetime lubrication. Burnished films of MoS_2 adhere better to metals than does graphite, probably due to strong sulfur-to-metal bonds. Table 3 (p. 82) gives the chemical analyses and particle-size distribution of typical MoS_2 powders that are commercially available.

Particle size must be suited to the application [7a], and the choice depends upon the surface roughness and other factors. If the particles are too large, they cannot enter all of the crevices in the surface to be lubricated, and

TABLE 5.   Typical Applications and Recommended Forms of MoS_2 Lubricants

Typical applications	Recommended forms				
	Dry powder	Dispersions	Greases	Concentrates[a]	Bonded coatings
Assembly	X	X	X	X	X
Bearings					
ball and roller		X	X		
sleeve	X	X	X	X	X
spherical, rod end, etc.			X	X	X
Cables		X	X		
Cams and followers		X	X	X	X
Closed gears		X	X		
Compressor liners			X		
Cold-metal forming (coining, heading)	X	X	X	X	X
Chassis lubrication, general			X		
Cutting tools		X			
Deep drawing	X	X		X	
Diesel liners			X		X
Drills and taps		X		X	X
Engine cylinder liners	X			X	
Forging and extruding presses				X	
Gear boxes		X	X		
Hot-metal forming (forging, extruding)	X	X			
Late centers an steady rests			X	X	
Lathe chucks and collets	X			X	
Machine tool ways and guides	X	X		X	X
Metal cutting		X			
Metal-forming dies	X	X			
O-rings and seals	X	X	X	X	X
part of composition	X		X		
Open gears			X	X	X
Oven conveyor chains		X			X
Packings	X	X	X	X	
Plastic components, part of composition	X				
Plug and thread gages	X	X	X	X	X

TABLE 5 (*Continued*)

Typical applications	Recommended forms				
	Dry powder	Dispersions	Greases	Concentrates[a]	Bonded coatings
Powder and lead screws			X		X
Press-fitting	X	X	X		
Punches				X	X
Punching and stamping	X	X		X	X
Railroad centerplates				X	
Relays and switches	X				X
Shrink fitting	X				
Sintered metals, part of composition	X				
Solenoid plungers	X			X	
Spline drives		X	X	X	X
Swaging	X				
Taper sleeves				X	
Threaded connections			X	X	X
Universal joints			X	X	X
Valves (stems, seats, etc.)	X	X	X	X	X
V-belts	X				X
Wearing-in (breaking-in)	X	X	X	X	X

[a] Concentrates are heavily loaded greases that have a paste consistency and special compounds added for specific purposes.

coverage will be inadequate. Particles that are too small are not as effective lubricants. Colloidal particles are useful for special applications, such as dispersions. Parts can be tumbled in MoS_2 powder plus cork, pine cones, or asbestos to aid in burnishing on a thin, uniform coating.

Table 6 lists a number of dispersions of MoS_2. These dispersions are often a more convenient form than dry powders for applying uniform coatings. Fine powders are used more often than coarse ones, and the solids content can cover a wide range. The dispersions are applied by spraying, dipping, or brushing, and can be applied from aerosol dispensers. Volatile carriers, such as alcohol and trichlorethylene, evaporate after application and leave a film of dry powder.

TABLE 6. MoS₂ Dispersions[a]

Dispersed substrate	Carrier	Solids content (%)	Particle size[b]	Density (lb/gal)	Diluent	Special characteristics	Typical applications
Colloidal MoS₂	Petroleum oil	10	A	8.4	Petroleum oil	Fine particles for low settling rates and better, more even usage of solids	Additive for specialized oils for general industrial and automotive uses for extreme pressure and high-temperature applications; drilling and tapping lubricant
	Polyglycol (water insoluble)	10	B	8.9	Polyglycol (water insoluble)	Low residue, high-temperature resistant, liquid carrier	Extreme-temperature lubricant: for film-car and core oven bearings
	Isopropanol	20	B	7.9	Commercial alcohols, ketones, etc.	Rapid evaporating carrier to produce a nonresin bonded dry film	Dry-film lubricant: pressfitting, thread antiseize coatings, light load mechanisms
	Trichlorethylene	20	B	12.2	Trichlorethylene, chlorothene, etc.	Rapid evaporating, nonflammable carrier	Nonflammable dry-film lubricant; general light load applications
	Mineral spirits	25	B	8.0	Mineral spirits, Stoddard solvent, etc.	Medium evaporating and low residue formulation	General high-temperature lubricant: for conveyor chains, kiln car wheel bearings

TABLE 6 (*Continued*)

Dispersed substrate	Carrier	Solids content (%)	Particle size[b]	Density (lb/gal)	Diluent	Special characteristics	Typical applications
	Water	35	B	11.0	Water	Low residue, easily evaporated carrier	Metal-working, such as wire drawing
MoS₂	Petroleum oil	65	C	15.0	Petroleum oil	High solids content for minimum formula dilution	Formulated into specialty greases
Graphite + MoS₂	Petroleum oil	37	C	10.0	None required	A unique blend of two solids to promote low friction and good release	Antiseize thread lubricant

[a] Data from Acheson Colloids Co., Port Huron, Michigan.

[b] The fineness range of the particles contained in these products has been designated arbitrarily by the letters, A, B, and C (A representing the finest particle-size range).

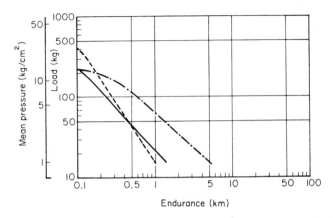

Figure 10. Variation of endurance with load for surfaces lubricated with MoS₂ dispersed in water (rubbing speed, 15.5 m/min). Symbols: ×, plain mild steel; +, phosphated mild steel; ⊙, sulfided mild steel. [A. A. Milne, Experiments on the friction and endurance of various surface treatments lubricated with molybdenum disulfide. *Wear* **1**, 92–103 (1957/1958).]

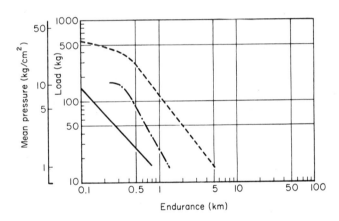

Figure 11. Variation of endurance with load for surfaces lubricated with MoS₂ dispersed in toluene (rubbing speed, 15.5 m/min). Symbols: ×, plain mild steel; +, phosphated mild steeel; ⊙, sulfided mild steel. [A. A. Milne, Experiments on the friction and endurance of various surface treatments lubricated with molybdenum disulfide. *Wear* **1**, 92–103 (1957/1958).]

The wear lives provided by MoS₂ are affected very much by the conditions of service and the manner of application. Figures 10–13 show typical variations of wear life with load for MoS₂ films applied from dispersions in water and toluene, with MoS₂–oil paste, and with a MoS₂

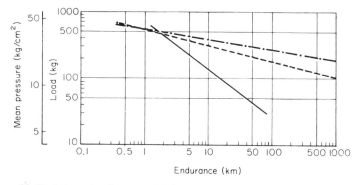

Figure 12. Variation of endurance with load for surfaces lubricated with molybdenum disulfide paste. (rubbing speed. 15.5 m/min). Symbols: ×, plain mild steel; +, phosphated mild steel; ⊙, sulfided mild steel. [A. A. Milne, Experiments on the friction and endurance of various surface treatments lubricated with molybdenum disulfide. *Wear* **1**, 92–103 (1957/1958).]

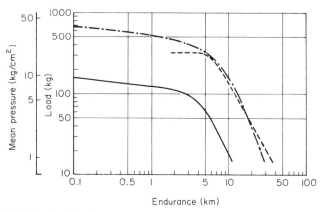

Figure 13. Variation of endurance with load for surfaces lubricated with molybdenum disulfide bonded with corn syrup (rubbing speed 15.5 m/min). Symbols: ×, plain mild steel; +, phosphated mild steel; ⊙, sulfided mild steel. [A. A. Milne, Experiments on the friction and endurance of various surface treatments lubricated with molybdenum disulfide. *Wear* **1**, 92–103 (1957/1958).]

film bonded with corn syrup. A paste of MoS_2 in oil* is particularly good. Although both phosphating and sulfiding increased the wear lives, as compared with untreated steel surfaces, the experimenters noted the following differences in the modes of failure [8]:

The phosphates surfaces failed by disruption of the coating and seizing and tearing of the underlying steel, accompanied by high and erratic friction, the

* 68–70% highly purified MoS_2, 26–28% light mineral oil, and 4% of a stabilizer.

transition from satisfactory running to failure being rapid. Failure of the sulphided surfaces was also accompanied by a rise in friction, but this was less marked than with the phosphated surfaces, while the immediate damage to the surfaces was also relatively slight. The residual protection of the underlying sulphide layer was also shown by some auxiliary experiments in which unlubricated surfaces had the moderate life of 11.2 km at a load of 15 kg ($\mu \approx 0.1$), seizure being immediate at higher loads.

E. BONDED FILMS

In order to increase wear life over that with loose powders, MoS_2 should be bonded to the surface to be lubricated. Table 7 illustrates the markedly superior wear life obtained by bonding MoS_2 powder with an organic resin binder, as compared to that obtained with unbonded MoS_2 powder.

TABLE 7.   Endurance Life of MoS_2 Used
in Various Forms[a]

Lubricant	Endurance at 35,000 psi (cycles to failure)
Resin-bonded MoS_2 film	9,860,000
Grease containing MoS_2	1,590,000
MoS_2 powder	130,000

[a] P. M. Magie, Moly bonded films. *Electromech. Des.* **4**, 50–54 (April 1960).

Bonded films of MoS_2 generally have better friction and wear characteristics than bonded films of other solid lubricants at room temperature. This is illustrated by the results summarized in Table 8.

As a result of their excellent combination of wear life and friction, bonded films of MoS_2 are used in many industrial and automotive applications, as well as in aircraft, rockets, missiles, satellites, and nuclear power plants where extreme environments and weight limitations are encountered. Next to oils and greases with MoS_2, bonded films are the most common manner of using MoS_2 as a lubricant. In many of these cases, the films are the sole source of lubrication; in others, they are used in conjunction with oils or greases.

The following factors affect the performance of bonded MoS_2 films*:

* Similar considerations apply also to bonded films of graphite and other solid lubricants, although the factors are not as well studied and documented as for MoS_2 films.

TABLE 8. Friction and Wear Lives of Bonded Films
of Solid Lubricants[a]

Solid lubricant[b]	Kinetic coefficient of friction	Wear life (cycles)
Molybdenum disulfide	0.036	103,680
Tungsten disulfide	0.034	100,460
Graphite	0.080	8,640
Cadmium iodide	0.088	4,320
Boron nitride	0.148	360

[a] B. C. Stupp, Molybdenum disulfide and related solid lubricants. *Lubric. Eng.* **14**, 159–163 (1958).

[b] *Test conditions:* Solid lubricants were bonded with a phenolic resin to a phosphated surface; rotary speed was constant at 72 rpm (25.9 fpm); coating thickness varied from 0.3 to 5 mils (0.0003–0.005 in.); all tests run at room temperature with no atmosphere control.

1. *Substrate conditions*—(a) base material, (b) hardness, (c) surface roughness, (d) surface pretreatment.

2. *Film conditions*—(a) binder material, (b) ratio of binder to MoS_2, (c) curing, (d) film thickness, (e) buffing and run-in.

3. *Operating conditions*—(a) mating parts, (b) humidity, (c) temperature, (d) presence of liquid lubricants, (e) presence of contaminants, (f) type of motion (g) sliding speed, (h) normal load, (i) vacuum, (j) radiation.

Base Material

Steel is the most common base material, but other metals and alloys are usually acceptable. Molded plastics and elastomers can also be coated, provided that the surface is properly roughened, chemically etched, or prepared and there is no adverse effect of the binder on the plastic or elastomer. Alternatively, the MoS_2 can be blended with the molding resins to produce solids with the lubricant dispersed throughout the body (see section G, this chapter, and chapters on plastics).

Hardness

The harder the substrate on which the MoS_2 film is coated, the lower is its coefficient of friction and the longer its wear life. Hard substrates provide a nonbuckling surface, whereas soft substrates allow a certain amount of flexing that disturbs the bond between the lubricant film and the substrate. When the rubbing surfaces of two parts have about equal areas and only one part is to be coated, it is usually preferable to coat the harder surface. The effect of hardness is negligible under low loads.

Surface Roughness

A slight degree of surface roughness is desirable, since it improves the adhesion between the binder and substrate. The optimum roughness for metals should be around 20 μin. RMS,* with a range from about 15 to 70 μin. If wear life is critical, the optimum roughness should be determined experimentally for the particular combination of film and substrate.

Surface Pretreatment

Most metals must be chemically processed to provide an etched surface or a chemical deposit on the surface that improves adhesion and increases the wear life. The treatments listed in Table 7 of Chapter 2 are generally specified. The difference between a good and bad pretreatment can result in an order-of-magnitude difference in the wear life of MoS_2 films. Each combination of substrate material, surface treatment, and dry film lubricant should be investigated if optimum performance is sought.

Binder Material

The purpose of the binder is to form a thin film that adheres strongly to the metal and resists abrasion and wear. Most failures of resin-bonded films are caused by breakdown of the binder rather than of the lubricating particles. The binders used in most commercial films today are organic resins such as the phenolics and epoxies (silicones and alkyds are also used) that require baking at temperatures up to 400° F. Air-drying films are also available; while these are sometimes more convenient to use, their properties are inferior to the oven-cured films. Other organic materials that have been used satisfactorily include varnish, glycerol, and corn

---

* This surface finish can be produced by sandblasting with 220-mesh alumina, Al_2O_3.

syrup. The results quoted in Table 9 illustrate the range of values for friction and wear life with different resins.

Inorganic binders include ceramics, sodium silicate, and metal matrices. These binders are useful in more extreme environments than can be tolerated by the organic binders, such as very high temperatures and nuclear radiation doses. Table 10 indicates the type of friction and wear behavior provided by metal-matrix bonded films of MoS_2. Silver-matrix bonded films provide friction and wear characteristics at room temperature that are very similar to those of phenolic-bonded films. (Compare data in Tables 9 and 10).

TABLE 9. Friction and Wear Lives of MoS_2 Films Bonded with Various Types of Organic Resins[a]

Type of resin binder[b]	Kinetic coefficient of friction	Wear life (cycles)
Phenolic	0.034	130,680
Phenolic–fluorocarbon	0.024	120,600
Phenolic–vinyl copolymer	0.040	102,660
Phenolic–vinyl acetate	0.040	96,120
Di-isocyanate–castor oil	0.060	96,750
Phenolic–acrylonitril	0.045	86,400
Di-isocyanate–phenolic	0.050	86,400
Corn-syrup	0.031	85,080
Phenolic–rubber	0.064	69,120
Phenolic–neoprene	0.035	68,000
Phenolic–acrylic	0.060	50,400
Phenolic–epoxy	0.063	36,000
Phenolic–amide	0.074	23,760
Phenolic–vinyl butyral	0.065	21,600
Vinyl chloride	0.070	21,600
Silicone	0.054	15,120

[a] B. C. Stupp, Molybdenum disulfide and related solid lubricants. *Lubric. Eng.* **14**, 159–163 (1958).

[b] *Test conditions:* coatings applied over a manganese phosphated surface. Rotary speed constant at 72 rpm (25.9 fpm). Thickness of coatings varied between 0.0003 to 0.0005 in. All tests run at room temperature and no atmospheric control.

TABLE 10.   Friction and Wear Lives of MoS_2 Films
Bonded with Various Types of Metal Matrices[a]

Metal matrix[b]	Kinetic coefficient of friction	Wear life (cycles)
Silver	0.032	103,680
Nickel	0.045	73,440
Chromium	0.040	43,200
Copper	0.086	38,880
Lead	0.110	860

[a] B. C. Stupp, Molybdenum disulfide and related solid lubricants. *Lubric. Eng.* **14**, 159–163 (1958).

[b] *Test conditions:* Rotary speed constant at 72 rpm (25.9 fpm). Thickness of coatings varied from 0.0004 to 0.0008 in. All tests run at room temperature without atmospheric control.

Ratio of Binder to MoS_2

The coefficient of friction and wear life varies with the relative amounts of binder and MoS_2* in the films. Too low a ratio of binder to MoS_2 results in poor bonding to the substrate, and too high a ratio gives poor lubricity. For resin-bonded films a ratio of about one part binder to two parts of MoS_2 is near optimum for normal applications in air.[†] This ratio can be modified for specific applications; for example, the MoS_2 can be increased to reduce friction, or a higher concentration of binder can be used where maximum wear life is important and the higher friction can be tolerated. For sodium–silicate bonded films, binder-to-MoS_2 ratios as low as 1 to 20 have been used.

Curing

Temperatures for curing or baking the binder vary with the type of binder used. Typical values are 200°–400° F for epoxy, silicone, and phenolic resin binders, 300°–400° F for sodium silicate binders, and up to

---

* Many commercially available MoS_2 films contain up to 10 or 20% of graphite mixed with the MoS_2.

† Normal range is from 1 binder: 1 MoS_2 to 1 binder: 4 MoS_2.

1000° F for ceramic binders. Curing times at these temperatures vary from 15 min to several hours. Curing is normally done in ovens with an air atmosphere. Volatile constituents should be removed slowly by initial baking at a low temperature. Rapid volatilization at too high an initial temperature can result in bubbling and a poor film. Curing temperatures should be below the point at which the substrate softens, distorts, or becomes dimensionally unstable.

Film Thickness

Resistance to wear is a maximum for a particular film thickness, and a properly applied film should generally be between 0.00015- and 0.0005- in. (0.15–0.5-mil) thick. Resistance to wear drops off rapidly at thicknesses below 0.15 mil. The decrease in wear life at thicknesses greater than the optimum is less pronounced, and is believed explainable by the fact that as the thickness increases, cohesion becomes less than adhesion of the film to the substrate, so that larger wear particles are produced.

Thickness can usually be controlled more satisfactorily by spraying than by dipping. By controlling the solids content and air pressure, a coating can be applied with a spray gun to within ± 0.00005-in. thickness.

The thickness of the films should be taken into account in dimensioning and specifying tolerances on drawings. Allowance should be made for the thickness of the film on surfaces that show a dimension to four decimal places, which usually involve a four-decimal tolerance. If chromium on hard nickel plating is to be used, either to provide a better surface beneath the MoS_2 coating or to ensure a smooth running surface to mate with a coated part, allowance should be made for the thickness of the plate.

When used on ball bearings, only the retainers are usually coated, but both the races and retainers can be coated if care is taken to keep the thickness on the races at a minimum (e.g., 0.0001–0.0002 in.) in order to avoid jamming of the bearings. Selecting balls that are slightly undersize or on the small side of the tolerances or selecting races on the proper side of the tolerances can be helpful in providing enough clearance so that the balls are not jammed by a thick film or coating. The coating on the retainer can generally be thicker than that on the races; a thicker coat here provides a reservoir for longer life, provided that the coating is not so thick that it has poor adherence. Small holes or indentations in retainers have been used to improve adhesion and increase the storage capacity.

Buffing and Run-In

New coatings of bonded MoS_2 films slough off slightly when first subjected to rubbing or sliding. For example, particles of the film flake off and contaminate the ball bearings so that the torque of freshly coated ball bearings is very high. Coatings should be run-in first by slowly rotating or sliding the mating parts over each other by hand, repeating this step in the opposite direction, and then blowing off the surfaces with clean, dry air or nitrogen to remove any dislodged particles. The parts should then be bench-cycled at higher speeds and cleaned by blowing. Running-in under gradually increasing loads can increase the wear life by 200%, as compared to no run-in. Coefficients of friction are slightly reduced during run-in.

Mating Parts

When two wear surfaces are about the same size, it is preferable to coat both surfaces since this produces a longer life. If one surface is considerably larger than the other, however, the benefits from coating the smaller surface are doubtful, and only the larger surface need be coated. Conversely, if only one surface can be coated, it should be the larger one. When only one surface is coated, the uncoated one should be smooth and free of burrs that might cut or abrade the coating on the mating part.

When only one of the mating surfaces is in motion, always coat the part that is constantly presenting a fresh surface area to the point of pressure, regardless of which part is in motion except when the "mover" is smaller (e.g., small piston in cylinder). For example, coat the cam, not the follower; coat the machine ways, not the stock. This minimizes the film's temperature and distributes its wear over the greatest area. As an example of the benefits from observing this point, the wear life of a block riding against a rotating ring was 196,000 cycles when the rotating ring was coated and only 1000 cycles when the block was coated [9].

Humidity

Humidity can either increase or decrease the wear life. For example, the wear life of an epoxy-bonded MoS_2 film increased from 150,000 to 210,000 revolutions as the relative humidity increased from 40 to 100%;

under similar conditions, the wear life of a film of MoS_2 + graphite with a vinyl-butyral binder was reduced from 100,000 to 40,000 revolutions [9]. Where the effect of humidity is critical, it should be verified experimentally for the specific coating.

Type of Motion

The coefficient of friction is always lower for undirectional motion than for oscillating motion. This may be due to continual reorientation of the surface particles in oscillating motion.

Temperature

Changes in coefficient of friction with temperature are relatively small. The wear life of resin-bonded films used in air is relatively independent of temperature up to the level at which the film is cured, and then decreases as the temperature is increased further. Oxidation of the resin binder usually imposes an upper temparature limit in air. Higher temperatures are possible in vacuum or inert atmosphere.

Presence of Liquid Lubricants

Using a lubricating oil with some MoS_2 films reduces their coefficients of friction without affecting their wear lives significantly. However, the wear lives of many resin-bonded coatings are seriously reduced if they are wet by oil during operation. The compatibility of a specific coating with oils should be checked with the coating vendor.

Sliding Speed

The static coefficient of friction is always higher than the kinetic. The coefficient of friction generally decreases with increasing sliding speed to about 100–1000 fpm, and it then remains substantially constant with further increases up to 8000 fpm [10]. However, the wear life may be shortened with increasing speed, possibly because of the higher temperatures that are generated, which tend to decompose resin binders. Figure 14 shows typical results for MoS_2 films bonded with various binders.

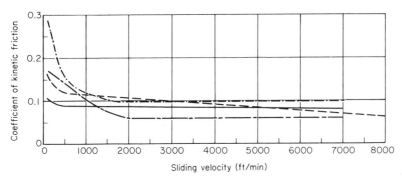

Figure 14. Effect of sliding velocity on the friction of steel specimens coated with films of MoS₂ applied with various bonding materials. [D. Godfrey and E. E. Bisson, *NACA Tech. Note* NACA TN **2802**.]

Normal Load

Increasing the normal load lowers the coefficient of friction but shortens the wear life.

Vacuum

Neither MoS_2 nor the binders commonly used are significantly volatile, and the various types of bonded MoS_2 films have demonstrated excellent behavior in vacuum.

Radiation

Present resin-bonded MoS_2 films are not significantly degraded by radiation and are useful up to dosages of at least 10^{11}–10^{12} ergs/gm(c) (or 10^9–10^{10} roentgens) [11–13].

F. FILMS FROM CHEMICAL FORMATION *IN SITU*

For effective lubrication, MoS_2 and other solid lubricating films must be firmly attached to the surface. An alternative to bonded films, which were considered in the preceding section, is to form the solid film *in situ* on the surface by chemical reaction. This can be done with molybdenum by heating it in the presence of gaseous atmospheres containing sulfur, such as hydrogen sulfide, H_2S. Table 11 presents data for the friction of MoS_2 formed in this manner on sintered molybdenum. Note that the coefficient of friction remained low at temperatures as high as 400° C (752° F). The wear and surface damage of steel sliding on sintered molybdenum containing MoS_2 were very slight, whereas on pure molybdenum they were severe.

TABLE 11.   Friction of MoS_2 Formed Chemically *in Situ* on Sintered Molybdenum[a]

Condition[b]	Coefficient of friction	
	Sintered molybdenum	Sintered molybdenum containing MoS_2
At room temp.		
initial	0.4	0.1
after repeated sliding	0.45	0.1
At various temps.		
15° C (59° F)	0.45	0.1
100° C (212° F)	0.5	0.08
200° C (392° F)	0.5	0.06
300° C (572° F)	0.5	0.06
400° C (752° F)	0.55	0.07

[a] F. P. Bowden, Frictional properties of porous metals containing molybdenum disulfide. *Research (London)* **3**, 383–384 (1950).

[b] *Test conditions :* data were obtained with a steel slider and a load of 4 kg (8820 lb).

Lubricating films of MoS_2, $MoSe_2$, WS_2, and WSe_2 can be produced on base metals such as steel and copper, as well as nonmetallic parts that can withstand the high processing temperatures needed, by electroplating molybdenum or tungsten over the substrate and then reacting in hydrogen sulfide or hydrogen selenide gas [14–17].* Nonmetallic surfaces are first

* Similarly, titanium can be reacted with iodine vapor to produce low-friction films of titanium di-iodide (Rowe [18]).

coated with an evaporated conductive film prior to electroplating. Chemical reaction conditions include gas pressures from 1 atm to 400 psi, temperatures up to 400° F, and reaction times up to 300 hr. The coefficients of friction of treated surfaces range from 0.05 to 0.08.

G. SOLIDS IMPREGNATED WITH MoS₂

Many plastics and powder metallurgy compacts can be impregnated with MoS_2 particles for gears, bearings, cams, seals, and similar applications. With such composites, the sliding process continues to feed a thin film of MoS_2 to the surfaces so that the friction remains low even after prolonged rubbing.

Table 2 lists values for the coefficients of friction of several plastics and porous metals, with and without MoS_2, and illustrates the marked reduction in coefficients of friction that can be achieved by impregnation with MoS_2. Equally important, wear rates are reduced by even greater factors. Other benefits obtained by adding MoS_2 to plastics include improving their resistance to cold flow, dimensional stability, and thermal conductivity.

Detailed information on plastics impregnated with MoS_2 is given in the chapters on the plastic materials. Tables 12 and 13 summarize data that illustrates the benefits of MoS_2 in metals. Impregnating MoS_2 into sintered bronze provides a greater improvement in friction and wear life than impregnation with graphite. MoS_2-filled metals also appear to retain their low coefficients of friction even after repeated sliding at elevated tem-

TABLE 12.   Friction and Wear of Sintered Bronze Bearings and Effects of Impregnation with Graphite and MoS_2[a]

Material[b]	Coefficient of friction	Wear (in.)	Time (hr)
Sintered bronze bearing	0.67	0.0025	70
with graphite	0.47	0.002	100
with MoS₂	0.34	0.001	400

[a] H. P. Jost, Pure molybdenum disulphide. *Sheet Metal Ind.* **33** (n. 354), 679–697 (1956).

[b] No oil lubrication.

TABLE 13.   Friction of Copper and Copper Containing MoS_2[a]

Condition[b]	Coefficient of friction		
	Solid copper	Sintered copper	Sintered copper containing MoS_2
At room temp.			
initial	~1.3	~0.3	0.15
after repeated sliding	~1.3	~0.8	0.13
At various temps.			
15° C (59° F)	1.3	0.3	0.13
100° C (212° F)	1.3	0.7	0.14
200° C (392° F)	~1.0	0.8	0.13
300° C (572° F)	~1.0	1.2	0.14
400° C (752° F)	~1.0	1.2	0.2

[a] F. P. Bowden, Frictional properties of porous metals containing molybdenum disulfide. *Research* (*London*) **3**, 383–384 (1950).

[b] *Test conditions:* data were obtained with a steel slider and a load of 4 kg. The rise in the coefficient of friction at 400° C (752° F) is believed to be due mainly to excessive oxidation of the copper.

peratures. A variety of sintered bronzes filled with MoS_2 is available commercially. Such materials can have porosities on the order of 10–25%, which permits them to be vacuum impregnated with a lubricating oil for further reducing friction.

The use of MoS_2 in carbon brushes for electrical use was discussed in Chapter 3.

H. OILS AND GREASES WITH MoS₂ AS AN ADDITIVE

The major use of MoS_2 is *not* where it is the predominant lubricant in the system, as in the cases considered above, but where it is only a contributing constituent to the lubrication provided by more conventional lubricants, such as oils and greases. For the past 10 years, automobile manufacturers and fleet operators have made increasing use of greases and oils containing micron- or submicron-size particles of MoS_2. The oils are generally petroleum oils and contain 2–3% MoS_2; greases typically contain 5–10% MoS_2, but may contain as much as 60% MoS_2.

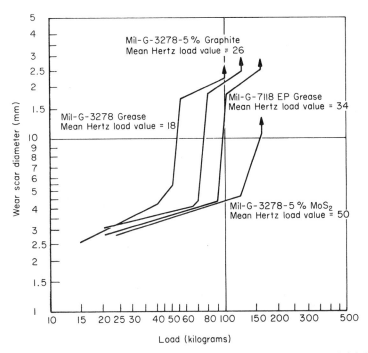

Figure 15. Shell four-ball test results with greases. [E. E. Smith, Molybdenum disulfide as a grease additive. *J. Nat. Lubric. Grease Inst.* **20,** 20–36 (1956).]

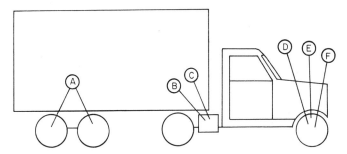

Figure 16. Cost savings with MoS₂ grease on truck fleets. Mobilgrease special with Moly: (A) 50% reduction in wheel bearing replacement costs, from $1015 in a single year to $443. (B) $25,300 labor savings through elimination of 1150 jobs per year by extending lubrication periods to 6000 miles. (C) Virtual elimination of monthly $24.50 U-joint replacements resulted in four-year savings of $1176. (D) Doubling and tripling of wheel bearing life resulted in an annual parts saving of $1036; labor, $150. (E) $1158 in parts and labor were saved by eliminating 24 king-pin replacements in the past four years. (F) Extension of chassis lubrication periods from 1000 to 3500 miles gave labor savings of $2211 yearly. [Courtesy of Mobil Oil Company. Source: *Molysulfide Newsletter*, **8,** no. 2, (1965). Climax Molybdenum Co.]

The heavily loaded greases have the consistency of paste and are known as "concentrates." If other additions are made for specific purposes, they are known in the industry as "compounds."

MoS₂-filled greases and concentrates are especially effective during the initial "run-in" of parts. They are commonly applied by brush or wipe methods during assembly to sliding surfaces, such as gear teeth. They are also effective under heavy loads. Figure 15 shows Shell four-ball test data that illustrates the superiority of MoS_2-containing grease over a conventional extreme pressure (EP) grease, a grease with graphite, and the grease alone. Figure 16 illustrates the areas in large trucks that have benefitted from such greases. Typical automotive applications include the following [19]: steering linkages, track rod joints, front drag links, intermediate lever systems, door and trunk mechanisms, gear mechanisms on windows, electric window regulators, ball joints, windshield wiper assemblies, wiper arm and nut, electric seat adjusters, propeller shaft

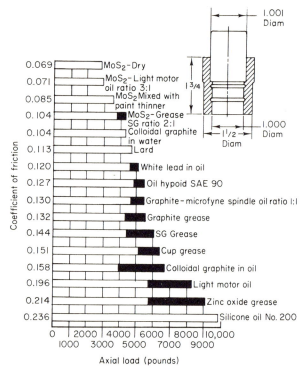

Figure 17. Coefficients of friction and axial forces required for interference-fit assembly with MoS₂ and other lubricants. [E. E. Smith, Molybdenum disulfide as a grease additive. *J. Nat. Lubric. Grease Inst.* **20**, 20–36 (1956).]

splines, turn signal switches, and outside remote control mirrors. Significantly, some of these applications involve intermittent operation under exposure to all types of weather conditions, including rain and freezing temperatures. Other applications under heavily loaded conditions include landing gear on large aircraft and railroad car centerplates, which are the connecting link between the body of the car and the truck unit which includes the wheels.

MoS₂-filled greases and concentrates are also used as press-fitting lubricants to reduce pressing forces required at assembly and disassembly. Figure 17 compares the axial forces and coefficients of friction obtained with various lubricants for press-fitting a 1.001-in. pin into a 1.000-in. bushing. Note that the grease containing MoS₂ had a coefficient of friction of 0.104 under these conditions, as compared with 0.132 for a graphite grease and 0.214 for zinc oxide grease.

MoS₂-filled greases and concentrates are also used as antigalling compounds to permit critical bolts, nuts, and studs to be drawn up to greater tightness without excessive torque (e.g., at heat exchanger heads), and as antisizing compounds on important threaded connections that may later require disassembly. Figure 18 compares the torque required to loosen a 1.25-in. × 7-in. long stud-nut assembly after 5000 hr at 1000° F. Under these severe conditions, MoS₂ allowed the part to be disassembled with the least effort.

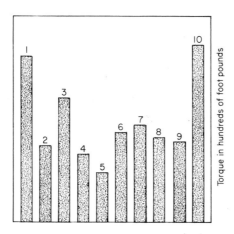

Figure 18. Torque for loosening stud-nut assembly after 5000 hr at 1000° F: 1. no lubricant. 2. graphite powder; 3. colloidal lead; 4. colloidal copper; 5. molybdenum disulfide; 6. aluminum powder; 7. calcium base grease; 8. silicone grease; 9. Colloidal zinc; 10. colloidal graphite. [E. E. Smith, Molybdenum disulfide as a grease additive, *J. Nat. Lubric. Grease Inst.* **20**, 20–36 (1956).]

REFERENCES

1. I.-M. Feng, Lubricating properties of molybdenum disulfide. *Lubric. Eng.* **8**, 285–289 (1952).
2. J. W. Midgley, The frictional properties of molybdenum disulphide. *J. Inst. Petrol. London* **42** (n. 395), 316–321 (1956).
3. D. Godfrey and E. C. Nelson, Oxidation characteristics of MoS_2 and effect of such oxidation on its role as a solid film lubricant. *NACA Tech. Note* NACA TN **1882**.
4. E. E. Bisson, The influence of solid surface films on the friction and surface damage of steel at high velocities. *Lubric. Eng.* **9** (1953).
5. M. B. Peterson and R. L. Johnson, Friction and wear characteristics of molybdenum disulfide. I: Effect of moisture. *NACA Tech. Note* NACA TN **3055** (1953).
6. D. G. Flom, A. J. Haltner, and C. A. Gaulin, Friction and cleavage of lamellar solids in ultrahigh vacuum. *Trans. ASLE* **8**, 133–145 (1965),.
7. V. R. Johnson and G. W. Vaughn, Investigation of the mechanism of MoS_2 lubrication in vacuum. *J. Appl. Phys.* **27**, 1173–1179 (1956).
7a. E. R. Braithwaite, Friction and wear of graphite and molybdenum disulfide. *Sci. Lubrication (London)* **18** (5), 17–21 (1966).
7b. E. R. Braithwaite, The mechanisms of lubrication with MoS_2. *Meccan. Ital.* **33**, 45 (1970).
8. A. A. Milne, Experiments on the friction and endurance of various surface treatments lubricated with molybdenum disulphide. *Wear* **1**, 92–103 (1957–1958).
9. A. DiSapio, Bonded coatings lubricate metal parts. *Prod. Eng.* **31**, 48–53 (1960).
10. R. L. Johnson, D. Godfrey, and E. E. Bisson, Friction of solid films on steel at high sliding velocities. *NACA Tech. Note* NACA TN **1578** (1948).
11. W. L. R. Rice, D. A. Kirk, and W. B. Cheney, Jr., Radiation-resistant fluids and lubricants. *Nucleonics* pp. 68–71 (1960).
12. S. L. Cosgrove, The effect of nuclear radiation on lubricants and hydraulic fluids. *REIC Rep.* n. **4**, addendum (1959).
13. M. T. Lavik, High temperature solid dry film lubricants. WADC-TR-57-455. Midwest Res. Inst., June 1959.
14. J. E. Brophy and R. W. Ingrahm, Application of solid lubricant coatings to surfaces, U. S. Patent 2,902,417, September 19, 1956).
15. J. E. Brophy, R. W. Ingrahm, and C. Pettus, Low friction coatings with good bond strength. *Mater. Des. Eng.* 10–11 (September 1961).
16. G. W. Rowe, Coatings on molybdenum for high temperature sliding. *Sci. Lubric.* **12**, 12–15 (1959).
17. C. E. Vest, Adaptation of a MoS_2 *in Situ* process for lubricating spacecraft mechanical components. Paper presented at *AIAA Ann. Struct. Mater. Conf. 5th*, 1964.
18. G. W. Rowe, *Brit. J. Appl. Phys.* **7**, 153 (1956).
19. J. T. McCabe, How the automotive industry uses solid lubricants. *Metal Progr.* 109 (May 1966).

Chapter 5

Miscellaneous
Inorganic
Compounds

While graphite and molybdenum disulfide continue to be the most commonly used inorganic solid lubricants, a number of other inorganic compounds have been suggested for special applications, particularly at high temperatures. Actual use of these materials is very limited, however.

A. DICHALCOGENIDES

Dichalcogenides of interest as self-lubricating solids include the disulfides, diselenides, and ditellurides of the metals molybdenum, tungsten, niobium, and tantalum.* Molybdenum disulfide is the most commonly used of these compounds, and it has been considered in detail in the preceding chapter.

Whereas MoS_2 occurs naturally, the other dichalcogenides are produced synthetically by direct combination of the elements at elevated temperatures. Typically, they are marketed with less than 0.5% impurities. They are relatively expensive and specialized materials, and they can generally be considered as direct substitutes for MoS_2 where MoS_2 is limited by its relatively poor oxidation resistance above 750° F or by its relatively high electrical resistivity.

---

* These are crystallographically similar lamellar-type compounds between metals from either Groups VB or VIB and nonmetals from Group VIA of the periodic table. "Niobium" is used in preference to "columbium" for the element of atomic number 41, in accordance with the recommended chemical nomenclature.

TABLE 1. Properties of the Dichalcogenides of the Group VB and VIB Metals[a]

Property	Disulfides				Diselenides				Ditellurides			
	MoS_2	WS_2	NbS_2	TaS_2	$MoSe_2$	WSe_2	$NbSe_2$	$TaSe_2$	$MoTe_2$	WTe_2	$NbTe_2$	$TaTe_2$
Molecular weight	160.08	248.05	157.04	245.01	253.87	341.84	250.83	238.80	351.17	439.14	348.13	436.10
Crystal structure[b]	Hex	Hex	Hex	Hex	Hex	Hex	Hex	Hex	Hex	Ortho	Trig	Trig
Lattice constants (Å)												
a	3.16	3.29	3.31	3.32	3.29	3.29	3.45	3.43	3.52	14.03	10.90	10.90
b	—	—	—	—	—	—	—	—	—	3.49	—	—
c	12.29	12.97	11.89	12.30	12.80	12.95	13.00	12.74	13.97	6.27	19.89	20.08
Volume resistivity[c]												
Ωin.	336	5.7	0.0012	0.0013	0.0073	44.9	0.00021	0.00088	342	0.0012	0.00023	0.00054
Ωcm	851	14.4	0.0031	0.0033	0.0186	144	0.00054	0.00223	869	0.0031	0.00057	0.00137

[a] D. J. Boes, New solid lubricants: Their preparations, properties, and potential for aerospace applications. *IEEE Trans. Aerospace* **2**, 454–466 (1964).

[b] Hex, hexagonal; Ortho, orthorhombic; Trig, trigonal.

[c] Measurements made on 1 × 0.250 × 0.125-in. bar hot-pressed at 200° C and 30,000 psi; measurements were made perpendicular to the pressing direction. Comparative volume resistivity of graphite is 0.00104 Ωin., or 0.00264 Ωcm.

114

Properties

Table 1 summarizes information on the crystal structure and electrical resistivity of these materials. Like MoS_2, the other dichalcogenides are blue-gray to black in color. They are relatively stable and inert. They are insoluble in water, oils, organic solvents, alkalis, and most acids (except aqua regia and hot concentrated hydrochloric, sulfuric, and nitric acids). They are attacked by the alkali metals (i.e., Li, Na, K, Rb, Cs, and Fr).

Friction Characteristics

Table 2 gives comparative data on the coefficients of friction of the various dichalcogenides. These tests were conducted with hot-pressed buttons of the dichalcogenides riding against disks of 440C stainless steel in ambient air. The coefficients indicated in this table have very likely been affected by the method of sample preparation, since the values given for MoS_2 are substantially higher than the values normally obtained and are, in fact, higher than the usual value for graphite. Nevertheless, the disulfides and diselenides of all four metals appear to offer coefficients of friction that are at least as low as that of MoS_2, and probably lower. $MoTe_2$ had a poor coefficient at high surface speeds and wore the disk lightly at the high-speed, high-load condition; the other three ditellurides had poor coefficients and wore the disk badly under all conditions, probably because of their unfavorable crystal structures. The sulfides and selenides of niobium and tantalum deposited heavier transfer films than those of molybdenum and tungsten.

Figure 1 summarize data on the effects of speed an load on the coefficients of friction of MoS_2, WS_2, WSe_2, and $NbSe_2$. These values were obtained with the solid lubricants in the form of thin films deposited by hand burnishing the powder onto metal surfaces.

WS_2 is an effective lubricant in vacuum; it behaves very similarly to MoS_2 [1, 2].

Oxidation Resistance

Tungsten disulfide, WS_2, provides significantly better oxidation resistance during heating in air than MoS_2, as indicated by the results in Table

TABLE 2. Coefficients of Friction for Dichalcogenides of Mo, W, Nb, and Ta[a,b]

Surface speed (fpm)	Load (psi)	Disulfides				Diselenides				Ditellurides				Graphite	Teflon TFE
		Mo	W	Nb[c]	Ta[c]	Mo	W	Nb[c,d,e]	Ta[c,d]	Mo[f]	W[g]	Nb[g]	Ta[g]		
7	80	0.228	0.166	0.165	0.066	0.22	0.174	0.12	0.136	0.105	0.29	0.64	0.48	0.13	0.058
35	80	0.21	0.142	0.098	0.033	0.178	0.13	0.12	0.084	0.20	0.38	0.70	0.53	0.14	0.138
70	80	0.17	0.136	0.098	0.068	0.20	0.10	0.15	0.10	0.34	0.38	0.61	0.55	0.16	0.21
7	170	0.228	0.173	0.155	0.05	0.20	0.185	0.11	0.106	0.11	0.27	0.31	0.41	0.11	0.055
35	170	0.185	0.175	0.092	0.055	0.167	0.09	0.12	0.08	0.19	0.44	0.74	0.60	0.14	0.224
70	170	0.166	0.148	0.074	0.062	0.174	0.10	0.17	0.095	0.19	0.34	0.74	0.59	0.14	0.25

[a] D. J. Boes, New solid lubricants: Their preparation, properties, and potential for aerospace applications, *IEEE Trans. Aerospace* **2**, 457–446 (April 1964).

[b] *Test conditions*: compacts prepared by hot-pressing 200-mesh powder of pure dichalcogenides in air at 200° C and 100,000 psi. Compacts tested by rotating against flat disks of 440C stainless steel in air at room temperature.

[c] Friction values are those before increase due to heavy film build-up.

[d] Friction became erratic after ~5 min due to film build-up.

[e] Unannealed.

[f] Wore disk lightly at high-speed, high-load condition.

[g] Wore disk—all conditions.

3. Tungsten disulfide has an advantage of about 200° F over MoS_2 with respect to oxidation resistance and thermal stability. The relatively slow rates of oxidation of WS_2, as well as WSe_2, are thought to be due to the formation of tungsten trioxide, WO_3, which is somewhat more protective against further oxidation and provides a lower coefficient of friction

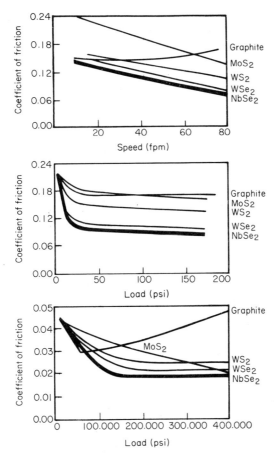

Figure 1. Effects of speed and load on the coefficients of friction of graphite, MoS_2, WS_2, WSe_2, and $NbSe_2$. [Tech. Data Sheet 207, Bemol Inc., Newton, Massachusetts, June, 1965].

than molybdenum trioxide, MoO_3. Dynamic coefficients of friction are about 0.2–0.3 for WO_3 and 0.5–0.6 for MoO_3 [3]. Tantalum disulfide, TaS_2, and tantalum diselenide, $TaSe_2$, are also reported to be more resistant to oxidation than MoS_2 [4].

TABLE 3. Comparative Oxidation Resistance of MoS_2 and WS_2[a]

Thermogravimetric analysis

Condition	WS_2 (°F)	MoS_2 (°F)
Inflection point indicating initial weight loss	860	662
Incipient point of slow oxidation rate	860	716
Incipient point of rapid oxidation rate	1475	1100
Inflection point indicating weight gain	2120	1436

Two-hour tube furnace test in air

Temperature (°F)	Sulfur percent loss by weight in air	
	WS_2	MoS_2
600	0.0	0.0
700	0.0	12.1
800	1.2	76.1
900	28.1	100.0
1000	77.7	100.0

[a] Tech. Data Sheet No. 201. Bemol, Inc., Newton, Massachusetts, August 1962.

Vacuum Stability

Figure 2 shows outgassing curves for several of the dichalcogenides and for graphite. WSe_2 and $NbSe_2$ provide significantly lower outgassing rates than graphite and MoS_2.

Electrical Resistivity

The electrical resistivity values quoted in Table 1 indicate that hot-pressed buttons of $NbSe_2$ are excellent conductors (better, in fact, than graphite). This property, together with a low coefficient of friction, makes

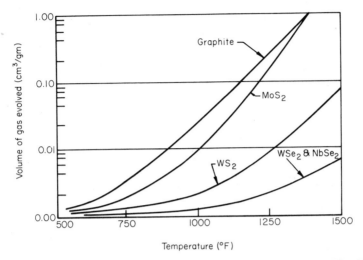

Figure 2. Outgassing characteristics in vacuum of graphite, MoS_2, WS_2, WSe_2, and $NbSe_2$. [P. M. Magie, "A Review of the Properties and Potentials of the New Heavy Metal Derivative Solid Lubricants." Bemol, Inc., Newton, Massachusetts, 1966.]

$NbSe_2$ appear promising for use in sliding electrical contacts. (However, note that satisfactory sliding electrical contacts have been made with MoS_2, which has a much higher resistivity in the form of hot-pressed buttons; cf. Chapter 4.)

Radiation Stability

Although the disulfide are normally stable under radiation doses encountered in most nuclear applications, they are less stable at very severe doses than the diselenides and ditellurides.

Composite Materials

A variety of metal-matrix composite materials incorporating the dichalcogenides is commercially available. These are similar to those with MoS_2 discussed in the preceding section. Table 4 lists properties of one such group of composite materials. Typical shapes produced from these materials include ball and roller bearings, bushings, seals, valve seats, gears, motor brushes, slip rings, and electrical contacts.

TABLE 4.   Properties of Composite Materials[a]

Composition (by wt.)	Density (gm/cm³)	Coeff. of friction	Hardness (Rockwell)	Max service temp. (°F)	
				Vacuum	Air
90–10 Ag–CbSe₂	8.82–9.31	0.10–0.18	M50–70	750	660
85–15 Ag–CbSe₂	8.57–9.04	0.08–0.17	M50–70	750	660
80–20 Ag–CbSe₂	8.32–8.78	0.07–0.15	M50–70	750	660
70–30 Ag–CbSe₂	7.85–8.28	0.06–0.14	M50–70	750	660
80–15–5/Ag–CbSe₂–C	7.35–7.76	0.08–0.17	—	Unstable	660
90–10 Ag–C	6.92–7.30	0.12–0.17	—	Unstable	660
80–20 Ag–CS	5.45–5.76	0.11–0.20	—	Unstable	660
90–10 Ag–MoS₂	8.45–8.92	0.10–0.19	—	750	500
80–20 Ag–MoS₂	7.63–8.06	0.08–0.18	—	750	500
85–15 Ag–WSe₂	9.22–9.73	0.10–0.18	M60–80	750	350
75–25 Ag–WSe₂	9.07–9.57	0.07–0.15	M60–80	750	350
70–20–10/Ag–PTFE–CbSe₂	6.14–6.48	0.06–0.15	H60–80	500	500
70–20–10/Ag–PTFE–WSe₂	5.29–5.59	0.06–0.15	H60–80	500	500
90–10 Ni–WS₂	7.87–8.31	0.12–0.20	B90–110	1000	660
80–20 Ni–WS₂	7.72–8.14	0.08–0.15	B85–105	1000	660
65–35 Ni–WS₂	7.52–7.94	0.05–0.12	B75–95	1000	660
95–5 Ni–CaF₂	7.35–7.76	0.30–0.40	B60–70	1200	1200
90–10 Ni–CaF₂	6.67–7.04	0.28–0.35	B65–80	1200	1200
85–15 Ni–CaF₂	6.31–6.66	0.28–0.33	B70–85	1200	1200
90–10 Ni–CbSe₂	7.69–8.12	0.12–0.20	B90–110	1200	660
80–20 Ni–CbSe₂	7.38–7.79	0.08–0.18	B85–105	1200	660
85–15 Ni–WSe₂	8.02–8.46	0.11–0.20	B110–120	1200	660
75–25 Ni–WSe₂	8.04–8.48	0.09–0.17	B95–105	1200	660
90–10 Ni–MoS₂	7.24–7.64	0.08–0.15	B70–80	750	500
85–15 Ni–MoS₂	7.10–7.50	0.07–0.15	B70–80	750	500

[a] Data from Bemol, Inc., Newton, Massachusetts.

B. LEAD COMPOUNDS

Lead monoxide, PbO, and lead sulfide, PbS, are among the more promising high-temperature solid lubricants. Although both compounds have been studied extensively since the mid-1950's, neither has yet been used much in practice.

TABLE 5. Friction and Wear Behavior of PbO and Other Solid Lubricants at 1000° F[a,b]

Lubricant[c]	Crystal structure	Melting point (°C)	Thermal stability	Method of application	Coefficient of friction	Surface conditions after test
None	—	—	—	—	>0.41	Severe galling
PbO	Orthorhombic	885	Stable to 753° C	Powder	0.08–0.12	No damage; nearly continuous lubricant film
				Evaporated metal film, then oxidized	0.07	No damage; nearly continuous lubricant film
Pb_3O_4				Powder	0.21	Discontinuous film; some metal contact; some rider wear
Ag				Evaporated film	0.25	Film worn and penetrated, allowing contact of base metals
Bi_2O_3				Powder	0.31	Very thin film with local metal contacts, formed after some galling
CdO	Cubic		Decomposes 950° C	Powder	0.34	Very thin film with local metal contacts
In_2O_3	Cubic	2000	Decomposes 850° C	Evaporated metal film, then oxidized	0.36	Very thin film with local metal contacts
WO_3	Orthorhombic or tetragonal		Stable to 700° C	Powder	>0.41	Failed; surface galled
Sb_2O_3	Orthorhombic	655		Powder	>0.41	Failed; irregular film; metal contact
PdO	Tetragonal		Decomposes 750° C	Powder	>0.41	Severe galling
BN				Powder	>0.41	Severe galling
Talc				Powder	>0.41	Severe galling

[a] M. B. Peterson and R. L. Johnson, *Lubric. Eng.* **13**, 203–207 (1957).

[b] Lubricants are listed in order of decreasing lubricating effectiveness.

[c] Solid lubricants were tested with a disk of Inconel X against a rider of Inconel; load and speed not specified.

Lead Monoxide*

The coefficient of friction of PbO is about 0.20–0.30 at room temperature. It decreases with increasing temperature to 0.05–0.10 at 500°–1000° F.[†] Table 5 compares the friction and wear at 1000° F for PbO with various other oxides, metallic silver, boron nitride, and talc. In these tests, PbO had the lowest coefficient of friction and provided the least wear of all the lubricants.

Ceramic-bonded films of PbO can be prepared by mixing the PbO with 5% SiO_2 and firing at 1650° F [6, 7]. The SiO_2 combines with molten PbO during firing at 1650° F and forms lead silicate which, upon solidifying, acts as a binder for the PbO phase of the coating. The powdered oxides are mixed by tumbling or pebble-milling, after which they are applied to the metal substrate either dry or, preferably, sprayed on as an aqueous slurry. A well-atomized spray should be used and the metal should be heated to about 300° F. Under these conditions the liquid carrier evaporates instantly, so that uniform coatings of appreciable thickness can be built up. Parts are fired at 1650° F until all the coating material is molten and then air-cooled. The optimum film thickness for minimum friction and wear is between 0.001 and 0.003 in. (1–3 mils).[‡]

Figure 3 shows the effect of sliding velocity and temperature on the coefficient of friction of 0.001-in. thick coatings of PbO–5% SiO_2. Increasing either the sliding velocity or the temperature lowers the friction. At high velocities (above 5000 fpm) the coefficient is constant at about 0.05 for all temperatures, from room temperature to 1200° F. At low velocities, the coefficient is higher and decreases more rapidly with increasing temperature. The effects of increasing velocity and temperature are probably due to the fact that both changes increase the surface temperature of the coating, which is the controlling factor.

Figure 4 compares the wear life of coatings of PbO–5% SiO_2 with resin-bonded films of MoS_2. At room temperature, the wear life of the MoS_2 films is ten times that of the PbO film. Increasing the temperature reduces the wear life of the MoS_2 film and improves that of the PbO film, however, so that at 500° F the wear life of the PbO film is approximately

---

* PbO (yellow lead) is converted to Pb_3O_4 (red lead) during oxidation at low temperatures; Pb_3O_4 reverts to PbO above 1000° F.

[†] These values were obtained with Inconel sliding against Inconel X, using PbO powder as the lubricant, at a load of 40 lb and a sliding velocity of 5.7 fpm [5].

[‡] These thickness values are based on tests under sliding friction at 1250° F, 430 fpm, and 1000-gm load.

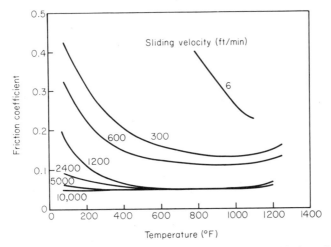

Figure 3. Effects of sliding velocity and temperature on the friction of PbO–5% SiO$_2$ coatings. *Test conditions:* film thickness, 0.001 in.; load, 1000 gm. [H. E. Sliney, *Natl. Advisory Comm. Aeron.* RM E58B11, Fig. 3 (1958).]

equal to that of the MoS$_2$ film at room temperature. Even at 1250° F the wear life of the PbO film is approximately equal to that of the MoS$_2$ film at room temperature.

Table 6 summarizes test data on the lubrication of ball bearings at

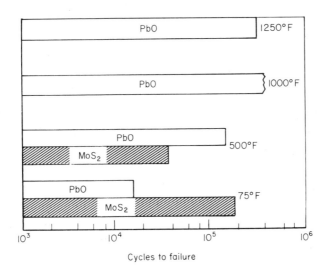

Figure 4. Endurance of coatings of PbO–5% SiO$_2$ and MoS$_2$ at various temperatures. [H. E. Sliney, *Natl. Advisory Comm. Aeron.* RM E58B11, Figs. 4 and 5 (1958).]

TABLE 6.   Some Results with Ball Bearings Lubricated with PbO Coatings
at Elevated Temperatures[a]

Test 1	
Ball bearings:	20-m bore, races and balls of M-10 tool steel, retainers of Monel, inner-race riding
Coating:	PbO film, 0.001-in. thick, applied to the inner-race riding surfaces and to the ball pocket surfaces of the retainers
Load:	15 lb, thrust
Speed:	2400 and 5000 rpm
Temp.:	1000° F
Results:	Bearings ran 2 hr at each speed without failing; unlubricated bearings failed in 1 min

Test 2	
Ball bearings:	35-mm bore, races of René 41 nicklel-base alloy, balls of Stellite, retainers of Ni-resist cast alloy, outer-race riding
Coating:	PbO film, 0.001-in. thick, applied to the outer-race riding surfaces and to the ball pocket surfaces of the retainers
Load:	100 lb, thrust
Speed:	5750 rpm
Temp.	1200° F
Results:	No lubrication failure in 44 hr operation of two bearings. Bearings were reassembled and run another 10 hr at 10,000 rpm and 1200° F without failure of the lubricant

[a] H. E. Sliney, NASA data.

elevated temperatures with PbO coatings. These data indicate that the PbO coating performs well in this difficult application.

Ceramic-bonded PbO films are intended primarily for use at elevated temperatures. Although they have relatively high friction at room temperature, their wear lives are sufficient so that they can be useful in high-temperature applications involving starting or cycling through room temperature. Their endurance lives are a maximum at around 1000° F.

Lead Sulfide

The coefficient of friction of PbS is about 0.25 at 1000° F and somewhat higher at room temperature [8].* Boric oxide, B_2O_3, has been used as a binder for bonded films of PbS; a weight ratio of six parts PbS to one part B_2O_3 is used. PbS films bonded with B_2O_3 provided a coefficient of friction of 0.12 together with good wear life at 1000° F, but friction was high at lower temperatures [9].

C. FLUORIDES

Mixtures of calcium fluoride, CaF_2, with other fluorides have been investigated as bonded films and as additives to metal composites. These are reported to be potentially useful as solid lubricants up to 1900° F [10–12]. Fused coatings of binary mixtures of the fluorides of calcium, barium, and lithium (CaF_2, BaF_2, LiF) have been shown useful on nickel–chromium alloys submerged in liquid sodium at 1000° F, as well as in hydrogen, vacuum, and air at elevated temperatures [13].

Bonded Films

Figure 5 illustrates the usefulness of the ceramic-bonded films of CaF_2 at temperatures above those at which films of MoS_2 or $PbO–SiO_2$ are useful. Although the coefficients of friction and wear rate of the CaF_2 film are inferior to those of the other two films below 650° F, both characteristics improve with increasing temperature so that the CaF_2 film is superior to the other two films above 800° F. As is typical for many ceramic-bonded films of solid lubricants, the coefficient of friction and wear rate are most favorable under conditions conducive to high surface temperatures, such as high ambient temperatures, high sliding velocities, and high load. In the temperature range of most interest for using ceramic-bonded films of CaF_2 (i.e., from about 600° to 1900° F), the coefficient of friction is about 0.10–0.15 and the wear rate is comparable to that of a good resin-bonded film of MoS_2 at room temperature.

---

* PbS was tested in the form of pellets riding on polished metal at 128–326-gm load and 500-fpm sliding velocity. Measurements of the coefficient of friction at room temperature were erratic, but were generally between 0.27 and 0.47.

The ceramic binder used with CaF_2 is a mixture of the oxides of cobalt, barium, and boron,* and it is used in the proportion of one part of ceramic binder to three parts of CaF_2. Adding 1–3% molybdic oxide, MoO_3, improves the properties, due to increasing the fluidity of the molten ceramic binder during firing and enhancing the wettability of the CaF_2 particles by the molten ceramic. Adding 3% bentonite clay (a suspending agent) improves spraying characteristics and wear life.

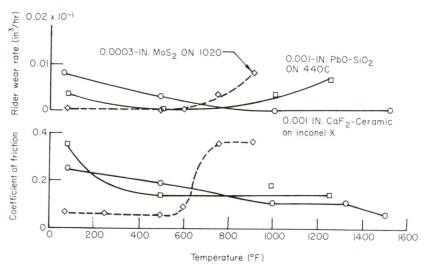

Figure 5. Effect of temperature on wear and friction with solid films. *Test conditions:* cast Inconel riders; sliding velocity, 430 fpm; load, 1000 gm. [E. E. Bisson and W. J. Anderson, *Advanced Bearing Technology. NASA Spec. Publ.*, NASA SP-**38**, p. 233, Fig. 8-23 (1964).]

Processing involves mixing the CaF_2, ceramic binder, and additives in a pebble mill, preparing a slurry from the mixture, and spraying the slurry onto the substrate to be coated. Steel substrates should be prepared by sandblasting and heating for a few minutes to 1700° F to produce a thin, blue interference oxide film to promote adhesion. A coating is built up to a thickness of 1–2 mils (0.001–0.002 in.) by repeated passes of the spray. The coating is fired at 2150° F. For use at 1000°–1600° F, rubbing a very thin film of a binary fluoride eutectic (62% BaF_2, 38% CaF_2) on the surface improves the friction coefficient of the ceramic-bonded coating.

---

* The powdered ceramic binder or frit has the composition 60%, CoO, 20% BaO, and 20% B_2O_3; it is available commercially from the Ferro Corp., Cleveland, Ohio.

Figure 6 summarizes information of friction and wear of fused fluoride coatings on a nickel–chromium alloy at a temperature of 1000° F and in environments of liquid sodium and a mixture of hydrogen and nitrogen gas. Firing temperatures for these coatings ranged from 1550° F for the 81.4% CaF$_2$ + 18.6% NaF coating to 1950° F for the 80% CaF$_2$ + 20%

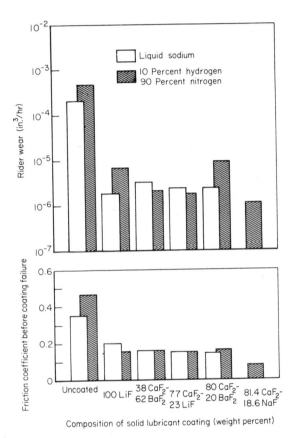

Composition of solid lubricant coating (weight percent)

Figure 6. Lubrication of nickel–chromium alloy with fused fluoride coatings. *Test conditions :* environment, liquid sodium and 10% H$_2$ + 90% N$_2$; temperature, 1000° F; coating thickness, 1–2 mils (0.001–0.002 in.); sliding velocity, 2000 fpm; load, 500 gm; specimens, 0.1875-in. radius hemispherical riders sliding against coated disks. (*NASA Tech. Note*, NASA TN D-2348, p. 10, Fig. 5.)

BaF$_2$ coating. The CaF$_2$ + BaF$_2$ coatings gave the best overall performance, considering compatibility of the coatings with liquid sodium together with the friction and wear behavior.

CaF$_2$–BaF$_2$ films bonded with aluminum phosphate, AlPO$_4$, (6% by volume) are reported to perform quite well at elevated temperatures, with a coefficient of friction of 0.10 at 800°–1400° F [14]. Friction and wear are both poor at room temperature, but they can be improved by adding gold or graphite powder to the film.

Although laboratory tests indicate that CaF_2–BaF_2 lubricants appear promising for high-temperature uses, application studies to date on bearings have not been too successful (e.g., [15]), and this type of lubricant must still be considered experimental.

Composites

The CaF_2–BaF_2 eutectic mixture, impregnated into porous nickel and nickel-chromium alloys with a concentration of 35% by volume of the eutectic, provided a coefficient of friction of about 0.20 at temperatures around 1450° F ($\sim$800° C). The friction and wear of these metal–base composites was also reported to be low at room temperature [16].

D. BORON NITRIDE

The crystal structure of boron nitride, BN, is similar to that of graphite [16a],* and, like graphite, fine powders of BN feel slippery when rubbed between two fingers. However, the coefficient of friction of BN films is normally about 0.35–0.40, which is substantially higher than that provided by graphite films under similar conditions, and bonded films of BN have relatively low load capacities and short wear lives.

Boron nitride is a soft material, having a hardness between 1 and 2 on the Mohs' scale. It has good oxidation resistance to about 1300° F, which is about the limiting temperature for using it in powder form in an oxidizing atmosphere. In solid form, BN is useful to about 1800° F in air and to 3000° F in an inert atmosphere [17].

The main use of BN is as an electrical insulator. Its use for applications involving friction and wear has been very limited [18, 19].

---

* Crystal structure of BN is hexagonal, with $a = 2.50$, $c = 6.66$, and $c/a = 2.66$.

REFERENCES

1. D. G. Flom, A. J. Haltner, and C. A. Gaulin, Friction and cleavage of lamellar solids in ultrahigh vacuum. *Trans. ASLE* **8**, 133–145 (1965).
2. M. T. Lavik, G. E. Gross, and G. W. Vaughn, Investigation of the mechanism of tungsten disulfide lubrication in vacuum. *Lubric. Eng.* **15**, 246–249, 264 (1959).
3. P. M. Magie, "A Review of the Properties and Potentials of the New Heavy Metal Derivative Solid Lubricants." Bemol, Inc., Newton, Massachusetts.
4. J. K. Lancaster, Composite self-lubricating bearing materials. *Proc. Inst. Mech. Eng.* **182**, pt. 1 (1967–1968).
5. M. B. Peterson and R. L. Johnson, Solid lubricants for temperatures to 1000° F. *Lubric. Eng.* **13**, 203–207 (1957).
6. H. E. Sliney, The lubricating properties of lead monoxide-base coatings of various compositions at temperatures to 1250° F. *NASA MEMO.* **3-2-59E** (1959).
7. H. E. Sliney, Effect of sliding velocity on friction properties and endurance life of bonded lead monoxide coatings at temperatures up to 1250° F. *Natl. Advisory Comm. Aeron.* RM E58B11 (1958).
8. M. T. Lavik, Ceramic bonded solid-film lubricants, WADC-TR-60-530, Wright Air Develop. Center, Wright-Patterson Air Force Base, Ohio. 1960.
9. B. D. McConnell, Solid-film lubricants for extreme environments. *Prod. Eng.* **32**, 70–73 (1961).
10. H. E. Sliney, Improved ceramic-bonded calcium fluoride coatings for lubricating nickel-base alloys in air at temperatures from 500° to 1700° F. *NASA Tech. Note* NASA TN D-**2688** (1965).
11. H. E. Sliney, Lubricating properties of ceramic-bonded calcium fluoride coatings on nickel-base alloys from 75° to 1900° F. *NASA Tech. Note* NASA TN D-**1190**, (1962).
12. H. E. Sliney, Lubricating properties of some bonded fluoride and oxide coatings for temperatures to 1500° F. *NASA Tech. Note* NASA TN D-**478** (1960).
13. H. E. Sliney, T. N. Strom, and G. P. Allen, Fused fluoride coatings as solid lubricants in liquid sodium, hydrogen, vacuum, and air. *NASA Tech. Note* NASA TN D-**2348** (1964).
14. V. Hopkins, R. D. Hubbel, and M. T. Lavik, Improved high-temperature solid film lubricants, AFML-TR-67-223, Pt. II, Air Force Materials Lab., Wright-Patterson Air Force Base, Ohio, February 1969.
15. C. S. Armstrong, Airframe bearings for advanced vehicles, AFDL-TR-69-66, Air Force Flight Dynamics Lab., Wright-Patterson Air Force Base, Ohio, August 15, 1969.
16. H. E. Sliney, Self-lubricating composites of porous nickel and nickel-chromium alloy impregnated with barium fluoride-calcium fluoride eutectic. *NASA Tech. Note* NASA TN D-**3484** (1966).
16a. E. R. Braithwaite and G. W. Rowe, Principles and applications of lubrication with solids. *Sci. Lubrication* (March 1963).
17. *Boron nitride*, Tech. Bull. from the Carborundum Co.
18. G. W. Rowe, Some observations on the frictional behavior of boron nitride and graphite. *Wear* **3**, 274–285 (1960).
19. R. F. Deacon and J. F. Goodman, Lubrication by lamellar solids. *Proc. Roy. Soc. Ser. A.* **243**, 464–482 (1958).

Chemical Seals

Hydraulic Pump Bearings

Vane Pump Parts

Meter and Valve Parts

Self-Expanding Piston Rings

Jet Engine Bearing Seals

See facing page for legend.

Molded phenolic bearing for the textile industry. Bearing was made from macerated fabric-phenolic molding compound. This application requires that the bearing be non-corrosive and that it must not discolor threads. (Source: Formica Corp., subsidiary of American Cynamid, Cincinnati, Ohio.)

Facing page illustration: Typical applications of carbon-graphite. **Chemical Seals:** Surface speeds to 5000 ft/min. Temperature range: 100–600° F. Sealing: acid solutions, alkaline solutions. Industrial solvents, petroleum derivatives. **Hydraulic Pump Bearings:** For military aircraft. Operating in hydraulic fluid (MIL H–5606) at 3000 psi. Temperature range: −65–275° F. Shaft speeds: 3500–12,500 rpm. **Vane Pump Parts:** Engineered for hot-air compressor-inlet temperature, 180° F; discharge, 380° F. Operating speed: 1750 cpm (150 ft/min). Cylinder is stainless steel. **Meter and Valve Parts:** Piston and seat for high accuracy; positive displacement meter used to measure water, oil, gasoline, acids, alcohol, and solvents. Mating materials: 316 SS and bronze. Operating speed: up to 200 cpm. **Self-Expanding Piston Rings:** Designed to operate without lubrication in an aircraft camera pump—air from −65–250° F—at altitudes from sea level to 60,000 ft. Stainless steel rotor assembly revolves at 7200 rpm. **Jet Engine Bearing Seals:** Surface speeds to 17,00 ft/min. Temperature range: −65–1100° F. Sealing: hot air at 30–120 psig and aircraft turbine oils at atmospheric pressure. (Source: Pure Carbon Co., Inc., St. Marys, Pennsylvania.)

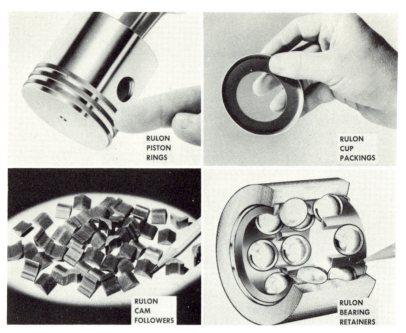

Typical applications of Rulon reinforced Teflon. (Source: Dixon Corp., Bristol, Rhode Island.)

Impeller assembly of injection-molded "Nylatron GS" nylon for submersible centrifugal pump. Use of MoS_2-filled nylon eliminated problems caused by dimensional changes in conventional nylon impellers due to water absorption. Other benefits were less friction and wear and closer molding tolerances. (Source: The Polymer Corporation, Reading, Pennsylvania.)

Wear strips of ultrahigh molecular weight polyethylene serve in a large brewery's bottling and canning operations. The plastic strips, at one-third the cost, outwear phosphor bronze formerly used by two-to-one. (Source: Polymers Dept., Hercules Inc., Wilmington, Delaware.)

Typical plug valve lubricated by a bonded film of MoS_2. Greases and oils could not be used as lubricants because they were removed by the water-laden gasoline carried by this valve, after which the valve corroded until the torque became so high that the valve was inoperative. The use of a corrosion-resistant bonded film of MoS_2 solved the problem. (L. C. Horwedel, Solid lubricants as organic finishes, *Ann. Tech. Proc. Amer. Electroplaters' Soc.*, *47th*, 1960, Fig. 5.)

Chapter 6

Soft
Metals

Soft metals have a number of properties that make them attractive as solid lubricants for special situations. For example, in addition to the fact that they have low shear strengths and can be applied as continuous films over harder metals, they are good conductors of heat and electricity, and they are stable at elevated temperatures as well as in vacuum* or exposed to nuclear radiation. Thin films of silver have been used for many years to lubricate high-speed ball bearings on rotating anode X-ray tubes. More recently, they have been used on satellite parts operating in space, and on other equipment exposed to high temperatures and nuclear radiation.

A. GENERAL CHARACTERISTICS

Table 1 lists the hardnesses and melting points of the soft metals of most interest as solid lubricants. Their hardnesses lie between 1 and 3 on the Mohs' scale (i.e., their hardnesses are similar to those of talc, gypsum, and calcite, which have Mohs' hardnesses of 1, 2, and 3, respectively). Coefficients of friction for thin films of these metals on hard substrates are typically on the order of 0.30.

Of the metals listed in Table 1, gold alone does not oxidize under normal conditions, and the other precious metals (silver, platinum, and rhodium) oxidize only slightly. Silver oxide, Ag_2O, decomposes at around 300° F. The other metals oxidize more readily, and their oxides reduce wear life in normal air operation. Oxidation is not a problem in vacuum,

---

* Exceptions include zinc and cadmium, which have relatively high vapor pressures.

TABLE 1. Properties of Soft Metals[a]

Metal	Moh hardness	Melting point (°F)
Indium	1	311
Thallium	1.2	572
Lead	1.5	621
Tin	1.8	449
Cadmium	2	610
Barium		1300
Silver	2.5–3	1761
Gold	2.5	1945
Platinum	4.3	3224
Rhodium	4.5–5	3571

[a] M. B. Peterson, S. F. Murray, and J. J. Florek, *Trans. ASLE* **2**, 225–234 (1960).

however, and reactive metals such as barium have demonstrated excellent lubricity on ball bearings operating in evacuated X-ray tubes.

Although they are also soft metals, the alkali metals (e.g., sodium and potassium) are omitted from Table 1 because of their low melting points. They are of more interest for liquid metal lubrication. The same is true of another soft metal, gallium, which melts at 86° F.

B. THIN FILMS OF SOFT METALS

Preparation

Thin films are commonly deposited by vacuum deposition, chemical plating, and mechanical burnishing. Obtaining good adhesion between the films and substrate is the major problem in securing long wear life. Careful cleaning to remove greases, oxide films, and other contaminants is the first step. Chromium oxide is difficult to remove from stainless steels, and it has also been reported to introduce abrasive particles that shorten wear life. Electron bombardment and thermal etching prior to vacuum deposition improves adherence and the wear life [1]. Silver and gold films usually adhere better to low-alloy steels, such as SAE 52100 chrome steel, than to steels such as 440 C stainless steel. A thin film of nickel over stainless steels improves the adherence of vacuum-deposited silver films. Tool steels and 440 C stainless have been used satisfactorily at high temperatures. Care should be taken not to disrupt the films by mishandling when the coated parts are assembled.

Although the metal films should adhere strongly to the metal substrate, they should not diffuse into the mating parts and bond them together. Experience with metal gaskets for demountable vacuum seals is pertinent to this requirement. Soft nickel gaskets are not suitable with steel flanges, for example, because the nickel diffuses into the steel (the atomic diameter of nickel and iron are about equal) and makes it difficult to break open the joints after the vacuum is released. Thin rings of soft copper sheet or of gold wire have been most satisfactory for high vacuum seals and provide tight joints that can be easily broken when desired. This capability may be important where short periods of operating sliding parts are followed by long hold-times, as on some satellite duty cycles. Material selection and film processing should be concerned, therefore, with obtaining good adhesion to a hard substrate and minimizing the possibility of subsequent film diffusion into the mating hard surface during long stop-times in vacuum.

The coefficient of friction is generally a minimum at film thicknesses on the order of 10^{-5} in. (0.01 mil). Thicker films of the soft metals result in larger areas of real contact and thereby increase the coefficient of friction at a gradual rate. Thinner films cause an abrupt increase in the coefficient of friction, apparently because they do not prevent the substrate from interacting with the mating part and thus forming stronger junctions. There is also some indication that thinner films can give low coefficients of friction if the surfaces are highly polished [2, 3]. In one study [4] of the relationship between the thickness of evaporated thin silver films varying from 300–2000 Å on the operation of ball bearings in vacuum of 10^{-8} mm Hg, thicknesses of 300 and 1100 Å gave longer operating lifetimes and generally lower torque than either intermediate film thicknesses or thicknesses greater than 110 Å. Results were erratic and apparently influenced by other factors, such as surface finish. The silver films in this investigation were applied by vacuum deposition onto 1/16-in. diam stainless steel balls. The balls were assembled into rings of 440 C stainless steel and operated at speeds from 1000 to 1690 rpm. No tests were run for longer than 100 hr. Evaporated silver coatings that were impregnated with molybdenum disulfide particles and ranging in thickness from 930 to 2000 Å gave generally better results than the plain silver films.

The need for a uniform film thickness has not been clearly established, although most evidence indicates that uneven films aggravate wear. Other studies conclude that an initial nonuniformity is not a problem and that any high spots will be quickly evened off during operation. With films of barium, for example, a liquid phase is thought to form at the rubbing surfaces so that the film is distributed uniformly during operation, thereby eliminating the initial nonuniformity in thickness as a problem [5].

Properties

The coefficients of friction provided by thin films of soft metals are not particularly low, being on the order of 0.3 for most conditions. Figure 1 shows values for the coefficient of silver films under various conditions.

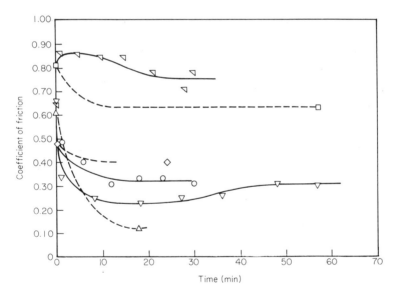

Figure 1. Coefficient of friction with various silver films. *Test conditions*: hemispherical rider of Inconel sliding back and forth on a flat surface of Inconel X; load, 4.14 lb; speed, 18 in./min; atm, air; temperature, 1200° F. Symbols: ◁, solid silver; □, ○, ▽, rolled silver film, 9.5 mils thick; ◇, △, plated silver film, 2 mils thick.

Increasing either the temperature or the load reduces both the coefficient of friction and the wear life [2]. The effect of temperature on the friction coefficient may be due to a reduction in the shear strength of the metal film.

Figure 2 is a plot of the vapor pressure of a number of metals against temperature. Except for mercury, Hg, which is quite volatile, the vapor pressures of the metals are less than that of most oils and greases. Thin films of metals such as silver (Ag) and gold (Au) are quite stable in vacuum, whereas films of cadmium (Cd) and zinc (Zn) may sublime at significant rates, depending upon the substrate temperature. (During vacuum deposition, the metals are heated to temperatures at which their vapor pressures are about 10^{-2} Torr; evaporation is sufficiently rapid at this level to form useful films in a reasonably short time.)

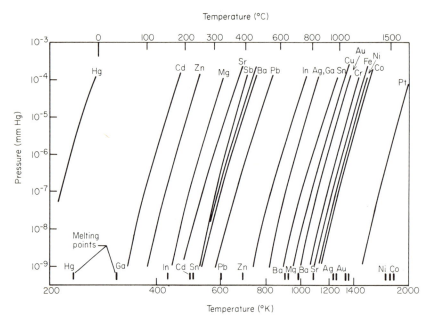

Figure 2. Vapor pressure versus temperature for soft and other selected metals. [R. Honig, Vapor pressure data for the solid and liquid elements. *RCA Rev.*, **30**, 285–305 (1969).]

The films are normally too thin to protect the metal substrates against corrosion, so that the base metals themselves should be sufficiently corrosion-resistant for the intended service. Temporary protection can be provided by oil films over the soft metal films, it being understood that the oil films will not be adequate lubricants during actual service. Silver films react to form sulfides in air or in oils containing sulfur, but they are compatible with lubricating oils that are essentially free of sulfur.

Uses

The two service conditions for which soft metal films have received most use or attention are vacuum and elevated temperatures.

Soft metal films have been used successfully as lubricants both in equipment that has been evacuated and sealed off and in equipment that has operated while exposed to the vacuum conditions of space. Ball bearings for rotating anode X-ray tubes are a good example of the use of soft metal films in evacuated and sealed equipment. This application uses instrument-size ball bearings operating at light loads and at speeds on the order of several thousand revolutions per minute. The bearings are heated by conduction from the X-ray target to temperatures estimated as high as 1100° F. The vacuum in the tubes is on the order of 10^{-6}–10^{-8} Torr, and it must not rise above this level during the entire lifetime of the tube. The tubes are customarily baked-out under vacuum at temperatures up to 800° F before sealing in order to minimize the subsequent release of gases from the materials inside. These requirements cannot be met by conventional lubricants, such as oils and greases.

Thin films of silver, deposited by tumbling the bearing balls in contact with small pieces of silver, are used by one manufacturer of rotating anode X-ray tubes [6]. These films provide minimum lifetimes of 1000 hr at the operating conditions and have attained lifetimes of 10,000 hr, and more, in some cases. At room temperature, lifetimes are said to be greater than 10,000 hr. Circle C tool steel, which does not soften at the operating temperature, is the preferred material for the ball-bearing races and balls.

Another example of the use of silver-coated ball bearings in evacuated and sealed-off equipment is provided by a special electron tube for a satellite application. In addition to requirements similar to those imposed by rotating anode X-ray tubes, the ball bearings in this instance had to be able to conduct small electric currents between the inner and outer races during operation. Balls that had been specially processed and vacuum-deposited with silver provided an average life of about 1000 hr under conditions of light load, a speed of 1600 rpm, and a vacuum of 10^{-6}–10^{-8} Torr.

Barium films have also been evaluated for use in rotating anode X-ray tubes. Research reported in 1940 noted that the following improvements were obtained with thin films of barium, as compared to dry, unlubricated ball bearings, for this type of application [5]: speed increased from 3100 to 3650 rpm; the coast time (time for bearings to slow down and come to rest after motor was turned off) increased from 12 sec to 8 min; and the noise level dropped from 87 to 68 dB. The films were said to be permanent for hundreds of hours of rotation at room temperature (i.e., provided the tube was not generating X-rays) and for at least 50–100 hr of rotation at the elevated temperatures during X-ray generation.

Additional metals tried on ball bearings of Circle C tool steel included zinc, magnesium, strontium, calcium, silver, gold, copper, iron, nickel, cobalt, platinum, and chromium. Some of these gave results similar to those with barium, but none gave better results, and a number of them were poorer. The chromium and cobalt films were the only ones specified by Atlee *et al.* [5] as providing poorer lubrication in vacuum than the barium films.

TABLE 2. Results of Tests with Barium Films Vaporized onto Balls of Different Materials[a]

Ball material	Results
Circle C tool steel (4.5% Cr, W, Co)	Good lubrication and wear
SAE 52100 steel (1.5% chromium, 1.0% carbon)	No lubrication; slight increase in stickiness
18% Chromium stainless steel	Good lubrication; poor wear and short life due to softness of the stainless steel
Carboloy (25% tungsten carbide, 75% cobalt)	No lubrication; "impossible to cover the sharp crystals of tungsten carbide by the cobalt–barium layer."
Monel metal (67% nickel, 30% copper)	Slight lubrication; failure due to distortion
SAE 52100 steel with layer of cobalt between the steel and the barium film	Good lubrication; poor wear and short life because of inability of cobalt to alloy with the substrate
SAE 52100 steel with a layer of chromium between the steel and the barium film	Excellent lubrication and wear
SAE 52100 steel with combination layers of barium with aluminium, manganese, rhodium, and zirconium	Good to excellent lubrication

[a] Z. J. Atlee, J. T. Wilson, and J. C. Filmer, Lubrication in vacuum by vaporized thin metallic films. *J. Appl. Phys.* **11**, 611–615 (1940).

Results with barium films vaporized on the balls of different materials are summarized in Table 2. The significant points demonstrated are that when cobalt and/or chromium were present in the hard steel used for the balls, as in the case of the tool steel, the barium films were unsatisfactory. Interposing a layer of cobalt, chromium, aluminum, or several other metals between the SAE 52100 steel and the barium film improved the lubrication. For wear resistance, the intermediate layer should alloy with the base steel. This result was apparently with chromium as the interlayer but not with cobalt.

Several investigations have been conducted to evaluate the usefulness of silver and gold films on ball bearings for spacecraft applications, in which the parts must operate while exposed to the vacuum of space [7–11]. Instrument-size ball bearings lubricated with such films have operated successfully under light loads and at speeds on the order of 8000–10,000 rpm for as many as 2600 hr, although there has been substantial scatter in the results.

REFERENCES

1. T. Spalvins and D. H. Buckley, Vapor-deposited thin gold films as lubricants in vacuum (10^{-11} mm Hg). *NASA Tech. Note* NASA TN D-**3040** (1965).
2. F. P. Bowden and D. Tabor, The lubrication by thin metallic films and the action of bearing metals. *J. Appl. Phys.* **14**, 141–151 (1943).
3. Y. Tsuya and R. Takagi, Lubricating properties of lead films on copper. *Wear* **7**, 131–143 (1964).
4. R. E. Azud, Study to establish principles of dry lubricant coatings in ball bearings for space application, Final Rep. of the CBS Lab. to the Army Ballistic Missile Agency under Contract No. DA-19-020-506-ORD-5171, March 1961.
5. Z. J. Atlee, J. T. Wilson, and J. C. Filmer, Lubrication in vacuum by vaporized thin metallic films. *J. Appl. Phys.* **11**, 611–615 (1940).
6. J. W. Skehan and G. J. Agule (assigned to Machlett Lab., Inc.), Vacuum tube apparatus, U. S. Patent 2,315,280, March 1943.
7. H. E. Evans and T. W. Flatley, Bearings for vacuum operation–Retainer material and design. *NASA Tech. Note* NASA TN D-**1339** (1962); also as *J. Eng. Ind.* **85**, 129–134 (1963).
8. H. E. Evans and T. W. Flatley, High speed vacuum performance of gold plated miniature ball bearings with various retainer materials and configurations. *NASA Tech. Note* NASA TN D-2101 (1963).
9. T. W. Flatley, High speed vacuum performance of miniature ball bearings lubricated with combinations of barium, gold, and silver films. *NASA Tech. Note* NASA TN D-**2304** (1964).

10. W. Voigtlander, Final technical progress report, soft metal film lubricant study, LMSD-TR-61, Lockheed Missiles and Space Co., Sunnyvale, California, March 1963.
11. P. Lewis, Evaluation of dry film lubricated ball bearings for use in a spatial environment - Phase III, *Rep.* No. GIGL48, General Eng. Lab., General Elec. Co., Schenectady, New York, February 1961.

Chapter 7

Plastics:
General

Plastics are successfully used in many applications involving friction and wear. Nylon,* for example, has long been used for quiet-running gears, and Teflon* is often used for sleeve bearings that operate dry with little friction. Less well known are the new polyimide[†] resins and phthalocyanine films, which extend the service limits of organic materials to temperatures as high as 1200° F.

Plastics bearings and gears are made in all sizes, from small electromechanical components to slipper block bearings for rolling mills and ships' rudder bearings. They are operated either dry, with water lubrication, or with conventional oils and greases under marginal-to-full hydrodynamic lubrication. Plastics are used in pure bulk form or with various fillers to improve their frictional and mechanical properties. In still other cases, plastics and other organic materials are used in the form of thin films or as impregnants into porous solids.

A. ADVANTAGES

For applications involving friction and wear, plastics can generally offer advantages in the following areas:

1. *Self-lubricity.* Many plastics have low coefficients of friction, even when run dry, and this is one of the main reasons for using them. As a result, plastic parts can operate under conditions where oils and greases

---

* Nylon and Teflon are registered trademarks of the Du Pont Company.

† The polyimides should not be confused with the polyamides (nylon), which are members of an entirely different polymer family.

could not be used (e.g., cryogenic applications, where oils and greases would freeze; consumer products, where the user cannot be relied upon to relubricate on schedule; food-processing equipment, where contamination by oils or greases would be a problem; parts that must operate after long periods of storage). Although plastics can operate dry, their performance is greatly improved by lubrication.

2. *Antiwelding characteristics.* Plastics can be selected that have little tendency to "stick" or cold-weld to metals, even under extreme conditions. The antisticking characteristics of Teflon, for example, are well known, even to housewives.

3. *Vibration absorption.* Plastics have good capacity for absorbing vibration, and they are especially useful where noise or vibration must be controlled. This characteristic is well known in the case of gear trains of nylon.

4. *Impact resistance.* Some of the plastics have excellent impact strength. This has permitted them to be used for ball bearings for armored-vehicle turrets, where the bearings must survive recoil and other heavy loads without appreciable wear or brinelling.

5. *Density.* The densities of plastics are as low as 1/6 or 1/7 that of steel and about half that of magnesium. Thus, plastic parts generally weigh less than comparable metal parts.

6. *Tolerances.* Plastics deform more readily than metals to conform to mating parts. Tolerance are less critical for plastics, and less accurate mounting and alignment are required.

7. *Machinability.* Plastics have good machinability and can be molded to close tolerances. They also have good dimensional stability. There are, however, some notable exceptions (e.g., where moisture absorption occurs, as in the case of molded nylon).

8. *Contamination.* Plastics have less tendency to attract dust than oils and greases, and contamination by dust and wear debris is less of a problem with plastics than with metals. The plastics themselves are abrasion resistant, and they allow contaminants to be embedded into them, thus preventing scoring of the mating part. This property makes sealing against contamination less critical with plastic components than with those fabricated from metal.

9. *Corrosion.* Plastics are free from corrosion by most acids and other chemical agents.

10. *Compatibility.* Plastics are compatible with oils, greases, and many chemicals so that such materials can be added for lubrication or to protect

other parts against corrosion without harming the plastic components with which they come into contact.

11. *Durability*. Plastics have low wear rates and outlast metals in many applications.

12. *Low cost*. Many plastics can be injection molded in large quantities and at low cost. Complex shapes can be molded in one operation, where metals would require several machining steps. While bearing alloys of lead, copper, tin, and zinc are becoming more expensive, plastics are generally becoming cheaper.

13. *Design flexibility*. Plastic parts can be molded in intricate designs. Several parts can be combined in a single piece (e.g., shaft, gears, cam, and bearing), thereby reducing total part and assembly cost.

14. *Electrical insulation*. The plastics are generally good electrical insulators, and can thereby electrically isolate metallic parts from one another.

15. *Low temperatures*. Many plastics retain their useful properties even at cryogenic temperatures, which are below those at which oils and greases become too viscous to be useful lubricants.

16. *Vacuum*. The volatility of plastic bodies is substantially less than that of oils and greases, so that they can be more useful than oils and greases under conditions of ultrahigh vacuum.

17. *Creepage*. Self-lubricating plastics are useful in instrument mechanisms and other devices where oils and greases creep away from the parts that require lubrication.

18. *Sterility*. Plastics can be steam cleaned without damage.

B. DISADVANTAGES

Plastics suffer certain disadvantages when compared to metals. It would be improper to generalize too widely here, since disadvantages are not always common from one plastic to another. Also, many specialty grades and techniques are available to overcome the disadvantages. With these reservations, the general disadvantages of plastics under conditions of friction and wear include the following:

1. *Thermal conductivity*. The thermal conductivity of plastics is much lower than that of metals. Consequently, they are less able to dissipate frictional heat generated at rubbing interfaces, and plastic parts run hotter than similar metal parts. This disadvantage can be overcome by using

the plastic as a thin film over a metal substrate so that the metal can conduct the frictional heat away more efficiently. Other techniques for accomplishing the same purpose include adding metal fibers or powders as fillers or using metal backing screens. Plastic parts are frequently operated submerged in liquids, which reduces frictional heating.

2. *Thermal expansion.* Plastics have high rates of thermal expansion. Their coefficients of thermal expansion are ten or more times than those of steels and other metals. Adding fillers can reduce the expansion rates of plastics.

3. *Temperature resistance.* Bulk plastics cannot be used at as high temperatures as can steels. They soften with heat and generally should not be used above 200°–300° F (93°–149° C), although polyimides are useful up to 600° F for continuous service.

4. *Operating speeds.* As a consequence of the three foregoing limitations, the use of plastics is restricted to lower speeds than those at which steels can be used.

5. *Structural strength.* Plastics are weaker than steels so that the load-carrying capacity of plastic gears and bearings is less than for the same size part in steel.

6. *Rigidity.* Plastics are much less rigid than metals, their moduli of elasticity being typically on the order of $0.1–1.5 \times 10^6$ psi, as compared to 30×10^6 psi for steels.

7. *Radiation stability.* Organic materials are less resistant to radiation than metals. Teflon, in particular, has very poor radiation stability, and nylon is not much better. However, published information on radiation stability can be misleading, unless the basis on which radiation stability has been judged is clearly established. In general, radiation stability data is reported in terms of the dose that reduces the mechanical strength by 10 or 25% of the initial strength of the pure plastic.

C. GENERAL COMPARISON

Table 1 compares the properties and usefulness of various types of plastics for applications involving friction and wear. Within each type, properties can be altered widely by using fillers or by other processing techniques. Although the list of typical uses is not exhaustive, it does indicate the diversity of applications. The individual types of plastics are discussed in greater detail in Chapters 8–11.

TABLE 1. General Comparison of Plastics for Applications Involving Friction and Wear[a]

Material type	Advantages	Disadvantages	Typical uses
Nylon	Low coefficient of friction; no lubrication required but can be used; tough; good conformability; low wear rate; high abrasion resistance; good chemical resistance; easily molded to close tolerances; reduces noise and vibration and provides quiet operation	Absorbs water; has low thermal conductivity and high thermal expansion; problems can be minimized by preconditioning and proper design	Automotive king pins, pedal shafts seat swivels, door handles, etc; typewriter shift levers; washing machine idlers; swinging shelves in refrigerators; baby carriage and tricycle wheels; hinge pins for dampers in industrial ducts; movie projectors; door rollers; jalousie windows and doors; farm macninery; textile machinery; marine steering and other controls; pin-ball machines; electric shavers; ventilating fan louvers; water and gas meters; foodwrapping machinery
Fluorocarbon (e.g., Du Pont's Teflon)	Very low coefficient of friction; no lubrication required but can be used; excellent resistance to heat; impervious to water, solvents, oils, and most chemicals; high shock resistance; useful at cryogenic temperatures; good machinability; good vibration absorption; low wear rate; readily molded with various fillers and reinforcements to provide special properties; available in fiber or fabric form	Relatively expensive; low thermal conductivity and high expansion	Automotive knuckle and ball joints; jet engine after-burners; instrument bearings; railroad car trucks; bridge bearings; roller conveyors; farm equipment; food and textile processing machinery; aircraft and missile control surface bearings

143

TABLE 1 (*Continued*)

Material type	Advantages	Disadvantages	Typical uses
Phenolic laminate	High resiliency and resistance to severe shock and impact; low wear rates; good machinability; can be lubricated by water; resistant to oils, greases, and mild chemicals; light weight; reduced vibration	Absorbs water; low thermal conductivity in large sizes	Marine shafts; steel mill and other heavy-duty machinery; automotive suspensions; pumps; aircraft landing gear; clock motors; electrical appliances and switchgear; retainers for high-speed, precision ball bearings
Acetal (e.g., Du Pont's Delrin)	Low coefficient of friction; no lubrication required but can be used; rigid but tough at high and low temperatures; low creep; resistant to water, lubricants, and most solvents; inexpensive	Low heat resistance; generous clearances required	Chair caster wheels; industrial truck wheels; door hinges; truck steering gears and pedals; drapery slides; lawn mower rollers; electric shavers; bicycle steering heads; egg beaters; conveyor belts
Chlorinated polyether (e.g., Hercules' Penton)	Low coefficient of friction; no lubrication required but can be used; excellent dimensional stability; resistant to water and most chemicals; very low creep under load at elevated temperatures; practically zero water absorption	Bearing properties not as good as most other plastics	Being evaluated for fertilizer mixers, in sump pumps for sewage disposal plants, and other applications

Material	Properties	Disadvantages	Applications
Polycarbonate (e.g., GE's Lexan)	Good resistance to heat and impact; good dimensional stability; good creep resistance; high impact strength; good machinability to close tolerances	High coefficient of friction	Being evaluated for various applications
High-molecular weight polyethylene	Excellent impact resistance and good wear properties	Relatively difficult to fabricate	
Acrylonitrile–butadiene–styrene	Low coefficient of friction; high abrasion resistance; low creep; low mold shrinkage; no lubrication required but can be used; high abrasion resistance		Lawn mower and roller-skate wheels, where wheels and bearings are integral; under evaluation for pulleys, drapery traverse rods, industrial dolly wheels
Polyimide (e.g., Du Pont's Vespel)	Low coefficient of friction; excellent resistance to high temperatures; high strength; low thermal expansion; resists solvents and most common chemicals; excellent bearing properties	Expensive	

[a] Mod. Plastic. 37 (May 1960),

D. BEARING DESIGN

When a plastic bearing fails, it is usually because frictional heat is generated faster than the bearing can dissipate it, so that the plastic part melts. Heat generation can be estimated from the combined effects of the load supported by the bearing and the sliding speed. Increasing either the load or the speed generates more heat, and this provides a starting point for designing plastic bearings.

PV Limit

The *PV* value of an application is the product of the unit load on the projected bearing area (in pounds per square inch) and the velocity of sliding (in feet per minute),* and to a first approximation it determines the severity of service. The *PV* limit of a material is the maximum combination of load and velocity at which it can be used, ignoring the factor of wear. Operation above the *PV* limit will generally cause rapid failure due to melting.

The *PV* limit of a material is established either by a pressure-stepping test or a wear test. The pressure-stepping test is more common, and it involves loading a specimen in small increments while the sliding velocity is held constant. After equilibrium is reached at each load, the specimen temperature and coefficient of friction are measured before increasing the load to the next step. Eventually, a limiting load is reached at which the temperature does not reach equilibrium but continues to rise, the friction becomes erratic, and there is other evidence of failure, such as melting or extrusion of the plastic. The product of the sliding velocity and the highest load at which satisfactory operation is maintained is the *PV* limit of the material. Figures 1 and 2 show typical equipment and test results for the pressure-stepping test. The second procedure involves measuring the rate of wear at a series of pressures and sliding velocities

---

* For sleeve bearings, formula $V = 0.262 \times$ rpm $\times D$ gives the sliding velocity in feet per minute when D is the shaft diameter in inches and rpm is the number of shaft revolutions per minute. The projected area of sleeve bearings is calculated by multiplying the bearing ID (in inches) by the bearing length (in inches), and the unit load is the total load (in pounds) divided by this project area (in square inches). For flat bearings, the sliding velocity is the speed at which the sliding surface moves across the mating surface, and the unit load on the projected bearing area is the total load (in pounds) divided by the total contact area (in square inches).

Figure 1. Equipment for pressure-stepping tests to evaluate *PV* limits. [DuPont *J. Teflon* **3** no. 2 (1962).]

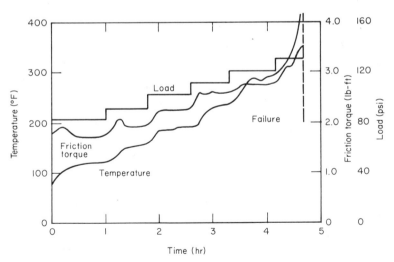

Figure 2. Typical results from pressure-stepping test. Bearing dimensions: 1 × 1 in.; shaft, cold-rolled carbon steel, 16 μin. (RMS); 18–22R$_c$; surface velocity; 100 fpm; *PV* limit at 100 fpm, 12,000. [Du Pont *J. Teflon* **3**, no. 2 (1962).]

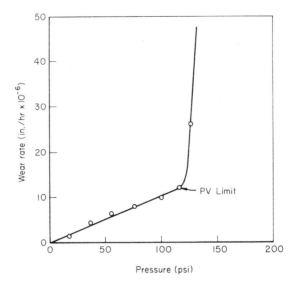

Figure 3. Wear rate of carbon-filled TFE resin versus pressure. *Test conditions*: mating material, AISI-1040 steel with 16 μin. finish and Rockwell C-22 hardness; rubbing velocity, 100 fpm; ambient temperature, —70° F; operated dry (no lubrication). [R. B. Lewis, Predicting the wear of sliding plastic surfaces. *Mech. Eng.* **86**, 32–35, Fig. 2 (1964).]

and then plotting the results. When wear rate is plotted against pressure for a given sliding velocity, as in Figure 3, the pressure at which the curve changes slope radically is the limiting pressure for that sliding velocity.

For a successful design, the *PV* value of the application must be below the *PV* limit of the material. This ensures that the temperature rise due to frictional heating is below the degradation level of the plastic. Figure 4 shows the maximum allowable unit loads as a function of sliding velocity for five plastics. Ideally, the *PV* product should be a constant over the entire range of *P* and *V* values, as is the case for unfilled Teflon PTFE (curve E). While this is approximately true for many materials, others are more sensitive to a high *P* than a high *V*, and vice versa, as is the case for filled and cast nylons (curve A), so that their *PV* limit varies slightly with the load and sliding velocity.

Wear

Wear is the primary basis for design and material selection, since it determines how long a part can operate before needing replacement.

Friction is generally of secondary importance, so long as it is low enough to avoid excessive drag and frictional heating. Unfortunately, there is no general relation between wear and the coefficient of friction of a material, and wear tests are necessary. Figure 5 shows typical results from a wear test. Note that the rate of wear during the break-in period is high, and the curve then flattens out to an essentially constant rate of wear. Rapid wear during break-in is due to factors such as misalignment, clearance,

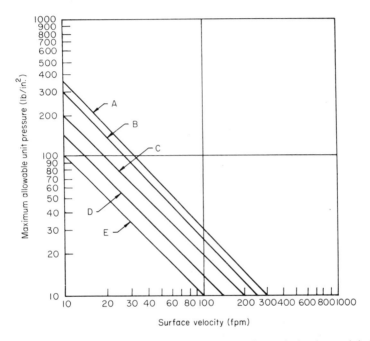

Figure 4. Maximum allowable unit pressure versus surface velocity for nonlubricated bearings. *Material code*: A, filled and cast nylons; B, nylon 66; C, filled Teflon PTFE; D, chlorinated polyether; E, unfilled Teflon PTFE. *Test conditions*: continuous service at 50% relative humidity at room temperature. [P. D. Mitchell, Design of bearings with plastic materials. *Brit. Plast.* **37**, 616–619, Fig. 1 (1964).]

surface finish, and thermal expansion. Break-in is normally completed in a few hours and does not account for much wear, whereas the steady-state wear is of principal interest in most applications.

Steady-state wear can be estimated by multiplying the PV value of the application by the time of operation (T) and the wear coefficient of the material (K); thus,

$$R = K \cdot PV \cdot T \tag{1}$$

where R is the radial wear. Wear coefficients can be established for various materials by relatively simple, inexpensive tests, and Equation (1) permits this information to be generalized and used for predicting service lives of bearings, seals, piston rings, and other components under a variety of loads and sliding velocities met in practice. Minor discrepancies can occur in the use of Equation (1) because the relationship between R and PV is not exactly linear, since the bearing temperature increases with PV. However, Equation (1) is approximately correct so long as the PV values are low enough to avoid overheating. If the sliding velocity varies during operation, the average sliding velocity should be used.

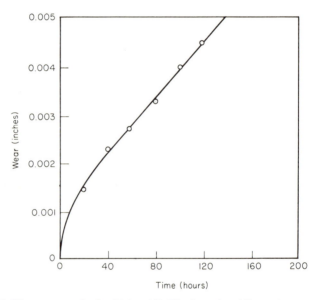

Figure 5. Wear test results for Nylon 6/6. Plastic, nylon 6/6; mating material, AISI 1040 steel; finish; 16 μin. (A A); hardness, 22R$_c$; pressure, 100 psi; velocity, 50 fpm; ambient temperature, $-70°$ F; lubrication, none. Wear factor, 70×10^{-10} (based on slope of wear versus time curve after wear-in.). [R. B. Lewis, Predicting the wear of sliding plastic surfaces. *Mech. Eng.* **86**, 32–35, Fig. 3 (1964).]

The wear coefficient is normally determined by measuring the amount of wear that a bushing suffers when operated for a period of time under specified conditions of shaft finish, ambient temperature, etc. Wear coefficients are nearly constant over the PV ranges of most plastics so long as other conditions are held constant. Small changes (less than 20%) in the wear coefficients of some plastics have been observed due to order-of-magnitude changes in the pressure and velocity.

One should note that the wear coefficient is not the same as or related to the abrasion resistance, which is commonly quoted in tables of properties of plastics. Abrasion resistance is the resistance to cutting by emery particles in a standard abrasion test.

Figure 6 is a nomograph for solving Equation (1) in terms of the wear rate, R/T. If the allowable wear rate is known or set for the application and a material with known wear coefficient is selected, the maximum allowable PV factor can be determined from this figure. For example, assume that a shaft bearing can tolerate radial wear of 0.001 in. per 1000 hr of operation and that a nylon bearing with a wear coefficient of 50×10^{-10}

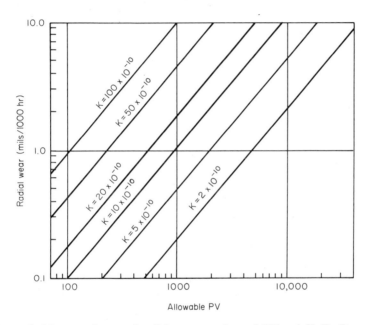

Figure 6. Nomograph rate of radial wear to values of PV and K. (Du Pont data.)

in³-min/lb-ft-hr was desirable from the standpoint of costs and fabrication techniques. The allowable PV of 200 can be read directly from Figure 6. Conversely, Figure 1 can be used to estimate the wear rate for known values of PV and K.

The wear resistance of plastics depends on their molecular weight, crystallinity, and other material processing factors. Figure 7, for example, illustrates how wear decreases as the molecular weight of a polymer increases. Generally, it is desirable to choose the highest practical molecular weight in order to reduce wear.

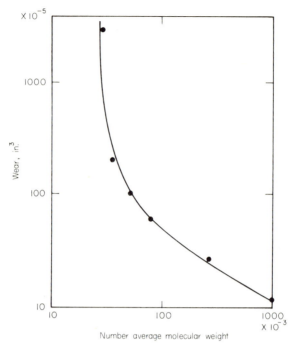

Figure 7. Effect of molecular weight on the wear of polyethylene. *Test conditions:* 64 hr under 16-lb load at 405 ft/min. [I. C. Pratt, Plastics as bearing materials, with particular reference to PTFE. *Plastics Inst. Trans.* **32**, 255–260 (1964).]

Wet versus Dry Operation

Although many plastics operate satisfactorily dry, lubrication improves their performance, as demonstrated by the data cited in Tables 2 and 3 and Figure 8. Figure 8 should be compared with Figure 4 in order to appreciate the marked improvement in the P-vs-V relation provided by lubrication for most of the plastics. Even a few drops of oil prior to break-in markedly improves the performance. Periodic lubrication can raise the PV limits by as much as 400%, depending upon the material. Under ideal conditions of continuous lubrication, operation may be limited only by the strength of the plastic.

When plastic bearings do seize, the shafts are seldom scored or galled, as with metal bearings, and the bearings can be readily replaced without refinishing the shafts. Plastic bearings are therefore used in preference to metal bearings where a temporary failure of the lubrication system would lead to expensive shaft damage.

TABLE 2. Coefficients of Friction under Dry and Oil-Lubricated Conditions for Various Plastics[a]

| Plastic[b] | Lubrication | | | |
| | None | | Oil | |
	max	min	max	min
Teflon	0.21	0.09	0.06	0.04
Rulon	0.19	0.12	0.06	0.04
Teflon–MoS$_2$ (1 : 1)	0.21	0.13	0.06	0.04
Teflon–MoS$_2$ (3 : 1)	0.22	0.13	0.06	0.05
Teflon–Graphite (1 : 1)	0.19	0.12	0.07	0.05
Teflon–Graphite (3 : 1)	0.19	0.12	0.06	0.04
Teflon–Asbestos (3 : 1)	0.21	0.14	0.05	0.04
Teflon–Cooper (1 : 1)	0.20	0.13	0.07	0.04
Cellulose acetate	0.53	0.18	0.16	0.08
Cellulose acetate butyrate	0.32	0.17	0.14	0.07
Ethyl cellulose	0.57	0.22	0.16	0.07
Kel–F	0.25	0.17	0.15	0.08
Methacrylate	0.47	0.16	0.19	0.10
Nylatron G	0.33	0.22	0.13	0.08
Nylon	0.33	0.15	0.14	0.09
Polyethylene	0.40	0.17	0.09	0.04
Polystyrene	0.45	0.12	0.13	0.06

[a] W. C. Milz and L. B. Sargent, Jr., Frictional characteristics of plastics. *Lubric. Eng.* **11**, 313–318 (1955).

[b] *Test conditions:* load, 1–5 lb; sliding speeds, 8–367 fpm.

TABLE 3. Effect of Initial Lubrication on Performance of Thermoplastic Bearings[a]

Material	Lubrication	PV value	Wear rate (in./hr $\times$ 10^{-6})
Nylon 66	None	6000	Seized after 3.5 hr
	Initial only	6000	Negligible after 400 hr
Delrin polyacetal	None	20,000	480
	Initial only	20,000	Negligible up to 450 hr, then 36

[a] G. C. Pratt, Plastics as bearing materials, with particular reference to PTFE. *Plastics Inst. Trans.* **32**, 255–260 (1964).

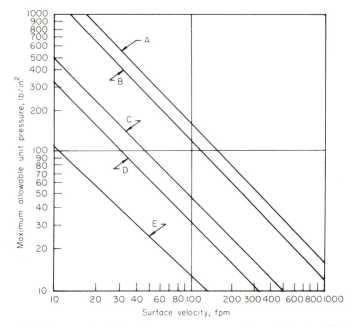

Figure 8. Maximum allowable unit pressure versus surface velocity for oil-lubricated bearings. Material code: A, filled and cast nylons; B, nylon 66; C, filled Teflon PTFE; D, chlorinated polyether; E, unfilled Teflon PTFE. *Test conditions*: continuous service at 50% relative humidity at room temperature. [P. D. Mitchell, Design of bearings with plastic materials. *Brit. Plast.* **37**, 616–619, Fig. 2 (1964).]

Interface temperature

Wear rates and *PV* limits are adversely affected by increasing the surface temperature at the sliding interface. The interface temperature depends not only upon the ambient temperature but also upon the amount of frictional heat generated and upon how easily the heat can be dissipated. Frictional heat, in turn, is proportional to the product of the load *P*, the sliding velocity *V*, and the coefficient of friction μ. If the heat generated is equated to the heat dissipated, one obtains

$$PV\mu = B(T_s - T_a) \tag{2}$$

where T_s is the interface temperature, T_a is the ambient temperature, and *B* is a proportionality constant or heat transfer coefficient. The dimensions of *B* are selected to coincide with the units selected for *P*, *V*, and *T*.

The value of B depends upon a number of service conditions that control the rate of heat transfer to the balance of the system and to the atmosphere. These conditions include (1) the thermal conductivities of the plastic bearing and the shaft and housing materials, (2) the intimacy of contact between mating parts, (3) cross-sectional areas and lengths of heat paths, and (4) convective cooling by the ambient air or by other coolants. Table 4 lists experimental values of B for two Teflon TFE

TABLE 4. Heat Transfer Coefficients for Teflon TFE Bearing Units[a,b]

Variable	Thrust-bearing tester	Sleeve-bearing tester
Bearing dimensions	1.125-in. OD × 1-in. ID	1-in. length × 1-in. diam
Bearing contact area	0.2 in.²	1.0 in.² (projected area)
Thickness of Teflon TFE	0.125 in.	0.125 in.
Contact metal	Carbon steel	Carbon steel
Metal surface	16 μin.	16 μin.
Heat transfere coefficient	10 ft-lb/in.²-min-°F	16 ft-lb/in².-min-°F

[a] Anon, Predicting bearing wear. *J. Teflon* **9**, No. 2, 9–11 (1968).
[b] Du Pont data.

bearing test units. Note that the value of B for the sleeve bearing tester was 60% higher than for the thrust bearing tester; this was primarily because of the much larger bearing contact area for dissipating heat in the sleeve bearing tester.

Table 5 shows the effects of some of the above service conditions on the PV limit, which, as indicated earlier, is adversely affected by increasing the interface temperature. For the thrust bearing conditions tested, doubling the thermal conductivity of the Teflon bearing material or of the metal improved the PV limit by 25 or 75%, respectively. On the other hand, doubling the thickness of the bearing reduced the PV limit by 12%, and doubling the length of the metal heat path reduced the PV limit by 37%. Reducing the coefficient of friction to one-half its initial value raised the PV limit by 100%.

TABLE 5. Effect of Geometry and Material on *PV* Limit[a,b]

Case	Thermal conductivity (btu/hr-ft²-°F-in.)		Effective heat path (in.)		Coefficient of friction	Change in *PV* limit (%)
	Teflon TFE	Metal	Teflon TFE	Metal		
Reference thrust bearing tester	2.8	320	0.1	3.8	Varies	—
Changes from reference tester (dimensionless values)						
Reference	Same	Same	Same	Same	Same	None
A	Double	Same	Same	Same	Same	+25
B	Same	Double	Same	Same	Same	+75
C	Same	Same	Double	Same	Same	—12
D	Same	Same	Same	Double	Same	—37
E	Same	Same	Same	Same	Half	+100

[a] Anon, Predicting bearing wear. *J. Teflon* **9**, No. 2, 9–11 (1968).
[b] Du Pont data.

Ambient Temperature

Although the surface temperature at the sliding interface is an important factor, as indicated in the preceding section, it is difficult either to measure or predict it accurately. The complexities of part geometry and fit-up generally preclude the designer from knowing the appropriate value of the heat transfer coefficient B, even though the values of P, V, μ, and T_a are known for inserting into Equation (2), and the designer is thereby prevented from calculating the surface temperature and basing his design upon it. For this reason, *PV* limits and wear factors are almost always referred to the ambient temperature conditions (i.e., to the temperature of the surrounding atmosphere).

Figure 9 shows multiplication factors for correcting the *PV* limit of several plastics for the ambient temperature. Since heat generally softens plastics, their *PV* limits are reduced as the ambient temperature is raised; conversely, lowering the ambient temperature allows a higher *PV* limit to be used, since there is a greater available temperature rise before the bearing will soften or fail. The data in Figure 9 show that at an ambient

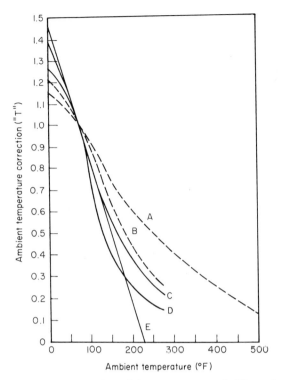

Figure 9. *PV* correction factors for ambient temperature. A, Fluorosint TFE; B, MC Nylon; C, Nylatron GS; D, Nylon 101; E, Teflon TFE. (Anon., "Plastic Bearing Design Manual," Form GT-la, Graph #1, p. 7. Polymer Corp., Reading, Pennsylvania,1965).

temperature of 200° F, for example, the *PV* limit of unmodified Teflon TFE is only 20% of its normal value, and the *PV* limit for Fluorosint TFE (a filled Teflon) is 60% of its value at room temperature.

Heat Dissipation

Because their thermal conductivity and thermal stability are less than those of metals, frictional heating must be dissipated before interfacial temperatures exceed the capability of the plastics. Useful techniques for improving heat dissipation from the sliding interface include using the plastics in thin sections, such as liners in metal sleeves; adding conductive fillers to the plastics, such as metal powders or fibers; providing an adequate mass of surrounding metal; extending the surface area for transmitting heat; and providing a flow of coolant.

Intermittent Operation

When bearings operate intermittently, heat generated during the "on" period can be dissipated during the "off" period, and the bearings can cool off between operating periods. For this reason, a higher *PV* limit can be used for intermittent operation than for continuous service. Figure 10 provides multiplication factors for converting the *PV* limit for continuous service to intermittent operation. For example, if a bearing operates for 30 sec and then remains stationary for 1 min (ratio of "off" to "on" of 2*X*), the bearing can operate at slightly more than twice its normal *PV* limit. Of course, the pressure must in no case exceed the static mechanical strength of the plastic, or the bearing will fracture when the load is applied.

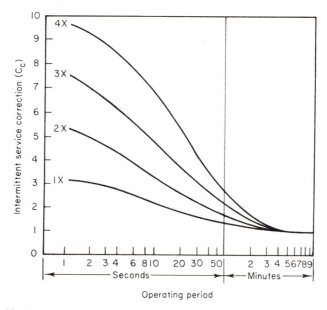

Figure 10. *PV* correction factors for intermittent operation.(Anon, "Plastic Bearing Design Manual," Form GT-la, Graph #2, p. 7. Polymer Corp.,Reading,Pennsylvania, 1965.)

Wall Thickness

Wall thickness should be kept to a minimum for bearings operating close to the *PV* limit of the material, as this will aid in dissipating heat into the bearing housings. If impact stresses are severe, wall thickness

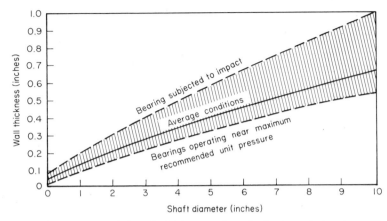

Figure 11. Recommended wall thicknesses for plastic journal bearings. (Anon, "Plastic Bearing Design Manual," Form GT-la, Graph #3, p. 8. Polymer Corp., Reading, Pennsylvania, 1965.)

should be increased. Figure 11 suggests a range of nominal wall thicknesses for different shaft diameters for average and extreme conditions. Running clearances, press-fit allowances, and tolerances are applied to the nominal dimensions to obtain the final design dimensions. Of course, if the plastic bearing is used to replace a bearing previously used in service, the wall thickness is already fixed by the shaft and housing dimensions of the existing design.

Length

The ratio of bearing length to shaft diameter should generally be on the order of one to one (i.e., bearing length equal to shaft diameter). As the bearing length is increased, local heating due to out-of-roundness and slight shaft vibration becomes more likely. On the other hand, very short bearings can be difficult to retain within the bearing housing.

Clearance

Insufficient running clearance is one of the most common causes of seizure with plastic bearings. Because their coefficients of thermal expansion are about ten times those of metals, plastic bearings require greater shaft clearances than customary for metal bearings. Plastics are more resilient and have better damping capacity than metals, so that the relatively large clearances used with plastics do not necessarily lead to vibration, deflection, noise, or other problems encountered when metal bearings are installed with excessive clearance.

The total running clearance for plastic bearings is the sum of three factors: (1) a basic shaft allowance, which is common for all plastic materials, (2) an allowance for wall expansion, which depends on the material, wall thickness, and ambient temperature, and (3) an allowance for close-down, which is added only when the bearing is press-fit into a housing.

Figure 12 is an average of recommendations from several sources for the basic shaft allowance versus shaft diameter. Generally, the recommended increase in shaft diameter is about 0.005 in./in. of shaft diameter for small bearings, and it decreases to about 0.003 in./in. for shafts as large as 10 in. Shaft allowances from Figure 12 are added to the nominal shaft diameter to obtain the internal diameter of the bearing.

The allowance for wall expansion depends upon the coefficient of thermal expansion of the plastic, the wall thickness of the bearing, and the increase in temperature above room temperature, which, in turn,

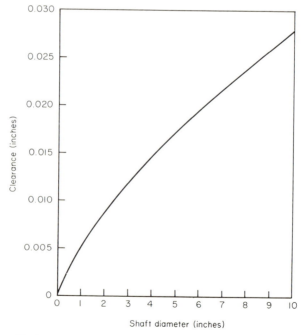

Figure 12. Recommended shaft clearances for plastic journal bearings.

depends upon the ambient temperature and the amount of frictional heating. An increase of 150° F above ambient temperature appears reasonably conservative for estimating frictional heating for most applications (i.e., where the bearing is not operating near its PV limit), and an average value for the coefficient of thermal expansion for the most commonly used plastics would be about 4×10^{-5} in./in.-°F. Thus, for example, for a bearing operating at room temperature, the expansion in wall thickness due to frictional heating would be

$$4 \times 10^{-5} \text{ in./in.-°F} \times 150° \text{ F} = 6 \times 10^{-3} \text{ in./in.}$$

or 6 mils/in. of wall thickness. The allowance on the internal diameter of the bearing would be twice this, to allow for both wall thicknesses, or 12 mils/in. of wall thickness. If the ambient temperature was raised to 175° F (i.e., 100° F above room temperature), the total expansion in wall thickness during operation would be

$$4 \times 10^{-5} \text{ in./in.-°F} \times (100 + 150)° \text{ F} = 10 \times 10^{-3} \text{ in./in.}$$

or 10 mils/in. of wall thickness, and the allowance on the internal diameter of the bearing would be 20 mils/in. of wall thickness. If the coefficient of friction is larger or frictional heating is likely to be more severe, the allowance should be increased accordingly. Based on their experience, some designers use expansion allowances 10–25% higher than those calculated by this procedure, apparently to allow for a small amount of shaft expansion and for close-down due to circumferential expansion of the bushing in its housing.

Plastic bearings are commonly press-fit into metal housings in order to keep them from rotating with the shaft. An average interference of 0.002 in./in. of outside bearing diameter is recommended, or data such as that shown in Figure 13 can be used for different materials. During press fitting, the resilient plastic bearings must conform to the internal diameter of the housing, and the internal diameters of the bearings "close-in" on the shaft. The amount of close-in is nearly equal to the press-fit interference, and it is conveniently compensated for by adding the interference on the outside diameter to the inner diameter of the bearings. Keys, set screws, pegs, bolted flanges, and other techniques are used for more positive retention, particularly under fluctuating service temperatures. Bearings should normally be installed so that they are free to expand lengthwise.

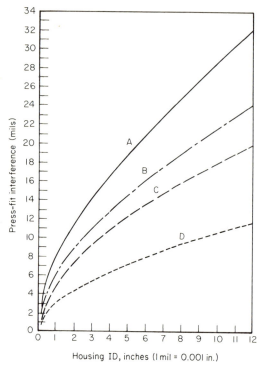

Figure 13. Recommended press-fit interference versus housing inside diameter. A, Teflon TFE; B, Nylon 101; C, MC Nylon and Nylatron GS; and D, Fluorosint TFE. (Anon, "Plastic Bearing Design Manual," Form GT-la, Graph #5, p. 10. Polymer Corp., Reading, Pennsylvania, 1965.)

TABLE 6.   Effect of Mating Material on the Wear
of Glass-Filled Teflon PTFE[a]

Mating material (finished to 16 μin.)	Relative wear
Carbon steel	1
Cast iron	1.2
Stainless steel	1.5–3.0
Hard chrome plate	10–20
Aluminum	20–50

[a] R. B. Lewis, Predicting the wear of sliding plastic surfaces. *Mech. Eng.* **86**, 32–35 (1964).

Mating Material

Table 6 presents data on the relative wear of glass-filled Teflon PTFE operated against different materials. Mating surfaces of low- and high-carbon steel, stainless steel, tool steel, and cast iron cause the same order of magnitude of wear and provide essentially the same PV limits. If mating surfaces are of ceramics or other materials that have significantly lower thermal conductivities than metals, heat dissipation is reduced and the PV limit of the plastic bearing material is less than when operating against metal.

Shaft Finish and Hardness

Rough surfaces cause rapid wear, and finishes from 4 to 32 μin. are generally recommended, with the range from 8 to 16 μin. being most common. Increasing the hardness of the mating surface also generally reduces wear.

Chapter 8

Nylon

Nylon is the generic name for a family of thermoplastic polyamide resins.* All these resins are related, but not identical, in chemical composition. By definition, a nylon is any long-chain synthetic polymeric amide which has recurring amide groups as an integral part of the main polymer chain and can be formed into filaments in which the structural elements are oriented in the direction of the axis.

Nylon was one of the first plastics to be used on a large scale for parts subject to friction and wear. Although its coefficient of friction against steel is above 0.20, so that it is not strictly a solid lubricant, nylon has been widely used for gears, bearings, and other parts because of its excellent wear resistance, toughness, ability to dampen vibration and reduce noise, and its ability to operate without lubrication. In comparison to other thermoplastics, nylon has good tensile and impact strengths and a high modulus of elasticity. It is inexpensive and can be fabricated easily into a variety of shapes and sizes. It can be reinforced and filled with fiberglass, graphite, molybdenum disulfide, and other materials to improve its friction and other properties. Nylon parts can operate continuously at 250° F, and for short periods up to 400° F if the loads are light.

A. UNMODIFIED NYLON

The three most widely used types of general purpose nylon molding resins are Nylon 6/6 (a copolymer of hexamethylene diamine and adipic acid), Nylon 6 (a polymer of aminocaproic acid), and Nylon 6/10 (a copolymer

---

* Nylon was introduced by the Du Pont Company. Other suppliers of the basic molding resins include Allied Chemical Corporation (Plastics Division); Belding Chemical Industries; Catalin Corporation; Celanese Polymer Company; Firestone Plastics Company; Foster Grant Company; H. Muehlstein & Company, Inc.; Gulf Oil Corporation (Spencer Chemical Division); and Tenneco Chemicals, Inc. (Heyden Division). In addition, there are various other suppliers and fabricators of filled and unfilled nylons.

of hexamethylene diamine and sebacid acid). Nylon 6 has the advantages of low cost and relatively high impact strength (2.5 ft-lb/in. at room temperature), although its water absorption is higher than other nylons. Nylon 6/6 is also a low-cost nylon and has about half the water absorption of Nylon 6 grades. Nylon 6/10 is a premium family of nylon resins and is limited to specialized applications that require better electrical properties, lower moisture absorption, or improved chemical resistance. Other types of nylon include an alcohol-soluble type, Nylon 8 (an alkoxy-substituted modification), which is used to form films, coatings, wire jacketing, etc.; and Nylon 11 and 12, which are premium grades that are noted for flexibility, resistance to stress cracking and aging, low moisture pickup, and good resistance to impact, especially at low temperatures. Within each of these basic types, there are a variety of grades that include copolymers and blends tailored for specific uses. For example, special formulations of Nylon 6/6, which is probably the biggest family of nylons now in use, can provide the following: (1) lubrication for easier molding, (2) adding mold-release agents, (3) stabilizers to prevent discoloration during processing, (4) very rapid crystallization for faster molding, (5) resistance to embrittlement at high service temperatures, (6) better electrical properties, (7) resistance to hydrolysis and oxidation, (8) high viscosity for extrusion or extrusion coating, (9) superior toughness with moldability.

Nylon is a thermoplastic material—it melts on heating and resolidifies on cooling. It is usually injection molded, but it can also be extruded and cast. In contrast to thermosetting resins, which solidify on heating and cannot be remelted, nylon and other thermoplastics can be reheated and reshaped a number of times. Unlike most other thermoplastics, however, nylon has some degree of crystallinity, so that it has a relatively sharp melting point. It does not soften gradually when heated, but it remains rigid, although with decreasing stiffness, as the melting point is approached. Rapid cooling from the melt favors the formation of the amorphous form, whereas slow cooling produces high crystallinity. Articles with high crystallinity have superior hardness, stiffness, and dimensional stability, whereas articles that are highly amorphous are more flexible, have better impact strength, and are more transparent.

General Characteristics

Table 1 lists the most important types of nylon molding resins available from Du Pont under the tradename "Zytel." These powders differ pri-

TABLE 1. Comparative Characteristics of Zytel[a] Nylon Molding Powders[b]

Code	Usual methods of working	Rigidity	Major uses	Characteristics
101	Injection, extrusion	Rigid	General purpose moldings (i.e., mechanical parts, sterilizable items, etc.)	Highest melting nylon, high fluidity at molding temperatures, good machinability, high impact strength with maximum stiffness
103, 103E	Injection, extrusion	Rigid	Electrical parts, coil forms, fastening devices	Comparable to Zytel 101, stabilized for extended operations at elevated temperatures
105	Injection, extrusion	Rigid	Automotive, electrical parts, weather-resistant moldings	Black composition with excellent weathering characteristics; comparable to Zytel 101 in general properties
42	Extrusion, injection	Rigid	Tubing, film, bottles, extruded shapes	High viscosity extrusion grade generally comparable to Zytel 101
31[c]	Injection, extrusion	Rigid	Wire jacketing, special mechanical moldings	Low moisture absorption
33[c]	Molding, extrusion	Rigid	Wire jacketing, electrical parts	Thermally stabilized extrusion grade comparable to Zytel 31
211	Injection, extrusion	Semirigid	Impact devices, parts requiring exceptional toughness	Combination of high impact strength and resilience
3606	Extrusion	Flexible	Wire jacketing (field wire)	Heat and light-stabilized
63	Injection, extrusion, solution	Flexible	Wire jacketing, sheeting, packings, seals	Alcohol solubility (but good resistance to gasoline and oil), flow characteristics comparable to conventional thermoplastics
69	Injection, extrusion, solution	Flexible	Impact devices, jacketing for mechanical cables and ropes	Comparable to Zytel 63, with superior resistance to impact and flexural fatigue

[a] Zytel is the trademark of the Du Pont Co.

[b] Du Pont data.

[c] These are by class 610 nylons and are being replaced in Du Pont by 612 nylons. The designations corresponding are: 610, 31 = 612, 151; 610, 33 = 612, 153.

marily in melting point, stiffness, hardness, and viscosity in the molten state. General comments by Du Pont on the individual resins are as follows:

Zytel 101, 103, 105, and 42 have the highest melting points. Zytel 101 is the most widely used, particularly for injection molding, because of its excellent combination of properties and processing characteristics. Zytel 103 is essentially the same resin, with an added stabilizer to retard embrittlement at elevated temperatures. Zytel 105 is another of the same class — colored black and stabilized against the slow deteriorating action of the sun's rays.

Zytel 42 is an extrusion grade of nylon that is essentially identical in its properties to Zytel 101, but with a melt viscosity tailored for ready extrusion into shapes, rods, blown bottles, tubing, and similar forms.

Zytel 31 and 33 are nylons of a different type that are characterized by lower melting points and lower moisture absorptions. Zytel 31 is molded and extruded into many forms where dimensional changes due to variations in moisture content must be minimized. Zytel 33 is a heat-stabilized analog and is used primarily as jacketing for wire and cable.

Zytel 63 and 69 are two flexible, alcohol soluble, extremely tough nylons. Zytel 63 is compounded for molding an extrusion. Zytel 69 is the softer and tougher of the two. It is extruded for cable covering and molded into articles subject to extreme impact.

Properties

Table 2 lists typical values for the properties of Zytel 101,* which is the most commonly used resin for molded mechanical parts. This resin is the highest melting and stiffest of the commercial nylons available. Data are given in Table 2 for two moisture contents: (1) 0.2% water, which is typical of the as-molded condition; and (2) 2.5% water, which is typical of the equilibrium condition in normal air.

Mechanical Behavior

Figure 1 is a typical stress–strain curve in tension. The yield point is 8500 psi at 25% elongation, following which the specimen "necks down." Fracture occurs at about 300% elongation, and a stress of 11,000 psi, calculated on the basis of the original cross-sectional area. Working stress

* Formerly designated FM–10001.

TABLE 2. Properties of Nylon

Property	Units	Method	Nylon 6/6 (Zytel 101)		Nylon 6	
			0.2%[a] Water	2.5%[a] Water	0.2% Water	2.5% Water
Tensile strength						
40° F	lb/sq in.	D–638–52T	15,700	13,500		
73° F	lb/sq in.	D–638–52T	11,800	11,200	12,000	8200
170° F	lb/sq in.	D–638–52T	9,000	—		
Yield stress, 73° F	lb/sq in.	D–638–52T	11,800	8,500		
Elongation						
40° F	%	D–638–52T	20	20		
73° F	%	D–638–52T	60	300		
170° F	%	D–638–52T	340	—		
Flexural modulus						
40° F	lb/sq in.	D–790–49T	470,000	500,000		
73° F	lb/sq in.	D–790–49T	410,000	175,000	135,000	
170° F	lb/sq in.	D–790–49T	100,000	—		
Shear strength	lb/sq in.	D–732–46	9,600	—		
Impact strength, Izod						
40° F	ft lb/in.	D–256–56	0.6	0.45		
73° F	ft lb/in.	D–256–56	1.0	2.0	2.2	6.0

Property	Units	ASTM				
Compressive stress at 1% deformation	lb/sq in.	D-695-54	4,900	—		
Apparent modulus[b]	lb/sq in.	—	—	100,000		
Hardness, Rockwell	—	D-785-51	M79 R118	M59 R108	R110	B75
Melting point	°F	D-789-53T	482–500	—		
Coefficient of linear thermal expansion per °F[c]	—	D-696-44	4.5×10^{-5}	—		
Thermal conductivity	btu/hr/sq ft/°F-in.	[d]	1.7	—		
Specific heat	—	—	0.3–0.5	—		
Deformation under load, 122° F., 2000 lb/sq in.	%	D-621-51	1.4	—		
Deflection temp. (annealed)						
264 lb/sq in.	°F	D-648-45T	220	—		
66 lb/sq in.	°F	D-648-45T	470	—		
Dielectric strength, short-time	V/mil	D-149-55T	385	—		
Step-by-step	V/mil	D-149-55T	340	—		
Volume resistivity	Ωcm	D-257-54T	$10^{14} \times 10^{15}$	—		
Dielectric constant						
60 cycles	—	D-150-54T	4.0	7.6		
10^3 cycles	—	D-150-54T	3.9	6.4		
10^6 cycles	—	D-150-54T	3.6	3.6		
Dissipation factor						
60 cycles	—	D-150-54T	0.014	—		
10^3 cycles	—	D-150-54T	0.02	—		
10^6 cycles	—	D-150-54T	0.04	—		

TABLE 2 (*Continued*)

Property	Units	Method	Nylon 6/6 (Zytel 101)		Nylon 6	
			0.2%[a] Water	2.5%[a] Water	0.2% Water	2.5% Water
Water absorption						
24 hr	%	D-570-57T	1.5	—		
Saturation	%	D-570-57T	8	—		
Specific gravity	—	D-792-57T	1.14	—		
Mold shrinkage	in./in.	—	0.015	—		
Compression ratio	—	D-392-38	2.1	—		
Taber abrasion—CS-17 wheel 1000—gm wt.	mg/1000 cycles	D-1044-54T		6–8		

[a] Test values reported at 0.2% water are typical of those in the as-molded condition. Values at 2.5% water describe the states reached in equilibrium with the atmosphere at 50% R. H. The tensile tests (D-638–52T) were run at 2 in./min. Data shown are average values and should not be used for specifications. Many of these properties are determined on molded bars, and are subject to variation, depending on the molding conditions or design, or both.

[b] After 100 hr in flexure, maximum fiber stress 1000 lb/sq in., 73° F, conditioned to 2.5% H_2O (50% R. H.).

[c] These are approximate values. The coefficient of expansion is highly dependent on both temperature and moisture content. Details can be supplied on request.

[d] Thermal conductivity measured by Cenco–Fitch apparatus.

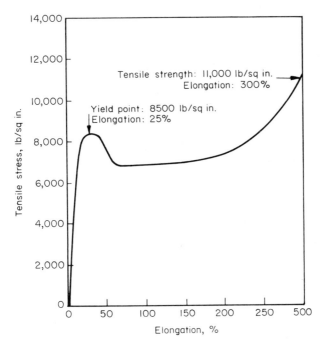

Figure 1. Typical stress-strain curve for Zytel 101 at 73° F and 2.5% moisture content; rate of loading, 0.25 in./min (Du Pont data). ("Designing with 'Zytel' Nylon Resin," Du Pont brochure. Du Pont Co., Wilmington, Delaware.)

should be less than the yield strength in order not to stress the part beyond the yield point. The working stress is determined by dividing the yield point by a safety factor. Depending upon the uncertainty in predicting the performance requirements and the seriousness of a failure, a safety factor between 4 and 10 is considered good design practice.

Deformation can be calculated from the working stress and the modulus of elasticity. The modulus of elasticity of Zytel 101 (i.e., the slope of the initial, straight portion of the stress–strain curve, Figure 1) is about 200,000 psi for 2.5% moisture and room temperature conditions. This value can be used up to a stress of about 3000 psi, beyond which there is some deviation from Hooke's law.

Figures 2 and 3 show the effects of temperature and moisture content on the yield point and modulus of elasticity of Zytel 101. Working stresses should be based on the values at the maximum temperature and moisture content that can be reasonably expected during a part's service.

Nylon continues to deform with time under stress. This is called creep or cold flow and is illustrated in Figure 4. In the case of Zytel 101 stressed

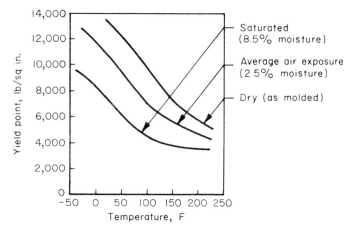

Figure 2. Effect of temperature and moisture content on the yield point of Zytel 101 (Du Pont data). ("Designing with 'Zytel' Nylon Resin," Du Pont brochure. Du Pont Co., Wilmington, Delaware.)

in tension at 1800 psi, for example, there is an initial, elastic extension of about 0.009 in./in. that takes place when the load is applied. Following this, the specimen continues to elongate with time, reaching an extension of about 0.018 in./in. at the end of 800 hr. Note that the major amount of creep takes place in the first 24 hr, and the rate of creep slows down thereafter. For design purposes, an apparent modulus of elasticity is used

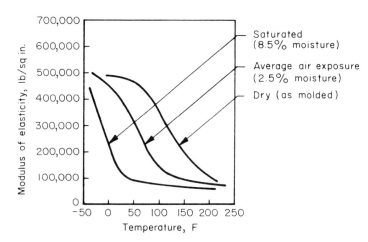

Figure 3. Effect of temperature and moisture content on the modulus of elasticity of Zytel 101. (Du Pont data). ("Designing with 'Zytel' Nylon Resin," Du Pont brochure. Du Pont Co., Wilmington, Delaware.)

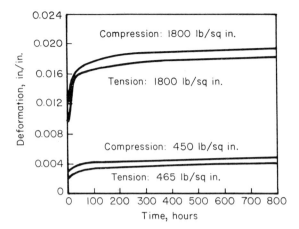

Figure 4. Deformation of Zytel 101 with time under stress (conditioned to average air exposure, Du Pont data). ("Designing with 'Zytel' Nylon Resin," Du Pont brochure. Du Pont Co., Wilmington, Delaware.)

that is based on the amount of deformation after a period of time. Figure 5 shows a plot of the apparent modulus of elasticity of Zytel 101 for normal conditions. Note that at the end of one year, the apparent modulus has decreased to a value about one-half of the initial value.

Molded bearings should be stress-relieved in hot oil to remove internal strains and improve dimensional stability. For general use, a temperature

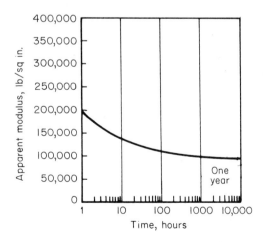

Figure 5. Apparent modulus of elasticity of Zytel 101 after creep deformation (at 73° F and 2.5% moisture, Du Pont data). ("Designing with 'Zytel' Nylon Resin," Du Pont brochure. Du Pont Co., Wilmington, Delaware.)

of 300° F is recommended with an immersion time of 15 min/$\frac{1}{8}$ in. of thickness. Temperatures 50° F above the maximum expected in service are recommended for applications at elevated temperatures. Unless molded parts are stress relieved, the parts will normally contract somewhat as the strains are relieved during service.

Nylon is hygroscopic. Although it does not deteriorate from exposure to either fresh or salt water, it absorbs moisture from the surroundings until an equilibrium is reached. As-molded nylon contains about 0.25% moisture by weight; for average exposure, the equilibrium moisture content is about 2.5%; immersion in water increases the value to about 8.5%. Moisture pickup improves toughness and impact strength but reduces strength and stiffness.

Figure 6 shows the change in dimensions of Zytel 101 with moisture content. This curve applies to nylon that was initially in a stress-free condition. Parts that have not been annealed increase only about 0.002 in./in. in going to equilibrium, because some shrinkage from stress-relief is compensated by the increase in dimensions as moisture is picked up from the air. These considerations should be discussed with the molder or fabricator of a part in order to determine the most economical molding conditions and treatments for dimensional control.

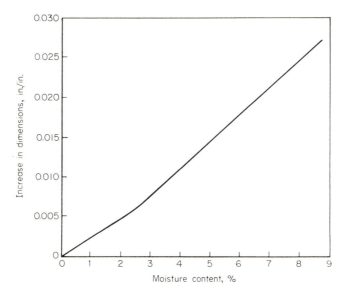

Figure 6. Change in dimensions of Zytel 101 with moisture content (Du Pont data). ("Designing with 'Zytel' Nylon Resin," Du Pont brochure. Du Pont Co., Wilmington, Delaware.)

For designing gears of nylon, the Lewis equation usually gives conservative results. One form of the Lewis equation that is used is

$$W = Spfy$$

where W is the load on the tooth (pounds), S is the design stress (pounds per square inch), p is the circular pitch (inches), f is the face width (inches), and y is the form factor.

The design stress is usually taken as two-thirds of the fatigue endurance limit. Table 3 gives typical values for the fatigue endurance limit of Zytel 101 for several conditions of temperature and moisture level.

TABLE 3. Fatigue Endurance Limits for Zytel 101 Nylon[a]

Moisture level[b]	Temp. (°F)	Fatigue endurance limit[c] (psi)
Dry (<0.3%)	73	5000
Average air exposure		
2.5%	73	3000
2.5% initially	212	2000
Saturated (8.5%)	212	1500

[a] "Designing with 'Zytel' Nylon Resin," Table 1, Du Pont brochure. Du Pont Co., Wilmington, Delaware.

[b] *Test conditions*: 1800 cpm with tension and compression equal.

[c] Defined as the stress causing failure in 2-million cycles.

Table 4 gives tooth form factors for lubricated gears cut from blanks of molded Zytel 101 and run at 2500 rpm. Nonlubricated gears should be operated at about one-half the stress for lubricated gears. Hall and Alvord [1] can be consulted for further details on calculating the load-carrying capacity of Zytel 101 gears.

Friction and Wear Behavior

Various values for the coefficient of friction on nylon have been reported. Table 5 gives some results obtained at very low speeds (about 0.25 in./min) in a modified Bowden–Leben-type machine, Table 6 gives some values for light loads and somewhat higher sliding velocities, and

TABLE 4.   Values for Form Factor in Lewis Equation[a]
(Load at Middle of Tooth)

Number of teeth	Value for specific tooth form	
	20° Full depth	20° Stub depth
15	—	0.556
18	—	0.603
20	0.544	0.628
24	0.522	0.664
30	0.606	0.698
75	0.735	0.792
300	0.801	0.855
Rack	0.823	0.881

[a] "Designing with 'Zytel' Nylon Resin," Table 7, Du Pont brochure. Du Pont Co., Wilmington, Delaware.

Table 7 reports some unusually low values obtained under rather high loads and high PV values. Comparison of the data indicates that the coefficient of friction is about 0.35 for nylon sliding without lubrication (dry) on a mating surface of either nylon or steel for normal conditions of load and speed. The coefficient decreases with increasing load, and

TABLE 5.   Coefficients of Friction for Nylon[a]

Lubricant	Nylon on nylon		Steel on nylon	
	Static	Kinetic	Static	Kinetic
Dry	0.46	0.37	0.37	0.34
Water	0.52	0.33	0.23	0.19
Ethylene glycol	0.58	0.19	0.20	0.16
Glycerol	0.36	0.19	0.23	0.18
Perfluorolube oil	0.58	0.24	0.30	0.19
Oleic acid	0.29	0.13	0.15	0.08
Methylpolysiloxane (DC 500 oil)	0.43	0.17	0.19	0.12

[a] R. C. Bowers, W. C. Clinton, and W. A. Zisman, *Ind. Eng. Chem.* **26**, 2416 (1954).

TABLE 6.   Spread in Coefficient of Friction Data[a,b]

Lubricant	*Nylon*	*Nylatron G*
No lubricant		
Max	0.33	0.33
Min	0.15	0.22
Water		
Max	0.18	0.21
Min	0.14	0.19
Oil		
Max	0.14	0.13
Min	0.09	0.08

[a] W. C. Milz and L. B. Sargent, Jr., Frictional characteristics of plastics. *ASLE Conf., Chicago, April* 1955.
[b] Applied loads, 1–5 lb; sliding speeds, 8–367 fpm.

reaches a value of 0.10–0.15 at high loadings. Water, oil, or other lubricants significantly reduce friction. Since the value of the coefficient of friction varies with the conditions, the above values can be used only as general guides. Where friction is critical, the coefficient should be measured under actual operating conditions.

TABLE 7.   Friction Data on Zytel 101 under High PV Values[a]

Lubricant	Mating surface	Coefficient of friction
Dry	Zytel 101	0.04–0.13
Water	Zytel 101	0.08–0.14
	Steel	0.3–0.5
	Brass	0.3–0.5
Oil	Zytel 101	0.07–0.08

[a] $P = 1050$ psi, $V = 156$ fpm, $PV = 163,500$.

TABLE 8. Typical *PV* Values for Bearings Made of Zytel 101 Nylon[a,b]

Type of lubricant	Type of service		
	Continuous	Intermittent[b]	Sporadic[c]
Dry	500	1,000	10,000
Initially lubricated	2,000	2,500	10,000
Water	2,500	2,500	No data
Wick lubrication	50,000	70,000	Not significant

[a] "Designing with 'Zytel' Nylon Resin," Du Pont Co., Wilmington, Delaware.

[b] Intermittent service is typically where the shaft is in motion approximately one-third of the time and continuous operation is less than 15 min/cycle.

[c] Sporadic service is typified by door-hinge bushings and drawer or door rollers.

Table 8 gives typical *PV* values for bearings made of Zytel 101 nylon resin, and Figure 7 indicates how the limiting bearing pressure and *PV* value change with sliding velocity. As Figure 7 indicates, the *PV* limit decreases from 4500 to 1800 as the sliding velocity increases from 100 to 600 fpm. For most designs, a value of 75% of the limiting *PV* values in Figure 7 is recommended.

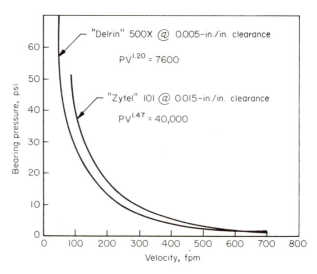

Figure 7. Bearing characteristics for Zytel 101 nylon and delrin acetal plastics. [L. H. Gillespie and Hudson, Design data for bearings of nylon, acetal, and TFE fluorocarbon resins. *Iron Steel Eng.* **37**, 151–156 (April 1960).]

B. FILLED MOLDED NYLON

Fiberglass, molybdenum disulfide, graphite, and other fillers are added to overcome some of the deficiencies of unfilled nylon. Fiberglass is the most common addition for improving mechanical properties. In addition to long glass fibers, short glass fibers have recently been introduced that are invisible to the naked eye, reduce the cost, and facilitate molding. However, nylon reinforced with long glass fibers is stronger, tougher, and more rigid.

The bond between nylon and glass is exceptionally good, so that relatively little glass reinforcement gives a dramatic improvement in strength; for example, only 30% glass reinforcement boosts the tensile strength of Nylon 6 by about 85%, to 23,000 psi. Cost also goes up with glass reinforcement; nylons with 30–40% glass reinforcement cost about 39% more than unfilled grades, 50% reinforcement costs about 37% more, and 60% reinforcement costs about 44% more. The range from 30 to 33% reinforcement appears to give the best combination of cost and properties and is the most popular level now.

Table 9 gives typical properties of fiberglass-reinforced nylons. These are furnished with up to 40% by weight fiberglass reinforcement in Nylon Types 6, 6/6, and 6/10. Tensile strengths up to 30,000 psi at room temperature can be obtained, as compared to about 14,000 psi for unfilled nylon. In addition to raising tensile strength, glass reinforcement also increases flexural modulus, impact strength, heat distortion temperature, *PV* bearing limit, fatigue strength, and dimensional stability.

Molybdenum disulfide is also used as a filler in Nylon Types 6, 6/6, and 6/10 to improve their wear, abrasion resistance, and frictional characteristics. Flexural strength, modulus, and heat resistance are also improved. The presence of MoS_2 promotes solidification and crystallite formation during molding of nylon, so that molded parts are less amorphous and have a more uniform crystalline structure than parts of unfilled nylon molded under comparable conditions. Table 10 compares typical properties of a MoS_2-filled nylon with unfilled nylon. As a dry bearing material, MoS_2-filled nylon can generally be used at 10–15% higher *PV* ratings than unfilled Nylon 6/6. Figure 8 illustrates the lower rate of wear of a MoS_2-filled nylon, Nylatron GS,* as compared to unfilled nylon.[†]

---

* Nylatron GS is a trademark of the Polymer Corporation, Reading, Pennsylvania.

† The test conditions for Figure 8 were more severe than normal practice in order to accelerate wear; it should not be implied that the material should be used at these *PV* conditions.

TABLE 9. Properties of Nylafil[a] (Fiberglass-Reinforced Nylon)[b]

Property	Unit	ASTM Test	G-1/30 Type 6-6	G-2/30 Type 6-10	G-3/30 Type 6	G-10/40 Type 6-6	G-13/40 Type 6
Tensile strength							
−40° F	psi	D638–60T	21,000	20,000	23,000	36,600	39,000
73° F	psi	D638–60T	20,000	19,000	21,000	30,000	30,000
170° F	psi	D638–60T	18,500	16,200	16,000	23,400	25,000
Elongation							
−40° F	%	D638–60T	1.6	1.8	1.9	6.4	2.0
73° F	%	D638–60T	1.5	1.9	2.0	1.9	2.0
170° F	%	D638–60T	1.9	2.1	2.1	2.2	2.3
Flexural modulus							
−40° F	psi	D790–59T	1,025,000	900,000	980,000	2,000,000	1,900,000
73° F	psi	D790–59T	985,000	860,000	970,000	1,800,000	1,500,000
170° F	psi	D790–59T	740,000	580,000	570,000	1,400,000	900,000
Impact strength, Izod							
−40° F ($\frac{1}{2} \times \frac{1}{4}$ bars)	ft-lb/in.	D256–56	3.0	3.7	3.5	4.2	4.5
73° F ($\frac{1}{2} \times \frac{1}{4}$ bars)	ft-lb/in.	D256–56	2.5	3.4	3.0	3.7	4.3
73° F ($\frac{1}{2} \times \frac{1}{2}$ bars)	ft-lb/in.	D256–56	2.1	2.5	2.8	18.7	—
Compressive strength	psi	D695–54	18,000	18,000	19,000	24,000	22,000

Property	Units	ASTM					
Flexural strength	psi	D790–59T	28,000	23,000	27,000	27,000	37,000
Shear strength	psi	D732–46	11,000	11,000	11,000	14,000	13,000
Hardness, Rockwell	—	D785–60T	E60–70	E70–75	E55–60	E75–80	E65–70
Deformation under load[c] 4000 psi	%	D621–59	0.6	0.9	0.8	0.4	0.5
Water absorption							
in 24 hr	%	D570–59aT	0.7	0.2	1.1	0.6	0.9
to saturation	%		5.65	1.84	6.4	4.0	4.0
Specific gravity	—	D792–60T	1.37	1.30	1.37	1.52	1.52
Mold shrinkage							
in $\frac{1}{8}$ av. section[d]	in./in.	—	0.0050	0.0045	0.0040	0.0045	0.0030
in $\frac{1}{4}$ av. section[d]	in./in.	—	0.0060	0.0050	0.0050	0.0055	0.0035
in $\frac{1}{2}$ av. section[d]	in./in.	—	0.0070	0.0060	0.0060	0.0065	0.0045
Taber abrasion, CS–17 wheel, 1000 G	mg/1000 cycles	D1044–56	25	18	14	32	5.0
Melting point	°F	D789–53T	480°–490°	430°	420°–435°	490°	435°
Coefficient of linear thermal expansion per °F	in./in.	D696–44	1.71×10^{-5}	1.33×10^{-5}	1.25×10^{-5}	0.9×10^{-5}	0.8×10^{-5}
Thermal conductivity (btu/hr-sq ft-°F-in.)	—	[e]	1.5	1.6	1.7		
Specific heat	—	—	0.304	0.347	0.324		
Heat distortion temp.							
264 psi	°F	D648–56	498°	420°	420°	502°	423°
66 psi	°F	D648–56	507°	437°	425°	509°	428°

TABLE 9 (*Continued*)

Property	Unit	ASTM test	G-1/30 Type 6-6	G-2/30 Type 6-10	G-3/30 Type 6	G-10/40 Type 6-6	G-13/40 Type 6
Dielectric strength							
short time	V/mil	D149–59	500	500	400	480	580
Step by step	V/mil	D149–59	400	450	375	400	460
Volume resistivity	Ωcm	D257–58	5.5×10^{15}	7.2×10^{14}	1.5×10^{15}	2.6×10^{15}	3.0×10^{14}
Dielectric constant							
60 cycles	—	D150–59T	4.0	4.2	4.6	4.45	4.4
10^3 cycles	—	D150–59T	3.9	4.0	4.4	4.40	4.1
10^6 cycles	—	D150–59T	3.4	3.5	3.9	4.10	4.0
Dissipation factor							
60 cycles	—	D150–59T	0.018	0.026	0.022	0.009	0.020
10^3 cycles	—	D150–59T	0.022	0.025	0.024	0.011	0.016
10^6 cycles	—	D150–59T	0.017	0.022	0.019	0.018	0.021
Arc resistance	sec	D495–58T	148	98	92	100	

[a] Nylafil is the trademark of Fiberfil Division, Dart Industries Inc., Evansville, Indiana.
[b] Data from Fiberfil, Inc., Evansville, Indiana.
[c] This test normally runs at 2000 psi, but loading was doubled to get a significant result.
[d] Data from laboratory specimens. For mold design a figure of 20–25% of mold shrinkage of unreinforced material is recommended.
[e] Thermal conductivity is measured by Cenco–Fitch apparatus.

TABLE 10.   Properties of Nylatron GS and Unfilled Nylon 6/6[a]

Property	Units	Nylatron GS (MoS₂-filled Nylon 6/6)	Unfilled Nylon 6/6
Tensile strength at 73° F	psi	9,500–15,000	9,000–12,000
Modulus of elasticity at 73° F	psi	450,000–600,000	250,000–400,000
Flexural strength at 73° F	psi	15,000–18,000	12,500–14,000
Tensile impact at 73° F	ft-lb/in.²	50–150	90–180
Heat distortion temp. at 264 psi	°F	200–300	140–200
Coefficient of thermal expansion	in./in.-°F	4.0×10^{-5}	5.0×10^{-5}
Brittleness temp.	°C	—10 to +10	—40 to —10
Deformation under load	%	0.5–2.5	1.0–3.0
Hardness at 73° F	Durometer	D80–90	D80–85
	Rockwell	R110–125	R110–120
Kinetic coefficient of friction dry, against steel	—	0.16–0.20	0.2–0.3
Specific gravity	—	1.14–1.17	1.14–1.15
Water absorption			
24 hr	%	0.5–1.4	0.6–1.5
saturation	%	6–7	6–8
Color	—	Steel gray	Buff white

[a] Data from Polymer Corp., Reading, Pennsylvania.

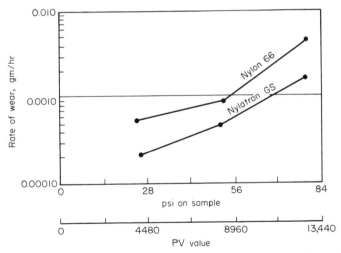

Figure 8. Comparison of rates of wear of MoS₂-filled Nylon (Nylatron GS) and unfilled Nylon 6/6. [Both specimens were run dry against steel cleaned with carbon tetrachloride at a rubbing velocity of 160 fpm (1165 rpm shaft speed). These were accelerated tests conducted at higher *PV* values than recommended for normal service.] (Data from the Polymer Corp. Reading, Pennsylvania.)

TABLE 11. Properties of Fiberglass-Reinforced Nylon with Lubricating Additives[a]

Property	Unit	ASTM test	Nylafil[b] G-1/30/TF/22	Nylafil[c] G-1/30/TF/44	Nylafil[d] G-1/30/MS/5
Tensile strength					
−40° F	psi	D638-60T	—	—	21,800
73° F	psi	D638-60T	19,000	16,000	20,000
170° F	psi	D638-60T	—	—	18,000
Elongation					
−40° F	%	D638-60T	—	—	3.3
73° F	%	D638-60T	1.8	1.6	1.6
170° F	%	D638-60T	—	—	1.9
Flexural modulus					
−40° F	psi	D790-59T	—	—	1,260,000
73° F	psi	D790-59T	—	—	1,900,000
170° F	psi	D790-59T	—	—	790,000
Impact strength, Izod					
−40° F					
($\frac{1}{2} \times \frac{1}{4}$ bars)	ft-lb./in.	D256-56	3.7	2.7	2.5
73° F ($\frac{1}{2} \times \frac{1}{4}$ bars)	ft-lb/in.	D256-56	2.7	3.0	2.2
73° F ($\frac{1}{2} \times \frac{1}{2}$ bars)	ft-lb/in.	D256-56	—	—	7.9
Compressive strength	psi	D695-54	19,000	16,000	21,000
Flexural strength	psi	D790-59T	24,500	21,000	26,000
Shear strength	psi	D732-46	10,500	9,000	12,000
Hardness, Rockwell	—	D785-60T	E50-55	M90	E65-75
Deformation under load[e] 4000 psi	%	D621-59	0.4	0.75	0.35
Water absorption					
in 24 hr	%	D570-59aT	0.45	0.30	0.7
to saturation	%	—	—	—	4.51

TABLE 11 (*Continued*)

Property	Unit	ASTM test	Nylafil[b] G-1/30/TF/22	Nylafil[c] G-1/30/TF/44	Nylafil[d] G-1/30/MS/5
Specific gravity	—	D792-60T	1.49	1.63	1.41
Mold shrinkage					
in ⅛ av. section[f]	in./in.	—	0.005	0.006	0.0045
in ¼ av. section[f]	in./in.	—	0.006	0.007	0.0050
in ½ av. section[f]	in./in.	—	0.007	0.008	0.0060
Taber abrasion, CS-17 wheel, 1000g	mg/1000	D1044-56	—	—	10
Melting point	°F	D789-53T	—	—	490
Coefficient of linear thermal expansion per °F	in./in.	D696-44	1.6×10^{-5}	1.43×10^{-5}	1.4×10^{-5}
Heat distortion temp.					
264 psi	°F	D648-56	493	498	498
66 psi	°F	D648-56	—	—	510

[a] Nylafil is the trademark of the Fiberfil Division, Dart Industries, Inc., Evansville, Indiana.

[b] Nylafil G-1/30/TF/22 is Nylon 6/6 with 30% fiberglass and 22% Teflon.

[c] Nylafil G-1/30/TF/44 is Nylon 6/6 with 30% fiberglass and 44% Teflon.

[d] Nylafil G-1/30/MS/5 is Nylon 6/6 with 30% fiberglass and 5% MoS_2.

[e] This test normally run at 2000 psi, but loading was doubled to get a significant result.

[f] Data from laboratory specimens. For mold design figure of 20%–25% of mold shrinkage of unreinforced material is recommended.

An additional benefit is the reduced coefficient of thermal expansion, about one-half that of unfilled nylon, which provides better dimensional control and more accurate molding tolerances. Primary uses for filled nylon are in bearing sliding parts such as aircraft fuel-pump bearings, oven-door slides, sleeve bushings, wear pads, and thrust washers. The improved heat resistance also offers some advantages in certain electrical insulating applications.

TABLE 12. Typical Properties of 30% Glass-Reinforced Nylon with and without Lubricating Additives[a]

Property	Type 6	Type 6+5% MoS_2	Type 6/6	Type 6/6+5% MoS_2	Type 6/6+15% TFE	Type 6/10
Specific gravity	1.37	1.43	1.37	1.43	1.51	1.30
Water absorption (24 hr) (%)	1.2	1.0	0.80	0.7	0.5	0.20
Mold shrinkage (in./in.)	0.004	0.004	0.005	0.004	0.005	0.004
Tensile strength (psi)	23,000	18,500	26,600	20,000	23,000	21,000
Elongation (%)	—	3–4	—	3–4	4–5	—
Flexural modulus (1000 psi)	1200	1100	1300	1200	1200	1100
Izod impact strength (ft, lb/in.)						
Notched	2.3	3.4–3.8	2.0	1.6–2.0	1.5–1.8	2.4
Unnotched	20	12	17	10	—	20
Rockwell hardness	M92, R121	M94	M96, R121	M97	E50	M93, R120
Heat distortion temp. at 264 psi, °F	419	420	489	475	>420	420
Coef. of linear expansion (10^{-5} in./in.-°F)	2.2	1.9	2.3	2.0	1.6	2.5
Flammability	Slow burn	—	Slow burn	—	—	Slow burn
Dielectric strength (V/mil)	450	—	440	—	—	440
Dielectric constant, 60×10^5 Hz	4.20–3.60	—	4.20–3.50	—	—	4.20–3.50
Dissipation Factor, 60×10^5 Hz	0.009–0.018	—	0.009–0.018	—	—	0.013–0.015

[a] Data from Liquid Nitrogen Proc. Corp. as quoted by R. J. Fabian, Wide selection, better grades keep nylon competitive. *Mater. Eng.* **68**, 34–36 (March 1969).

Fiberglass-reinforced nylon that also contains MoS_2 or Teflon is also available. Teflon is commonly added as fine powder, 5–10 μ in size. Tables 11 and 12 summarize properties of several that are commercially available. Figure 9 indicates the higher load-carrying capacities of these materials

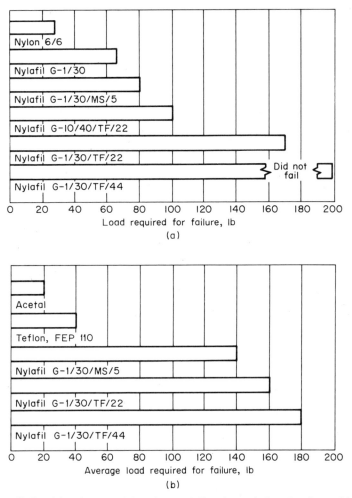

Figure 9. Load-bearing capacities of several fiberglass-reinforced nylons with lubricated additives. (a) New shafts (20 μin. RMS is the surface finish) on each evaluation; phenolic bearing retainer; no lubrication, 400 rpm; bearing 1-in. diam. × 1.25 in. × 0.125 in. (b) 1-in. shaft (CRS) at 215 rpm; bearing dimensions 1 in. × 1.25 in. × 0.125 in.; no lubrication and phenolic bearing holder; test under extreme conditions, no lubrication, no heat dissipation, scored steel shaft, loaded on one edge. [Data from Fiberfil Division, Dart Industries, Inc., Evansville, Indiana. Nylofil is the trademark of Fiberfil.]

TABLE 13. Limiting PV Values for a Wide Range of Reinforced Thermoplastics[a]

Thermoplastic	52 fpm	78 fpm	110 fpm
Polycarbonate and 22% TFE	>8050	1,810	1,680
Polycarbonate	1200	1,810	NR[b]
Polycarbafil			
20% glass	820	NR	NR
20% glass and 44% TFE	4930	1,810	1,680
20% glass and 22% TFE	2820	—	2,520
40% glass and 22% TFE	2410	12,100[c]	NR
40% glass and 12% TFE	2410	1,210	NR
20% glass and 12% TFE	2410	3,020	NR
20% glass and 12% TFE (cooled)	—	4,830	—
FEP Teflon 110	2420	2,420	1,680
FEP Teflon and 25% glass	>8050	>12,100	>16,800
Acetal	2010	1,210	NR
Acetal and 22% TFE	5225	NR	NR
Nylon, Type 6-6	>8050	9,070	1,680
Nylon and 44% TFE	>8050	9,675	6,750
Polyamide and 5% MoS_2	3220	1,210	NR
Nylafil			
30% glass	>8050	9,070	5,900
30% glass and MoS_2	>8050	9,070	5,900
30% glass and 22% TFE	>8050	9,675	13,500
30% glass and 22% TFE (fibrous)	>8050	>12,100	>16,800
20% glass and 22% TFE and 4% MoS_2	>8050	10,280	7,070
30% glass and 44% TFE	>8050	>12,100	>16,800
40% glass and 22% TFE	>8050	9,675	7,550
Polypropylene	2420	NR	NR

[a] Data from Fiberfil Division, Dart Industries, Inc., Evansville, Indiana. Polycarbofil and Nylafil are the trademarks of Fiberfil.

[b] NR, not recommended.

[c] Charred

in comparison to unfilled nylon and several other thermoplastics, as well as fiberglass-reinforced nylon that does not contain lubricating additives. Table 13 summarizes limiting PV values for a range of reinforced thermoplastics, including several grades of nylon.

Teflon-filled nylon is also available. Properties for Plaslube NY-1/TF/44,* a proprietary molded nylon containing 44% Teflon, are given in Table 14, and the improvement in load-bearing capacity is indicated by the results for sleeve-bearing tests presented in Figure 10.

C. SINTERED NYLON

Nylon powders can be precipitated from solution and subsequently pressed and sintered by a process somewhat similar to powder metallurgy. Sintered nylon was originally conceived as a practical means for reducing the dimensional instabilities found in injection-molded polyamides. Because of its higher crystallinity as compared with injection-molded nylon, sintered nylon has superior frictional and wear qualities and higher compressive strength, although its tensile strength, elongation, and impact strength are lower. Various additives and fillers, including MoS_2, are easily blended with the fine nylon powders to give special properties.

Sintered nylon parts are made by cold-molding at high pressure (in excess of 20,000 psi), and then heated or sintered. For satisfactory bonding, the powder must be prepared by chemical precipitation; powder produced by mechanically grinding molding pellets does not give satisfactory strength when cold-pressed and sintered. Precipitation from high-temperature solution gives a powder that has a relatively high percentage of crystallinity, usually about 80%. On the other hand, injection-molded nylon articles often have a highly amorphous skin resulting from quick cooling of the molten material against a cold die surface, and normally have an average crystallinity of about 43%. Although this skin condition does no harm in many applications, it appears detrimental where minimum wear and best load-carrying capacity as a bearing material are required. Finished parts, produced by pressing and sintering the precipitated nylon powders, are available in the following material grades: (1) Nylasint† type 66, which has the higher rigidity, modulus of elasticity,

---

* Product of Fiberfil, Inc., Evansville, Indiana.
† Nylasint is a registered trademark of the Polymer Corp., Reading, Pennsylvania.

TABLE 14. Properties of Plaslubes[a]

Property	Unit	ASTM test	NY-1/TF/44[b] (nylon–Teflon)	PC-50/TF/12[b] (polycarbonate–Teflon)	PC-50/TF/22[b] (polycarbonate–Teflon)	PC-50/TF/44[b] (polycarbonate–Teflon)	AC-80/TF/22[b] (acetal–Teflon)	PP-60/MS/5 (polypropylene–MoS₂)
Tensile strength, 73° F	psi	D638–60T	5,500	7,500	6,500	6,000	5,800	5,000
Modulus of elasticity, 73° F	psi	D790–59T	300,000	220,000	180,000		300,000	
Tensile elongation	%	D638–60T	2.0	10.0	12.0		5.0	30.0[c]
Izod impact								
73° F	ft-lb/in.	D256–56	0.5	1.5	2.0	1.8	0.50	0.70
−40° F	ft-lb/in.	D256–56	0.5	1.2	1.1		0.50	0.30
Coefficient of linear thermal expansion per °F	in./in.		4.5×10^{-5}	3.5×10^{-5}	3.9×10^{-5}		5.5×10^{-5}	3.20×10^{-6}
Flexural strength	psi	D790–59T	8,000	9,600[d]	10,300[d]	7,600[d]	7,500	4,500
Heat distortion temp.								
264 psi	°F		180	275	265	260	205	140
66 psi	°F		210	290	285		315	
Water absorption, 24 hr	%	D570–59aT	0.55	0.11	0.14	0.06	0.25	0.0028

Property	Units	ASTM Method						
Deformation under load								
4000 psi 122° F	%	D621-59	3.9	4.25	0.40	0.30	0.32	6.0
2000 psi 122° F	%	D621-59					—	2.4
Rockwell hardness	—	D785-60T	L80	M65-75	L77	M57	L92	M55
Shear strength	psi	D732-46	4,000	4,000	5,300	5,900	8,000	6,000
Specific gravity	—	D792-60T	0.93	1.48-1.55	1.40	1.33	1.27	1.43
Compressive stress, 1% Deformation	psi	D695				1,600	1,800	1,400
Compressive strength			5,000	10,000		9,000	9,000	6,000
Mold shrinkage								
in $\frac{1}{8}$-in. av. section	in./in.	—		0.013	0.009	0.0045	0.0045	0.007
in $\frac{1}{4}$-in. av. section	in./in.	—		0.017	0.010	0.005	0.005	0.020
in $\frac{1}{2}$-in. av. section	in./in.	—		0.023	0.011	0.006	0.006	0.042

[a] Data from Fiberfil Division, Dart Industries, Inc., Evansville, Indiana. Plaslube is the trademark of Fiberfil.
[b] Patent pending.
[c] Pulled at 2 in./min.
[d] No break.

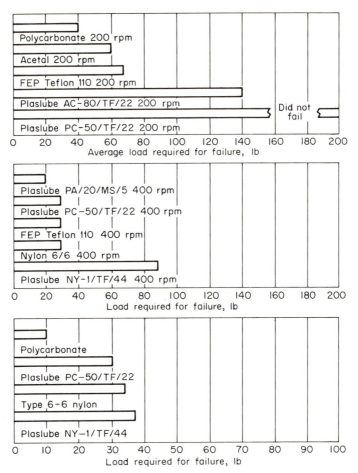

Figure 10. Load-bearing capacities of several unreinforced plastics with lubricating additives. (Data from Fiberfil Division, Dart Industries Inc., Evansville Indiana. Plastube is the trademark of Fiberfil.)

and melting point; and (2) Nylasint Type 64, in which fine powders are used and which has the higher impact strength and greater deformability.

Both compositions are also available with MoS_2 additive (Nylasint Type MS and Nylasint Type M4), which further improves their frictional performance in some applications. Compositions containing various percentages of either graphite or zirconium silicate are also available.

Sintered nylon parts can be impregnated with oil. "Microporous" Nylasint can absorb and maintain up to 25% of fluids by weight and provides a coefficient of friction of 0.01. Accelerated wear tests, sum-

TABLE 15. Comparative Wear and Friction Data from Accelerated Tests of Sintered and Injection-Molded Nylon[a]

Material	Type of lubrication	Load (psi)	Surface speed (ft/min)	Coefficient of friction	Total wear[b] (mil)	Pressure–velocity product (PV)[c]	Power consumption (FV)[d]	Running time (hr)
Nylasint 66	Sintered in Gulf Crest 55 (no other lubrication)	135	240	0.12 (smooth, no change)	1.5	32,400	3,890	48
	Sintered in Gulf Crest 55 (no other lubrication)	195	240	0.10 (smooth, no change)	1.5	46,800	4,680	34
	Sintered in Gulf Crest 55 (no other lubrication)	195	370	0.09 (smooth, no change)	1.5	72,200	6,500	24
Nylasint 64M	Sintered in Gulf Crest 55 (no other lubrication)	195	240	0.10 (smooth, no change)	1.5	46,800	4,680	24
Nylon 101, Injection molded	2 drops, Gulf Crest 55	195	240	0.11 (smooth, no change)	2.7	46,800	5,150	21
	2 drops, Gulf Crest 55	195	370	0.11–0.32 (very rough and variable)	0.6	72,200	8,000–23,000	Failed, 0.5
	None	29	240	0.26–1.18 (steady increase, rough during latter part of test)	1.6	6,900	1,800–8,200	Failed, 0.5
	None	52	240	0.19–0.67 (steady increase, very rough)	20.0	12,500	8,370	Failed, 3 min

[a] L. L. Stott, Sintered Nylon. *Mod. Plast.* **35**, 157–158 (1957).

[b] Wear based upon 24-hr test unless otherwise noted; values including deformation of samples.

[c] PV, load (in pounds per square inch) multiplied by velocity (in feet per minute).

[d] FV, frictional force (in pounds per square inch) multiplied by velocity (in feet per minute).

marized in Table 15, show the superiority of sintered nylon over injection-molded nylon in friction and wear. These data were obtained on thrust rings of oil-sintered nylon and injection-molded nylon which were rotated against hardened tool steel (Rockwell C-63–65, 1.5-μin. finish) at various speeds and loads. Sintered nylon is used in cams, slides, rollers, bearings, and other parts subject to wear in business machines, automotive equipment, aircraft instruments, and textile machinery.

REFERENCE

1. K. W. Hall and H. H. Alvord, Zytel spur gears. *Mech. Eng.* **81**, 50–53 (1959).

Chapter 9

Fluorocarbons

Fluorocarbons are essentially hydrocarbons in which all or nearly all of the hydrogen has been replaced by fluorine. Although the term "Teflon" has meant fluorocarbon to those not versed in its chemistry, Teflon is actually the tradename of Du Pont for its line of fluorocarbon products. Table 1 lists the four chemical types of fluorocarbons, their tradenames, suppliers, and general characteristics.

Fluorocarbon are thermoplastics. Their most noteworthy characteristic for applications involving friction and wear are their very low coefficients of friction and good resistance to heat. They can be used from —450° to about 500° F. They do not absorb water, and their dimensional stability is excellent. They retain their toughness and flexibility at cryogenic temperatures, are inert to most chemicals and solvents, and are excellent dielectrics. On the debit side, fluorocarbons have relatively high rates of thermal expansion, are subject to cold flow under stress, do not conduct heat as well as other plastics, and are relatively expensive.

To overcome these disadvantages, the basic fluorocarbon resins are often mixed with various additives. The filled products are proprietary and are sold under a variety of tradenames. Other useful forms are as thin films bonded to suitable substrates, as impregnants into porous metals, and as fibers and powders.

A. PROPERTIES AND CHARACTERISTICS OF FLUOROCARBONS

Teflon TFE (polytetrafluoroethylene) is the original fluorocarbon resin, and it has been used since the early 1940's. Teflon FEP (fluorinated ethylene propylene copolymer) was introduced in 1958 and is easier to extrude and injection mold. In comparison with Teflon FEP, the TFE type is harder, has a lower coefficient of friction, is more resistant to wear, and can be used to higher temperatures.

TABLE 1.   Types of Fluorocarbons

Chemical type	Abbreviation	Tradenames and suppliers	General characteristics
Polytetra-fluoroethylene	TFE or PTFE	Teflon TFE (Du Pont) Halon TFE (Allied Chemical Corp.) Fluon PTFE (Imperial Chemical Industries)	Very low coefficient of friction (~0.04) Good combination of mechanical and electrical properties, but relatively weak in cold flow unless reinforced by suitable fillers Useful from −450° to 500° F (continuous) or +600° F (intermittent) Nearly inert chemically, as are most fluorocarbons Nonflammable
Fluorinated ethylene propylene copolymer	FEP	Teflon FEP (Du Pont)	Similar to TFE, except its coefficient of friction is slightly higher and it is easier to mold Useful from −450° to about +400° F
Polychlorotri-fluoroethylene	CFE or CTFE	Kel-F (3M) Plaskon CTFE (Allied Chemical Corp.)	Stiffer than TFE and FEP, but does have some cold flow Useful from −450° to +390° F; inferior to TFE in physical properties at low temperatures and in sensitivity to stress cracking at high temperatures
Polyvinylidene fluoride	PVF	Kynar (Pennsalt Chemical Corp.)	One of the easiest of the fluorocarbons to process Stiff and more resistant to cold flow than TFE Useful from −80° to +300° F

Properties

Table 2 summarizes data on the properties of Teflon TFE and FEP and other fluorocarbons. The values quoted are typical for pieces that have been molded under good conditions. Many of the properties can be altered by changing the fabrication techniques. Teflon retains useful

TABLE 2. Typical Properties of Unfilled Fluorocarbon Plastics[a]

Property	Temp. (°F)	Teflon TFE	Teflon FEP	Halon G-10 and G-50	Halon G-80	Halon G-85	Kel-F
Ultimate tensile strength (psi)	−423	17,900	23,800				27,000
	−320	14,900	18,000				
	−200	9,100	12,200				
	−110	5,900	6,500				
	+77	4,500	4,000	2,500	5,200	4,200	5,200
	248						520
Tensile yield strength (psi)	−423	17,800	23,700				
	−320	13,300	19,000				
	−200	7,700	11,400				
	−110	4,700	5,600				
	+77	1,700	2,000				3,640
	500	550					
Tensile elongation (%)	−423	3	5				
	−320	7	7				
	−200	13	15				
	−110	31	33				
	+77	198	353	225	375	375	150
Tensile modulus of elasticity (psi)	−423	620,000	730,000				
	−320	470,000	580,000				
	−200	300,000	480,000				
	−110	200,000	300,000				
	+77	80,000	70,000	75,000	110,000	110,000	208,000
Compressive strength (psi)	−423	31,900	35,900				
	−320	21,100	30,000				
	−200	16,000	23,400				
	−110	7,400	13,300				
	+77	3,700	1,500				

197

TABLE 2 (*Continued*)

Property	Temp. (°F)	Teflon TFE	Teflon FEP	Halon G-10 and G-50	Halon G-80	Halon G-85	Kel-F
Compressive modulus of elasticity (psi)	−423	900,000	1,020,000				
	−320	800,000	920,000				
	−200	590,000	740,000				
	−110	280,000	390,000				
	+77	100,000	90,000				184,000
Compressive strength at 1% deformation (psi)	+77	600		600	800	800	
Flexural strength (psi)	−423	28,300	36,300				
	−320	25,800	26,700				
	−200	15,200	20,100				
	−110	6,900	9,600				
	+77	3,700	2,900				8,200
	158						1,500
Flexural modulus of elasticity (psi)	−423	740,000	770,000				
	−320	680,000	680,000				
	−200	460,000	570,000				
	−110	230,000	230,000				
	+77	170,000	200,000				182,000
Deformation under load (%)							
24 hr at 1000 psi	70	2.4					
24 hr at 1200 psi	122	6					
24 hr at 2000 psi	122	25		10	10	10	

Property	Temp (°F)						
Notched Izod impact strength, ft-lb/in. of notch	−423	1.40	1.83				
	−320	1.30	1.73				
	−200	1.40					
	−110	1.50	9.0				
	−70			2.0	2.0	2.0	
	+77	1.90	19.5	3.0	3.0	3.0	3.62
Specific gravity	+77	2.16	2.15	2.15	2.15	2.15	2.1
Hardness Rockwell	+77	J85					R113
Durometer		D58		D55	D58	D58	D80
Coefficient of friction against hardened steel	+77	0.04	0.04	0.04	0.04		
Tabor abrasion resistance, mg/1000 cycles (1000-gm load, CS-17F wheel)	+77	8.9					10
Melting point (°F)	620						
Coefficient of thermal expansion (in./in. °F)	73–140	5.5×10^{-5}		5.7×10^{-5}	5.5×10^{-5}		
Thermal conductivity (btu/hr ft² °F in.)	+77	1.7	1.4	1.9	1.9	1.9	1.74
Specific heat (btu/lb-°F)	+77	0.25	0.28	0.25	0.25	0.25	0.22
Heat distortion temp. (°F) at 66 psi		252	158	250	250	250	
at 264 psi		132	124				

a Values for Teflon TFE are Du Pont data for unfilled resin with 41–71% crystallinity. Values for Teflon FEP are Du Pont data for unfilled resin with 44–51% crystallinity. Values for Halon TFE G-10, G-50, G-80, and G-85 are Allied Chemical data for unfilled resin with average characteristics. Values for Kel-F are 3M data for unfilled resin with average characteristics.

mechanical properties at temperatures from $-450°$ to $500°$ F for continuous use (to $600°$ F for intermittent use). Compared to nylon, Teflon is somewhat soft and has a lower tensile strength. Because Teflon is a soft although tough material, hard foreign particles that may be introduced into gears and bearings will embed into it, thereby reducing the scoring of the mating part. Teflon is subject to cold flow, so that it continues to deform with time even after the initial strain that occurs on loading. Teflon is inert to most chemicals and solvents, but it can be attacked by molten alkali metals and by fluorine at elevated temperatures and pressures. Water has no effect on Teflon.

Teflon's unique properties are due to its molecular structure, which is characterized by a tightly bonded, impenetrable shield of fluorine atoms that surround and guard the long, interior chain of carbon atoms. This makes Teflon inert to most corrosive chemicals, makes it an excellent electrical conductor, and makes it so slippery that nothing sticks to it.

Friction and Wear Characteristics

The coefficient of friction for Teflon TFE is lower than that of graphite, MoS_2, or any other known solid. A value of 0.04 is usually quoted for its coefficient against steel, and a value as low as 0.016 has been reported for very high loads [1a].

The coefficient of friction varies with the test conditions, and Table 3 presents typical values. Figures 1 and 2 summarize the effects of load and sliding speed. High normal loads and slow sliding speeds generally provide the lowest friction.

In actual practice, thin films of TFE are transferred to surfaces sliding against it until the other surfaces are covered with it, so that the true condition is that of TFE sliding against TFE. At slow speeds (or high temperatures), the low friction of Teflon is associated with the formation of a thin, highly oriented transfer film of Teflon between 100 and 400 Å thick. The high friction at high speeds (or low temperatures) is associated with the transfer of relatively large fragments of Teflon [1]. Teflon undergoes a phase transition at room temperature; below room temperature its friction can be about one-half of the value above room temperature [2].

The coefficient also depends upon the condition of the wear track. Table 4 presents data showing the effects of speed and wear on the kinetic coefficient. When clean, newly prepared surfaces were used at low sliding

TABLE 3.   Coefficients of Friction Reported for Teflon TFE

Test conditions	Coefficient of friction
Teflon TFE on steel in Bowden–Leben machine; speed, 0.02-2 fpm; load, 2–9 lb; temp., 68°–392°C	0.04[a,b]
Load, 22 lb; speed, less than 2 fpm	0.10[c]
Steel slider on heat-polished Teflon TFE in Bowden–Leben machine	0.15[b]
Teflon TFE in journal bearing application	0.20–0.27[d]
Micropolished steel ring on constrained ring of Teflon TFE at very high loads (up to 3500 psi)	0.016–0.029[e]
Teflon TFE against ground cast iron, scraped cast iron, and ground steel; load, 50 lb	0.070–0.087[f]
Crossed cylinders of Teflon TFE and polished steel; load, 1–5 lb; speed, 8–367 fpm	0.09–0.21[g]
Sintered Teflon TFE film on copper, tested in Bowden–Leben machine (sliding); temp., 20° C; load, 4 kg; speed, 0.1 cm/sec	0.04–0.14[h]
Teflon TFE films against Teflon TFE film; load, 1–100 gm; speed, 0.01 cm/sec	0.15[i]
0.25-in. diam hemispherical rider of Teflon TFE riding against a 2-mil Teflon TFE film supported on a rotating steel plate; load, 100–1000 gm; speed, 0.001 cm/sec; temp., room	0.06–0.07[j]

[a] K. H. Shooter and P. H. Thomas, Frictional properties of some plastics. *Research* (*London*) **2**, 533–535 (1949).

[b] R. C. Bowers, W. C. Clinton, and W. A. Zisman, Frictional behavior of polyethylene, polytetrafluoroethylene and halogenated derivatives. *Lubric. Eng.* **9**, 204–208 (1958).

[c] K. H. Shooter, Frictional properties of plastics. *Proc. Roy. Soc. Ser. A* **212**, 488–491 (1952).

[d] H. S. White, Progress report on small oil-free bearings project for January 1 to March 31, 1954. NBS Rep. 3243. Nat., Bur. Std., Washington, D. C., April 1954.

[e] J. B. Thompson, G. C. Turrell, and B. W. Sandt, The sliding friction of Teflon. *J. Appl. Phys.* **26**, 1088–1092 (1955).

[f] L. H. Gillespie, How to design with Teflon pistons rings. *Appl. Hydraul. Pneumat.*

[g] W. C. Milz and L. B. Sargent, Jr., Frictional characteristics of plastics. *Lubric. Eng.* **11**, 313–317 (1955).

[h] E. Kay and E. D. Tingle, The use of polytetrafluoroethylene as a lubricant. *Brit. J. Appl. Phys.* **9**, 17–25 (1958).

[i] A. J. G. Allan, Wettability and friction of polytetrafluoroethylene film: Effect of prebonding treatments. *J. Polym. Sci.* **24**, 461–466 (1959).

[j] T. Fort, Jr., Adsorption and boundary friction on polymer surfaces. *J. Phys. Chem.* **66**, 1136–1143 (1962).

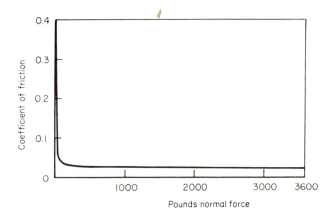

Figure 1. Effect of load on friction of Teflon TFE. [R. B. Fehr, Nonlubricated bearings and piston rings of polytetrafluoroethylene. *SPE (Soc. Plast. Eng.) J.* **16**, 943–948, Fig. 1 (1960).]

speed (1.1 cm/sec, or less), the coefficient was very low (0.05–0.08) and remained low for at least 4100 traversals over the same track. As the sliding speed was increased, the coefficient also increased. Furthermore, if the speed was reduced after first sliding at high speed and allowing time for the specimens to cool, the original low-speed value for the coefficient was no longer obtained. As the values in Table 4 indicate, the increase was substantial (on the order of two- or threefold) and irreversible. Refinishing the surfaces with a sharp tool was necessary to restore the low-speed coefficient to its original low value [2].

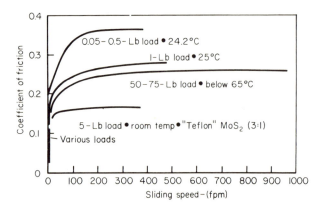

Figure 2. Effect of speed on friction of Teflon TFE. [R. B. Fehr, Nonlubricated bearings and piston rings of polytetrafluoroethylene. *SPE (Soc. Plast. Eng.) J.* **16**, 943–948, Fig. 2 (1960).

TABLE 4. Effect of Speed and Wear on the Friction of Teflon TFE[a,b]

Sliding speed (cm/sec)	Kinetic coefficient of friction	
	Fresh track	Track worn by prior sliding at 189 cm/sec
1.1	0.07	0.19
8.0	0.13	0.22
189	—	0.32

[a] D. G. Flom and N. T. Porile, Friction of teflon sliding on Teflon. *J. Appl. Phys.* **26**, 1088–1092 (1955).

[b] *Test conditions*: 0.150-in. diam rod of Teflon riding under a normal load of 108 gm against a rotating cylinder of Teflon in dry air at room temperature.

Replacing fluorine atoms in the fluorocarbon molecule by chlorine atoms increases friction and wear. For example, replacing only 10% of the fluorine atoms in Teflon TFE by chlorine atoms increases its kinetic coefficient of friction by sixfold. Similarly, the static coefficients of friction increased in the sequence 0.10, 0.30, 0.33, 0.45, and 0.69 for steel sliding against Teflon TFE, a 1 : 1 copolymer of tetrafluoroethylene and polyethylene, polyvinyl chloride, and polyvinylidene chloride, respectively [3]. These observations parallel the effects of halogen substitution on wettability, liquid adhesion, and surface free energy of polymeric solids.

The frictional characteristics of Teflon TFE are unique in that its coefficient of friction is only about one-third of the value of the ratio of its shear strength to its yield pressure, whereas the coefficients for other plastics and most metals are equal to or greater than this ratio.* This behavior is shown for Teflon TFE and three other plastics in Figure 3. As pointed out in Chapter 1, strong bonds normally form across the interface when clean materials are pressed together. If sliding then takes place, the bonds may hold fast and the structure of the softer material may break up. Shearing then takes place within the bulk of the material rather than at the surface, and the coefficient of friction should be approximated by the ratio of the shear strength to yield pressure. When Teflon TFE

* Equation (5) in Chapter 1 indicates that the coefficient of friction is given by the relation $\mu = S/P$, where S is the average shear strength and P is the yield pressure of the softer material.

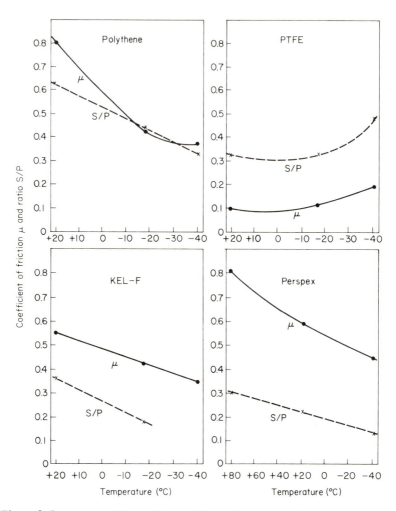

Figure 3. Comparison of the coefficient of friction (μ) and the ratio of the shear strength to yield pressure (S/P) of four plastic materials as a function of temperature. [R. F. King and D. Tabor, The effect of temperature on the mechanical properties and the friction of plastics. *Proc. Phys. Soc. London B* **65**, 728–736 Fig. 3. (1953).]

is pressed against another material, however, the molecular structure of TFE prevents bonds from forming across the interface, and shearing takes place along the surface. Another explanation is that the low friction is related to the intrinsically low adhesion between the TFE molecular chains or transfer films together with a relatively high bulk shear strength due to interlocking between rigid chains in the bulk of the plastic.

Vacuum Stability

The vapor pressure of Teflon is extremely low, and its stability in vacuum is excellent. Du Pont gives the following values for the vapor pressure of Teflon TFE: 2.5×10^{-25} atm at 80° F, 1.0×10^{-16} atm at 260° F, and 1.6×10^{-11} atm at 440° F. Weight loss is less than 0.003% even after 72 hr in a vacuum of 5×10^{-6} Torr at 212° F.

Radiation Stability

Even though its radiation stability is relatively poor among plastics, Teflon's radiation tolerance far exceeds the requirements of most applications, and it has been used successfully in nuclear power plants and in a variety of spacecraft. The threshold dose *in air* for detectable change in Teflon TFE is 2×10^4 rad.[*] Elongation is affected first; however, elongation remains above 100% for doses up to 2×10^5 rad, and it then drops rapidly to a small residual elongation at 10^6 rad. Teflon TFE retains 50% of its initial tensile strength after 10^6 rad, and 40% after 10^7 rad. Impact strength increases as much as 300–500% at doses up to $10^{6\cdot}$ rad in air before dropping at around 10^7 rad, while the flexural modulus increases slowly. Radiation does not affect the coefficient of friction.

Excluding oxygen improves the radiation tolerance of TFE and increases the above doses in air by a factor of 10 or more; for example, the threshold for detectable damage to TFE is raised to 2×10^6 rad in vacuum. Teflon FEP is more resistant to radiation than TFE; for example, Teflon FEP in air will tolerate a dose 10–100 times larger than TFE in air, and FEP in vacuum will tolerate a dose 10 times larger than TFE in vacuum.

Radiation breaks the bonds between adjacent carbon atoms in TFE and FEP, rather than the carbon-to-fluorine bonds, so that fragment radicals of C_3F_6 and higher are produced and the molecular weight is reduced. Free fluorine is *not* liberated, regardless of whether Teflon is irradiated in air or in vacuum.

---

[*] 1 rad = 1.2 roentgens = 100 ergs/gm. Data cited in this section is from *J. Teflon*, **10**, 3–5, (Jan.-Feb. 1969).

B. FILLED OR REINFORCED FLUOROCARBONS

Typical fillers include powders or chopped fibers of the materials listed in Table 5. The main purposes of these fillers or reinforcements are to reduce cold flow and increase the load-bearing capacity of the fluorocarbon resins. At the same time, wear rates are reduced by factors of several thousand, while the filled composites retain the same low friction as the unfilled resins. As a result, filled fluorocarbons are superior in friction and wear to any other plastic bearing material within their operating range.

TABLE 5. Typical Fillers for Fluorocarbons

Filler	Concentration range, percent by weight
Aluminum oxide	25–40
Aluminum metal powder	15–30
Asbestos	15–25
Bronze metal powder	25–70
Cadmium oxide	—
Carbon black	1–3
Copper metal powder	25–70
Coke fluor	15–25
Glass fibers	5–30
Graphite	5–20
Load monoxide	—
Mica	—
Molybdenum disulfide powder	5–30
Nickel metal powder	25–65
Zinc oxide	—
Zirconium oxide	—

In addition to the benefits already mentioned, fillers can also reduce mold shrinkage and cracking, lower the thermal expansion, and increase thermal conductivity.

Glass fiber is the most universally used TFE filler; it has the least effect on chemical and electrical properties, and it adds greatly to mechanical properties. Fibers are generally better than particles or powders in increasing compressive strength, rigidity, and load-bearing properties, but particle shape appears to have little effect on the wear of filled Teflon.

TABLE 6. Properties of Typical Filled Teflon TFE Materials

Property	Unfilled Teflon	Fluorosint[a]	Rulon A[b]	Rulon C[b]	Duroid 5813[c]	Fluorocomp 103[d]	Fluorocomp 174[d]
Fillers and percent by weight	0	Proprietary	Proprietary	Proprietary	Proprietary	15% Fiberglass	15% Fiberglass + 5% MoS_2
Specific gravity	2.18	2.3–2.5	2.2–2.25	3.1		2.20	2.27
Hardness		D70–75	D60–75 R27–29		Shore D73		
Tensile strength (psi)	3500–4500	750–2500	1400–1500	535–675	4000–8000	2800–3600	2200–3200
Tensile elongation (%)	300–400	10–200	50–200	2.0		320–330	280
Tensile modulus (psi)		190,000					
Flexural modulus (psi)		464,000					
Compressive modulus (psi)		253,000					
Dynamic coefficient of friction	0.12	0.16	0.12–0.24	0.16–0.18	0.18	0.14	0.14
PV limit	1200–2500		15,000–20,000	15,000–20,000		10,000–15,000	11,000–17,500
Wear factor in.³-min/lb-ft-hr	$20,000 \times 10^{-10}$					16×10^{-10}	9×10^{-10}
Izod impact (ft-lb/in.)	2.90		2.3		2.1	2.70	2.97

[a] Manufactured by The Polymer Corp., Reading, Pennsylvania.
[b] Manufactured by Dixon Corp. Bristol, Rhode Island.
[c] Manufactured by Rogers Corp., Rogers, Connecticut.
[d] Manufactured by Liquid Nitrogen Processing Corp., Malvern, Pennsylvania.

Metal powders are particularly effective in improving thermal conductivity, which helps dissipate frictional heating at high sliding velocities. Metal powders also reduce electrical resistance substantially, so that the metal-filled compositions are no longer good insulators. Graphite and molybdenum disulfide help to reduce the initial wear and starting friction, in addition to improving the mechanical properties. Asbestos has many useful properties but is variable and prone to outgas during processing; it is no longer recommended as a filler.

In addition to the fillers listed in Table 5, other types of reinforcement include metal screens, continuous filaments, perforated metals, and porous metals.

TABLE 7. Bearing Characteristics of Filled Teflon TFE and FEP[a]

Bearing material[b]	PV Limit at			K in-min per lb-ft-hr × 10⁻¹⁰
	$V=10$ fpm	$V=100$ fpm	$V=1000$ fpm	
Virgin "Teflon" TFE	1,200	1,800	2,500	10,000–20,000
30% Bronze-filled[c] TFE	12,000	28,000	45,000	3–6
35% Graphite-filled TFE	9,000	19,000	35,000	10–20
35% Glass-fiber-filled TFE	10,000	13,000	17,000	15–30
25% Glass-fiber TFE, metal-backed	17,000	17,000	17,000	15–30
TFE impregnated[d] bronze fabric	23,000	60,000	35,000	3–6
TFE impregnated graphite fabric	10,000	30,000	30,000	15–30
TFE impregnated glass fabric	20,000	30,000	10,000	20–40
TFE fabric	50,000	32,000	5,000	15–25
Virgin "Teflon" FEP	600	800	900	25,000–50,000
30% Bronze-filled FEP	9,000	12,000	10,000	X^e–20
20% Graphite-filled FEP	8,000	10,000	8,000	X–60
10% Glass-fiber-filled FEP	4,500	10,000	8,000	20–40
FEP impregnated graphite fabric	10,000	18,000	12,000	X–80

[a] *J. Teflon* **3**, No. 2 (1962).

[b] All percentages shown are by volume.

[c] A filled composition is any mixture of "Teflon" and discrete organic or inorganic particles of fibers.

[d] An impregnated composition consists of any porous structure having the interstices completely or partially filled with dispersions of "Teflon."

[e] X means that the lower limit has not been determined.

TABLE 8.   Comparative Friction and Wear Data on Reinforced Teflon TFE and Other Plastics[a]

Material[b]	Coefficient of friction		Wear (mils/million revolutions at 120 psi)
	New	Old	
Rulon A[c]	0.18	0.22	0.34
Rulon B	0.20	0.18	0.17
Rulon C	0.17	0.16	0.13
Teflon, unfilled	0.21	0.26	Too worn to measure
75% Teflon, 25% glass	0.26	0.23	0.50
75% Teflon, 25% mica	0.28	—	0.60
60% Teflon, 40% bronze	0.27	0.24	0.50
60% Teflon, 40% lead	0.23	0.25	0.31
60% Teflon, 40% graphite	0.19	0.19	0.77
Nylon, unfilled	0.37	0.54	4.20
Polyethylene, unfilled	0.73	—	Too worn to measure
Textolite 2001	0.24	0.43	0.90
Graphite	0.36	—	—

[a] Data from Dixon Corp., Bristol, Rhode Island.
[b] *Test conditions :* all tests were run dry with no lubrication of any type. Rulon values are averages of 5–20 pairs of bearings; other data may be for a single pair of bearings.
[c] Rulon is the trademark of the Dixon Corp. for their Teflon products.

Tables 6–10 and Figures 4 and 5 summarize the properties of a few commercially available filled Teflon materials in order to illustrate the benefits of the fillers. Many other specialty grades are available from plastic fabricators, and these should be consulted for their recommendations and for more complete information before making a final selection.

The compressive strength, modulus in tension and compression, and the creep strength are all raised by the additions, although there is generally a loss in tensile strength, elongation, and impact strength. Since filled Teflon is usually used in compression, the reduction in tensile strength is generally not significant. The loss in tensile elongation can be important where the material must be stretched for installation (e.g., continuous ring seals). Coefficients of thermal expansion are reduced substantially from that for unfilled Teflon, so that there is usually a better match with the coefficients of metal parts.

Of greatest importance for applications involving friction and wear are

TABLE 9. Static Coefficients of Friction for Teflon TFE and Other Materials[a]

Slider material	Test conditions[b]	Static coefficient of friction		
		Ground cast iron (20 μin. rms)	Scraped cast iron (20 contact points/sq in.)	Ground steel (20 μin. rms)
Unfilled Teflon TFE	D	0.079	0.070	0.087
	L	0.046	0.098	0.079
Glass-filled Teflon TFE	D	0.148	0.091	0.140
	L	0.090	0.094	0.095
Graphite-filled Teflon TFE	D	0.076	0.130	0.110
	L	0.075	0.084	0.087
Bearing bronze	D	0.260	0.250	c
	L	0.150	0.211	0.098
Cast iron	D	0.350	0.202	c
	L	0.142	0.30	0.123

[a] L. H. Gillespie, How to design with Teflon piston rings. *Appl. Hydraul. Pneumat.*
[b] D, dry; L, lubricated. *Test conditions*: 50 lb; period at rest, 1 min.
[c] Coefficient increased in successive tests.

the increase in the *PV* limit and the reduction in wear achieved with fillers. *PV* limits are increased approximately an order of magnitude, and wear factors are reduced approximately three orders of magnitude in comparison with unfilled Teflon. Average values for filled Teflon TFE compositions are 0.1–0.2 for the kinetic coefficient of friction, 10,000–20,000 psi-fpm for the *PV* limit, and 10×10^{-10} in.^{3}-min/lb-ft-hr for the wear constant. Under severe wear conditions (i.e., use above the normal *PV* limit), the wear constant for filled TFE increases to about 90×10^{-10} in.^{3}-min/lb-ft-hr, and wear involves the actual shearing away of the TFE. *PV* limits for filled Teflon vary somewhat with the operating load and speed in a manner similar to that for unfilled Teflon. Thus, high loads and low sliding speeds generally favor low friction and wear and permit a higher *PV* limit than low load/high speed conditions.

Wear resistance, which applies to rubbing against smooth surfaces, should not be confused with abrasion resistance, which applies to rubbing against sharp particles. Fillers that improve wear resistance can actually reduce abrasion resistance, since sharp particles can more easily penetrate

TABLE 10. Wear Rates for Sleeve Bearings of Molded Teflon TFE
with Various Fillers[a]

Material	Wear rate (mg/hr)	Test conditions
Unfilled Teflon	200	Bearings, 1-in. long × 0.75-in. ID; shaft,
Teflon and 25% graphite	0.7	410 stainless steel; load, 42 lb or 56 psi;
Teflon and 22% glass	0.2	speed, 60 fpm, *PV* product, 3360
Teflon and 25% copper	1.2	
Teflon and 25% graphite	0.7	Bearings, 1-in. long × 0.75 in. ID; shaft,
Teflon and 22% glass	0.4	410 stainless steel; speed, 215 fpm
Unfilled Teflon	0.74	Bearings, 0.50-in. long × 0.25-in. ID; shaft,
Teflon and 15–25% graphite	0.0015	303 stainless steel; clearance, 0.002 in.;
Teflon and 15–25% glass	0.0015	load, 250 lb or 2000 psi; speed, 150 rpm
Teflon and 4–8% copper	0.032	or 9.83 fpm; *PV* product, 19,660
Molybdenum disulfide	0.38	
Fabrics of oriented fibers of Teflon resins	6 × 10⁻⁶ (in./hr)	Bearings, 1-in. diam; speed, 25 fpm, load, 1150 psi
Reinforced Teflon resins	4 × 10⁻⁷ (in./hr)	Bearings, 1-in. diam; load, 2000 psi; speed, 100 rpm or 26.2 fpm; *PV* product, 52,400

[a] H. S. White, Small oil-free bearings, Research Paper 2709, *I. Res. Nat. Bur. Standards*, **57**, No. 4, 185–203, (1956). Engineering facts about Teflon, Bull. 6. E.I. Du Pont du Nemours and Co., Inc., Wilmington, Delaware, 1958.

and tear a filled plastic along the boundaries between the filler particles and the resin. This is important in selecting materials for applications such as lining chutes, where abrasive particles may be present; under such conditions, the best material may be an unfilled Teflon rather than a filled one.

As examples of the usefulness of filled Teflon for special applications, ball bearings with retainers of filled Teflon TFE have operated satisfactorily in liquid oxygen at −297° F [4], in liquid nitrogen at −320° F [5], and in dry hydrogen gas at −241° F [6]. During operation in liquid nitrogen at 2300 fpm and 1000-gm load, molded and extruded Teflon TFE provided coefficients of friction on the order of 0.10 and wear rates of 4 × 10⁻⁶ in.³/hr (ranges from 0.06 to 0.13 and from 2 to 40 × 10⁻⁶, respectively); for comparison, the corresponding values for halide- and phenolic-impregnated carbon seal materials were 0.18 for the coefficient of friction and 150–10,000 × 10⁻⁶ in.³/hr for the wear rate [7, 8].

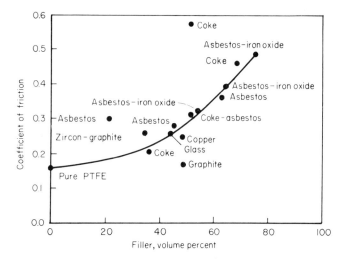

Figure 4. Effect of filler type and concentration on friction of filled Teflon TFE [S. B. Twiss, P. J. Willson, and F. J. Sydor, Friction of polytetrafluoroethylene dry bearings. *Lubric. Eng.* **14**, 255–261, 273 (1958).]

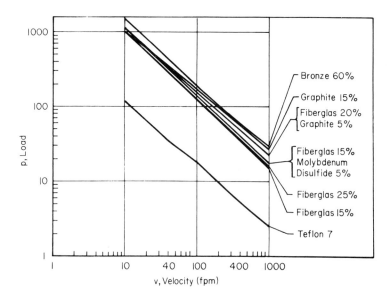

Figure 5. Limiting loads for filled-Teflon TFE compounds [Data from Liquid Nitrogen Processing Corp., Malvern, Pennsylvania.] (Limiting load was determined by a load-stepping test at constant velocity. The limiting load is the highest load at which the frictional torque and temperature stabilized.)

C. SHEET, TAPE, AND LAMINATES

Most fluorocarbons are available either as filled or unfilled sheet or tape in thicknesses down to 1 mil (0.001 in.). Using fluorocarbon in the form of thin sheets or tapes, either alone or laminated to metal foil or other backing, substantially reduces material costs. Other advantages may include easier part replacement, improved heat transfer, and better load-carrying capability.

Parts such as lip seals, pump cups, piston rings, and gaskets can be made by stamping from sheet or tape and forming to the desired shape. The "plastic memory" of the material, which tends to return the formed parts to a flat section, helps sealing and often makes it possible to eliminate springs and associated hardware.

Bearings can be easily made by snapping 15- to 30-mil thick tape into metal retainers. Such tape-lined bearings are available* with press-fit steel retaining shells ranging from 0.25 to 1.25 in. OD. Alternatively, the tape can be retained by shoulders on the shaft or by undercutting the housing. Tape-lined bearings are being successfully used on conveyors, farm machinery, typewriters, sewing machines, washing machines, phonograph turntables, pumps, electrical controls, textile machinery, and many other industrial and consumer applications. Tape-wrapped piston rings provide oilless operation and are low in cost, quiet in operation, and unaffected by most fluids.

Fluorocarbon sheet can be prepared for bonding by chemically etching one or both sides. These sheets can be bonded to a variety of materials, including steel, wood, glass, aluminium, titanium, copper, ceramics, and other plastics—in fact, any material for which commercial adhesives are made. These laminates can also be obtained with pressure-sensitive adhesive backing, so that they can be cut and attached easily to any desired surface. Bondable films and laminates can be used as coverings for rollers, slides, table tops, laboratory benches, splash guards, sanitary work surfaces, etc., that are used in handling foodstuffs, drugs, plastics, chemicals, and similar products. They are also useful as linings for chutes, guide bars, containers, trays, molds, ducts, hoppers, tanks, hoods, glue dispensers, drums, spray booths, etc.

---

* Rulon T-Liner bearings, tradename of Dixon Corp., Bristol, Rhode Island.

D. FLUOROCARBON COATINGS

Thin, tenacious fluorocarbon films can be applied to metal and other substrates by sintering or resin-bonding. Films deposited on hard substrates usually have lower coefficients of friction than solid fluorocarbons because of cold flow in the bulk solid. Metal substrates have good thermal conductivity and can dissipate heat better, so that frictional heating is less than when the fluorocarbons are used in bulk form. Thin fluorocarbon films permit higher speeds of operation without increase in friction, and they have good durability.

Sintered Films

Teflon TFE films produced from aqueous dispersions were developed at the U. S. Naval Research Laboratory as dry-film lubricants and protective coatings for weapons, ammunition cartridges, aircraft parts, and submarine parts [9, 10]. They have also been used for gears, hinges, shafts, bearings, valves, plugcocks, piston rings, and other industrial applications. The films are produced by the following techniques:

In practice, after the appropriate Teflon Suspensoid has been deposited on the solid surface, the films is allowed to dry in the air; evaporation of water must not be so rapid that Teflon particles are forced apart, creating larger pores in the coating. When the dried surface is heated to approximately 385° C (725° F); the Teflon particles quickly soften and sinter. After the surface has cooled, a thin, continuous film of Teflon is left adhering to the surface. However, many small pores in the film cannot be eliminated because of the high melt viscosity of Teflon.

Although pores do not limit lubrication applications, they offer points of attack for rusting or other types of corrosion. Therefore, when corrosion prevention is desired, one or more additional thin coatings are applied by repeating the operations. Two coats are usually sufficient for the applications described here. Each deposited Teflon layer should not exceed 0.0003 inch in thickness; otherwise, many cracks in the film may develop like the cracking of dried mud. When the film is to be used as a lubricant, total film thickness should not exceed 0.0006 to 0.0007 inch.

Teflon coating adheres best to steel, brass, and aluminium when the metal surface is cleaned and degreased without removing the surface oxide normally present. If excessively thick oxides have been removed—by acid pickling, for example—it is essential to heat the metal in air until a thin oxide layer has formed.

Adhesion is also increased by increasing the real surface area; thus a sandblasted or mat finish is better than a mirror finish.

The coefficient of friction of Teflon-coated surfaces can be decreased by roughening the surface of the metal substrate. However, durability under conditions of sliding friction is decreased when the metal roughness exceeds 32 microinches (rms). Roughness is produced most conveniently by sandblasting with No. 80 silica sand delivered by air to the nozzle at pressures of 70 to 90 psi. This soft mat finish dimensionally raises the surface 0.0001 inch by the peening action of the silica; in fact, this dimensional change was used as the limiting value for terminating the sandblasting operation. Finishes up to 62 microinches were leveled by by sandblasting to 32 microinches. This is an economic advantage in mass production. After being sandblasted, the metal surfaces are heated in air for oxidation prior to applying Teflon [9].

The use of a phosphate treatment on steel substrates is also reported to improve the wear life of sintered Teflon TFE films [11]. Porous, hard anodized coatings on aluminium have been impregnated with Teflon TFE to combine the lubricity of the fluorocarbon with the hardness and abrasion resistance of the anodized coating.

Teflon S finishes are a proprietary series of water-based dispersions of TFE and FEP resins introduced by Du Pont about 1966. They are described as a "stratified" finish. During processing, the more durable, nonstick TFE and FEP resin forces its way to the surface, where it concentrates in the top layers to improve the hardness and antistick properties; the lower layers retain substances that strengthen adhesion to the substrate. These films are much harder and more durable than the original Teflon finishes used on cookware. Even if severely scratched, enough of the coating stays on the metal to reduce friction.

Table 11 is a guide for selecting the proper Du Pont system for various applications. Teflon S finishes may consist of a single layer of primer, a coat of primer followed by a coat of enamel or clear finish, or a three-coat system of primer, enamel, and clear finish. The primers contain modifiers to promote adhesion to the metal or ceramic substrate. While the primers are often used as one-coat finishes, they must be topcoated with enamels or clear finishes for use in contact with food. Primers cannot be applied in multiple coats because of poor intercoat adhesion; if coatings thicker than 0.6 mil are required, primers must be topcoated with enamels or clear finishes. Pigmented primers are usually preferred to unpigmented ones because the pigment gives a visual check on film coverage and thickness, and they are less subject to intercoat failures if overbaked. The enamels and clear finishes must be applied over a primer to obtain satis-

TABLE 11. Guide for

End use	Requirement	Typical use	Total film thickness (mils)	Primer	
				Code	Thickness (mils)
Antistick, industrial	Moderate sticking, low abrasion service	Textile slasher cans	1.0–2.5	850–204 851–204 850–201 850–202	0.3
	Maximum abrasion resistance	Heat sealing bars, rubber curing rolls	0.7	850–311	0.7
	Severe antistick	Urethane and epoxy resin curing molds	2.0–5.0	850–204 851–204 856–301	0.3
	Ice release	Carburetor deicing, ice-making machine	0.8–1.3	850–204 851–204 856–301	0.3
	Substrates requiring low temperature cure	Wood, rubber tinplate, zinc	0.7	850–311	0.7
food	Consumer cookware	Frying pans, bakeware	0.8–1.2	850–300 Series, two-package primers	0.3
	Industrial food processing, moderate sticking	Dough rollers	1.0–3.0	850–204 851–204 850–201 850–202	0.3
	Industrial food processing, severe sticking	Candy equipment	2.0–3.0	850–204 851–204 850–201 850–202	0.3
Dry lubrication	Low load, low speed noncritical	Plug valves	0.3–0.7	851–204	0.3–0.7

Selecting Teflon S Finishes[a]

Enamel		Clear Finish		Comments
Code	Thickness (mils)	Code	Thickness (mils)	
851–line 855–line	0.7–2.2	852–201 852–202	0.7–1.0 0.7–2.2	
Cannot be topcoated				Nonfood contact uses only
856–204	0.7–3.7	856–200	1.0 min	
856–204 855–line	0.5–1.0	856–200 or 852–202	0.5–1.0	The FEP enamels and clear finish provide the ultimate in ice-release properties. 856–301 should also be considered as a one-coat finish at 0.2–0.7 mil.
Cannot be topcoated				
855–line	0.5–0.9			One-coat system prohibited
851–line 855–line	0.7–2.7			One-coat system prohibited
851–line 855–line	0.7–1.7	852–201	1.0 min	One-coat system prohibited
				One-coat finish usually sufficient

TABLE 11

End use	Requirement	Typical use	Total film thickness (mils)	Primer Code	Thickness (mils)
	Low surface speed, moderate abrasion	Delivery equipment for glass bottle manufacture	1.5–2.5	850–204 851–204	0.3
	High surface speed, low loads	Bearings	0.5–0.7	850–204 851–204	0.2
Electrical and electronic	High dielectric strength, low electrical loss characteristics	Coatings for resistors	4.0–5.0	850–204 851–204 850–201 850–202 856–301	0.3
	Antistatic	Idler rolls, paper and textile industries	1.0–1.5	850–204 851–204	0.3
	Nontracking	Ceramic insulators	2.0–2.5	850–204 851–204 850–201 850–202 856–301	0.3
Corrosion protection		Vessel lining	5.0 or greater	850–204 851–204 850–201 850–202 856–301	0.3
Nonwetting		Condenser tubes	0.2–0.4	851–204 856–301	0.2–0.4

[a] Du Pont Data.

(*Continued*)

Enamel		Clear Finish		Comments
Code	Thickness (mils)	Code	Thickness (mils)	
851–224 851–225 851–205	1.2–2.2			
851–214	0.3–0.5	852–201	0.3–0.5	Film thickness control important. Keep at 0.7 mil or below
		856–200 or 852–201 (either of these clears may be used)	3.7–4.7	
851–205 851–225	0.7–1.2			
		856–200	1.7–2.2	
		856–200 852–201	4.7 or greater 5–10	The degree of corrosion protection is dependent on the porosity of the film. Because of the many factors involved, it is recommended that test panels coated with selected systems be subjected to end use conditions
				850–311 should be considered if abrasion resistance is also a problem

factory adhesion. "Mud-cracking"* limits the maximum thickness per coat to about 1.0 mil, but total thicknesses up to 10 mils can be applied under extreme conditions by multiple coating, provided that each coat is separately baked.

Teflon S finishes are applied by conventional paint-spray techniques. The parts should first be air dried after spraying to remove the volatile constituents of the film. The finishes can be used on almost any material that can resist the baking temperatures of 575°–800° F.

Teflon S coated panels can be obtained with the Teflon S coating on 5-mil aluminium sheet. The sheet can be easily formed by bending to fit inexpensive supports and fastened in place with adhesives or nails, screws, bolts, etc. Foil is available with pressure-sensitive adhesive backing that makes it as simple to apply as preglued wallpaper.

Sintered films of Teflon FEP and chlorotrifluoroethylene (CTFE) are also used. Their main advantage over Teflon TFE is that they can be sintered at 600°–700° F and at 400°–575° F, respectively, which are below the sintering temperature required for Teflon TFE. Moreover, FEP and CTFE melt-flow during sintering, so that they form films that are less porous and more protective than TFE films. Their coefficients of friction are not as low as with TFE films, and their upper service temperatures are not as high. Where flexibility is needed, one can use coatings of vinylidene fluoride or fluoroelastomers, such as the copolymer of chlorotrifluoroethylene with vinylidene fluoride or hexafluoropropylene with vinylidene fluoride [12].

Resin-Bonded Films

Resins pigmented with fine particles of Teflon TFE provide Teflon films that can be cured at lower temperatures than required for the sintered films described in the preceding section. Table 12 lists types and uses. Phenolic-bonded films are cured at 300° F; they can be used up to 350° F for continuous service and up to 400° F for limited periods. Acrylic resins also are cured at 300° F and are used on flexible substrates. Air-drying resins are available for substrates that are very heat-sensitive or where curing facilities are not available. They cannot be used at as high operating temperatures as the thermoplastic, oven-cured type and

---

* Mud-cracking" occurs when a wet film is too thick and the particles are pulled apart due to shrinkage on drying.

TABLE 12. Types and Uses of Resin-Bonded Teflon TFE Dry-Film Lubricants[a]

Type	Applications
Phenolic resin Solution-I	Low-baking PTFE dry-film lubricant designed for heat-sensitive substrates (baked at 300° F for 1 hr)
Solution-II	A nonpigmented low-baking PTFE dry-film lubricant developed specifically for food-handling and food-processing equipment (baked at 300° F for 1 hr)
Acrylic resin latex	Low-baking PTFE dry-film lubricant developed primarily for flexible substrates such as O-rings and weather-stripping (baked at 300° F for 30 min)
Epoxy resin solution	PTFE dry-film lubricant for applications requiring improved stability and chemical resistance (baked at 350° F for 1 hr)
Thermoplastic resin Solution-I	Air-hardening PTFE dry-film lubricant for heat-sensitive substrates (air dry 2 hr at room temperature)
Solution-II	A nonpigmented, air-hardening PTFE dry-film lubricant developed specifically for food-handling and food-processing equipment (air dry 2 hr at room temperature)

[a] A. J. Stock, PTFE dry-film lubricants reduce friction and wear. *Mater. Des. Eng.* 97–99 (February 1965).

have poorer corrosion resistance. Resin-bonding permits Teflon TFE films to be applied to plastics, rubber, wood, and metals that would be softened by the high sintering temperature required for aqueous dispersions of TFE.

The resin-bonded films are normally applied by spraying, either by conventional spray equipment or from aerosol cans. Recommended surface pretreatments for the various types of substrates are given in the accompanying tabulation:

Substrate	Pretreatment
Steel	Degrease, sandblast, phosphate coat
Stainless steel	Degrease, sandblast, "Lubrite" SS
Aluminum	Degrease, sandblast, and/or anodize
Copper and its alloys	Degrease, sandblast, and/or chromate
Rubber and plastics	Degrease with appropriate solvent

Coefficients of friction for the resin-bonded Teflon TFE films are between 0.05 and 0.07. The coatings are free from pinholes and provide much better corrosion protection than the sintered TFE films. Phenolic-resin bonded films of TFE provide twice the wear life of pure sintered TFE films.

Epoxy-bonded coatings of Teflon TFE and ceramic fillers have demonstrated good properties for use in liquid nitrogen [13]. A 5-mil coating of 10 parts Teflon TFE, 40 parts epoxy adhesive, and 50 parts ceramic filler* on steel had a coefficient of friction of 0.07 in liquid nitrogen and provided a longer wear life than 5-mil films of sintered Teflon TFE or resin-bonded films of either Teflon TFE or MoS_2.[†] Adhesion was excellent; in fact, the Teflon–epoxy-ceramic coatings survived both quenching in liquid nitrogen at $-320°$ F and repeated hammer blows while cold without spalling. The coating was useful to higher sliding velocities when used over copper (above 16,000 fpm) than stainless steel (9000-fpm limit), apparently because frictional heating was dissipated more readily the copper substrate. The Teflon–epoxy-ceramic composition can also be cast into solid bodies for seals and bearings.

E. WOVEN PRODUCTS

Both Teflon fibers and fiberglass coated with Teflon are woven into commercially available products that are used for rod-end bearings, self-aligning spherical bearings, journal bearings, packing, and gaskets. Table 13 compares the mechanical properties of oriented Teflon TFE with resin and nylon fibers.

Figure 6 compares the frictional characteristics of a conventionally lubricated automotive ball-and-socket suspension joint and a similar but nonlubricated joint made with Teflon TFE fiber. The standard joint required 9.2 ft-lb to break away, and after several rather severe fluctua-

---

* Composition was 10 parts Teflon TFE powder (<8-mesh particle size), 40 parts epoxy resin (diglycidyl ether of bisphenol-A), and 50 parts ceramic (lithium–aluminum silicate, <325-mesh particle size) by weight plus 4 parts amine catalyst. Coatings were cured in air for 2 hr at 200° F.

† *Test conditions*: coatings applied to AISI 304 stainless steel disk and tested under sliding friction conditions against a rider of AISI 304 stainless steel. Load, 1000 gm; sliding velocity, 2300 fpm. Specimens submerged in liquid nitrogen ($-320°$ F).

TABLE 13.   Properties of Teflon TFE and Nylon Fibers and Resins

Property	TFE fiber[a]	TFE resin[a]	Nylon fiber	Nylon resin
Filament diam (in.)	0.008	—	0.0062	—
Density (gm/cm³)	2.1	2.2	1.14	1.14
Tensile strength (psi)[b]	43,000	3000–5000	61,000	11,200
Elongation at break (%)[b]	18	200–500	26	60–300
Initial modulus (psi)[b]	471,000	60,000	264,000	100,000

[a] Du Pont data.
[b] At 70° F and 65% relative humidity.

tions, the torque to maintain motion leveled off at around 6.5 ft-lb. The joint made with Teflon TFE fabric had much easier and smoother operation, requiring only 2.5 ft-lb for breakaway and 1.2 ft-lb to keep in motion. Bearings of this type are made with Teflon TFE fibers and fibers of either cotton or fiberglass woven into a double-faced fabric, Teflon on one side, cotton or fiberglass on the other. The woven fabric is formed into a cup insert for the type of bearing just described, and the cotton or fiberglass provides a bonding surface for adhesively bonding the fabric into a metal housing with a phenolic adhesive. In this condition the Teflon

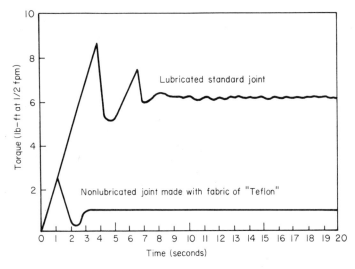

Figure 6. Frictional performance of automotive suspension joints (Du Pont data). *Test conditions*: 1000-lb compression load, 0.5 fpm sliding speed.

fibers are completely surrounded by supporting material and cannot flatten or extrude under heavy loads. This type of bearing is particularly suited for high-load applications requiring freedom from stick-slip action.

F. POWDERS

Special grinding techniques at cryogenic temperatures have been developed for producing Teflon TFE powders with an average particle size of 10 microns (4 to 25 microns range).* As a dry powder, Teflon TFE has many of the uses of graphite and MoS_2 powders, plus the advantage of having a white to light-gray color that is nonsoiling. This last characteristic has been responsible for its substitution for graphite powder on lace-making machines, where it has reduced scouring costs and yielded better and stronger fabrics. Aerosol dispersions of Teflon powder are used as mold release agents, and 0.25% of the powder can be blended with other plastic polymers to assist in their extrusion. The powders are also used in fluorocarbon-filled composites and greases, which are discussed in the following sections.

TABLE 14. Friction and Wear Characteristics of Some Molded Resin Products Incorporating Teflon as an Additive[a]

Composition (percent by volume)			Coefficient of friction		Wear rate (mils/hr)
Teflon[b]	Resin[c]	Filler	Initial	After 10 hr	
100	0	0	—	—	69
40	22	38[d]	0.25	0.35	3
30	26	44[d]	0.25	0.27	5
20	30	50[d]	0.25	0.38	4
37	31	32[e]	0.15	0.15	—

[a] S. B. Twiss, P. J. Willson, and E. J. Sydor, Friction of polytetrafluoroethylene dry bearings, *Lubric. Eng.* **14**, 255–261, 273 (1958).

[b] Coarse, general-purpose TFE powders.

[c] Phenolic type.

[d] Asbestos.

[e] Powdered lead.

* TL-126 powder from the Liquid Nitrogen Processing Corp., Malvern, Pennsylvania.

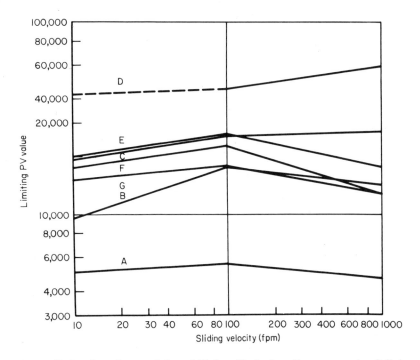

Figure 7. Bearing characteristics of Teflon-filled phenolic compounds. Cellulose-filled phenolic resin was used as base material; data were obtained in air by the step-loading technique. (Data from the Whitford Chemical Corp. West Chester, Pennsylvania.)

Code	Filler	% Filler by volume	Wear constant, K (in.^{3}-min/lb-ft-hr)		Break-in time (hr)	Coefficient of friction	
			Break-in	Equilibrium		Static	Dynamic
A	None	0	2500×10^{-10}	2000×10^{-10}	nil	1.13	0.98
B	TFE	5	60×10^{-10}	30×10^{-10}	48	0.73	0.82
C	TFE	10	51×10^{-10}	26×10^{-10}	48	0.68	0.70
D	TFE	15	35×10^{-10}	15×10^{-10}	60	0.32	0.45
E	TFE	20	35×10^{-10}	21×10^{-10}	48	0.36	0.49
F	MoS$_2$	10	51×10^{-10}	49×10^{-10}	nil	0.76	0.73
G	Graphite	10	44×10^{-10}	41×10^{-10}	nil	0.69	0.73

Fluorocarbon-Filled Composites

The lubricating qualities of the fluorocarbons can be used by adding them in powder or fiber form to cast or molded resin products. Both thermosetting (e.g., phenolic) and thermoplastic (e.g., acetal) resins are used in commercial products of this type. These products differ from filled or reinforced fluorocarbons, as discussed in the preceding section, in that bonding is done with a resin other than the fluorocarbon, and the fluorocarbon is used strictly as a lubricant. Reinforcing such as fiberglass, asbestos, cellulose, and powdered metals can also be added. The advantages of the resin-bonded materials are that they can be cast or molded at lower temperatures and pressures than necessary for fluorocarbons, and the wide choice of fillers and resins provides a range of physical properties.

Table 14 and Figure 7 give typical coefficients of friction, *PV* limits, and wear rates for phenolic resins filled with Teflon TFE particles and other fillers. Figure 8 gives similar information for several thermoplastic materials filled with Teflon TFE and other fillers. Further details are given in Chapter 10 and 11.

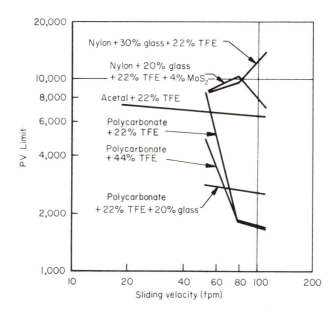

Figure 8. Bearing characteristics of Teflon-filled thermoplastic resins.

G. POROUS COMPACTS IMPREGNATED WITH FLUOROCARBONS

Materials are available that are essentially porous metal compacts impregnated with a fluorocarbon resin. These materials provide a film of the fluorocarbon at the surface. One of their obvious advantages is that the metal body provides a hard substrate with good thermal conductivity for dissipating frictional heat. Also, the pores provide means for storing the fluorocarbon, so that additional lubricant is available after the surface layers have been worn away.

Table 15 presents data demonstrating that impregnating sintered copper with Teflon gives very low friction, and this low friction is maintained up to high temperatures. At a temperature of 300° C (572 °F), where de-

TABLE 15.   Effect of Teflon Impregnation on the Friction of Copper[a]

Material	Coefficient of friction for unlubricated sliding against steel					
	Temperature					After cooling to 30° C (86° F)
	15° C (59° F)	100° C (212° F)	200° C (392° F)	250° C (482° F)	300° C (572° F)	
Sintered copper, impregnated with Teflon to a depth of about 1 mm	0.05	0.05	0.05	0.05	∼0.12	0.05
Sintered copper, untreated	0.24	0.24	∼0.7	∼0.8	∼1.2	∼1
Solid copper	1.3	∼1.3	∼1	∼1	∼1	∼1

[a] F. P. Bowden, Frictional properties of porous metal impregnated with plastic. *Research (London)* **3**, 147–148 (1950).

composition of the plastic started, the friction began to rise. On allowing to cool, however, the coefficient of friction again decreased to 0.05. The treated metal showed little sign of surface damage, whereas the untreated copper displayed marked adhesion, surface damage, and wear. Since the thin plastic film can be fed onto the surface by sliding, it was not worn away; in fact, repeated sliding led to a reduction in the friction. Sintered bronze impregnated with Teflon can provide much better wear characteristics than ordinary oil-impregnated bronze.

Sintered bronze, copper, and silver composites that incorporate Teflon TFE in their structure are available commercially from Booker–Cooper, Inc. (Sinitex) and Westinghouse.

A complex material containing Teflon, and suitable for sleeve and thrust bearings, is available under the name "DU." This material was developed by the Glacier Metal Co. of England and is marketed by Garlock Bearings, Inc. It consist of a tin-plated steel backing on which a thin lining of spherical bronze impregnated with a mixture of 80% Teflon and 20% lead is sintered and then overlaid with a thin surface layer of the same Teflon–lead mixture. The combination takes advantage of the low friction of Teflon and of the high thermal conductivity and low thermal expansion of the bronze and steel, as well as of the mechanical strength of the steel backing. The compressive strength of DU is high because of the support given by the steel backing. The addition of approximately 20% lead powder to the Teflon increases the wear resistance of DU manyfold and permits higher speeds and loads.

During initial operation, the thin surface layer (0.0008 in.) of lead-filed Teflon is lost by the shedding of flakes from the assembly, and the mating surface is coated with a thin film of Teflon. If the mating surface contacts a peak in the porous bronze, heat is developed and causes the

TABLE 16. Comparative Thrust-Washer Performance of Some Self-Lubricating Bearing Materials[a]

Material[b]	Testing time (hr)	Reason for stopping
DU (20% Pb, TFE in porous bronze on steel)	1000	Completed test
TFE in porous bronze on steel	213	0.005-in. wear
Graphite and lead bronze	158	0.010-in. wear
TFE plus 25% graphite	134	0.005-in. wear
Oil-impregnated porous bronze	105	0.010-in. wear
Phenolic resin plus MoS_2	73	0.005-in. wear
TFE plus 25% glass fiber	48	0.005-in. wear
MoS_2-treated steel	26	Seizure
Graphite (bearing grade)	24	0.005-in. wear
Porous bronze plus 25% MoS_2	17	0.005-in. wear
Resin-asbestos plus MoS_2	0.8	0.005-in. wear
Nylon	0.3	0.010-in. wear

[a] Data from the Glacier Metal Co., England.
[b] *Test conditions:* $PV = 50,000$.

Teflon–lead mixture to expand so that it is smeared over the contact area. After break-in, there is little further wear during the service life.

With loads from 10 to 1500 psi and speeds from 40 to 1000 fpm, DU has an average coefficient of friction of 0.13 (range from 0.10 to 0.16, independent of speed and load). At very slow speeds (1–20 fpm), the coefficient is about one-half of that at higher speeds. Table 16 compares the wear life of DU thrust washers with other self-lubricating solids.

H. GREASES

Fluorocarbon-based greases are a specialty item used for lubrication in highly reactive environments, such as contact with high-energy rocket propellants.

I. APPLICATIONS

Applications of fluorocarbons involving friction and wear include fairly conventional uses in sleeve bearings and other mechanical parts, as well as more specialized applications that also depend upon their chemical inertness and uniquely low coefficient of friction under high loads and low sliding speeds. Table 17 lists these general applications along with the important material properties for the applications.

Sleeve Bearings and Similar Bearing Surface for Mechanical Parts

The design of sleeve bearings and similar bearing surfaces for mechanical parts is based on PV values and wear rates, as discussed in Chapter 6. Such applications are being successfully made in very critical parts. For example, an analysis of maintenance records for various military and commercial airplanes indicates that Teflon bearings provide equal or better service lives than oil- or grease-lubricated bearings [14]. This study included bearings for various linkages, levers, actuators, pushrods, bellcranks, torque tubes, track rollers, and fairleads. The simplicity of design and the self-lubrication feature of Teflon bearings contributed to their lower requirements for maintenance.

TABLE 17. Applications of Teflon TFE

Application	Important properties of Teflon TFE	Alternate materials used	Useful forms of Teflon
Sleeve bearings and similar bearing surfaces for mechanical parts	Low friction and wear Low creep	Lubricated metals Ball and roller bearings Wood Other plastics	Filled Teflon Teflon-impregnated metals Teflon-filled plastics
Structural bearing pads	Low friction with no "stick-slip" at high loads and low sliding speeds Long life	Lubricated metals Roller bearings Rubber bearings	Films, sheets, and laminates TFE-impregnated metals
Static seals (gaskets)	Low creep Chemical inertness Temperature stability Nonstick	Numerous, including elastomers, compressed asbestos fibers, and metals	Filled and unfilled sheet
Dynamic seals (reciprocating and rotary)	Low friction and wear Low creep Chemical inertness Temperature stability	Carbon–graphite Lubricated metals Other plastics	Filled Teflon
Valve seats	Low creep Chemical inertness Temperature stability Nonstick	Elastomers Plastics Metals	Filled and unfilled moldings and machined parts Resin-bonded and self-bonded films

Structural Bearing Pads

Teflon TFE has been recognized for bearing pads by the International Conference of Building Officials since 1967, and it is being used increasingly for bearing pads for bridges, buildings, and other structures. Table 18 lists typical applications of Teflon TFE for bearing pads and

TABLE 18.   Teflon TFE Bearing Pads for Structural Use[a]

Applications

Bridges

Buildings with wide roof or floor spans, or whose foundations are liable to movement

Concrete and steel pipe lines, such as those used in hydroelectric installations, chemical process plants, etc.

Long horizontal structures and vessels, such as boilers, heat exchangers, and storage tanks

Large machinery, such as turbines and motors

Large doors, such as those on aircraft hangars

Between beams and joists, and hangars and purlins, where thermal expansion and contraction occur

As antivibration pads for machinery and structures

Roadway expansion joints

Chimney construction

Advantages of Teflon TFE for Structural Bearing Pads

Minimum friction (lower than lubricated metal and lower than other solid lubricants) and no stick–slip action

Indefinitely long life, since chemicals and weather have no effect on TFE

Easily installed either as a preassembled unit or "on site"

Far less bulky than alternatives, such as roller bearing assemblies

No maintenance required, unlike other sliding assemblies that require intermittent lubrication

Not subject to fatigue, as with elastomer bearings

Reduced construction costs by designing to allow for expansion rather than to withstand severe strains

Electrical and thermal insulation, which can be an added bonus to prevent galvanic corrosion and reduce heat loss

Vibrations are damped

Within reason, small foreign particles that may become embedded in the TFE do not cause the mating surfaces to bind

Reasonably constant operation over a temperature range from -420 to $480°$ F

[a] Filled TFE: Properties and application design data. Tech. Note F-13, Tables 20, 21, p. 36. Plastics Dept., ICI America Inc., Stamford, Conn.

the advantages of Teflon TFE for these applications. These applications are characterized by high loads and very slow speeds, which are the conditions of minimum friction for TFE. Various pad designs include (1) TFE bonded to aluminum or steel, either to a separate backing plate or directly to the main work, (2) freely floating or partially retained TFE or filled TFE disks, (3) TFE-impregnated porous sintered bronze with steel backing (DU material), and (4) TFE bonded to elastomers. Unit loads should be a minimum of 500 psi and can be as much as 4000 psi for filled TFE that is confined or bonded. A value of 0.1 for the coefficient of friction is conservative and can be used safely for designing, although the actual friction in practice is usually much less. Recommended pad thickness is from 0.06 in. for bonded pads to 0.20–0.25 in. for confined pads.

Static Seals (Gaskets)

This was one of the original applications of Teflon TFE where its chemical inertness, thermal stability, and nonstick characteristics were required. Plain gaskets are made of unfilled or filled Teflon TFE sheet as well as TFE-impregnated woven glasscloth. Unfilled TFE has excellent chemical resistance and is available in a wide range of sizes and thicknesses. Filled TFE has better resistance to creep but lower chemical resistance, depending upon the filler. Glass-filled grades are preferred in order to minimize the reduction in chemical resistance. TFE-impregnated woven glasscloth has still greater resistance to deformation under load, but it is not available in as wide a range of thicknesses. Plain gaskets should be designed for a maximum bolting stress of 1000 psi for unfilled TFE and 2000 psi for filled TFE. Sealing power can be increased either by (1) increasing the contact area by reducing the inside diameter and/or increasing the outside diameter, or (2) reducing the thickness to 0.06 in., or less, if possible. There are limits to both methods, since increasing the contact area increases the total bolt load required to exert a given stress, and the thickness must be enough to take up irregularities in the mating surfaces and allow for misalignment. Other suggested practices for plain gaskets of TFE are (1) recess the gasket into one or both flanges and (2) retighten to full bolting stress after a period of one day.

Envelope gaskets, consisting of an envelope of Teflon TFE tape with a core of asbestos fiber, combine the resilience of asbestos with the chemical resistance and nonstick properties of Teflon TFE. Spirally wound

TABLE 19. Dynamic Seals and the Use of Teflon in Them[a]

Type of seal	Description	Use of PTFE
Rotary Felt radial seals	Made from specified grades of felt, these are generally simple annular rings, impregnated with oil and used as an exclusion device and/or lubricator	PTFE is replacing felt as seals for "sealed for life" roller bearings and it could possibly be used as an impregnant for felt seals
Circumferential seals	These are high performance, low leakage contact-type seals for use in critical rotary applications. They are sophisticated versions of the reciprocating ring seals, involving several split rings, generally made from carbon, often with energizing springs	Carbon is the preferred material, operating up to 316° C (600° F). [538° C (1000° F) in a nonoxidizing atmosphere.] There appears to be no reason why filled PTFE should not be considered
Axial mechanical seals	These are characterized by having flat sealing faces usually located in a plane at right angles to the shaft. They generally replace conventional stuffing boxes at high pressures and are claimed to give reduced power loss (lower friction); to eliminate wear on the shaft; to have very low or controlled leakage; to be relatively insensitive to shaft deflection or endplay	Filled PTFE is frequently used as the face material, while unfilled PTFE is used as O-rings, bellows and for covering springs
Rotary and reciprocating Radial positive-contact seals[a]	These are lip seals and are the most common form of sealing device. They are often referred to simply as "oil seals" or "shaft seals" and are most frequently made from leather or elastomers. There are many different configurations, including cased (i.e., clamped between metal members) and bonded types, single and mul-	Filled PTFE is certainly used in this type of seal but currently only for specialist applications such as at high temperatures or where chemical resistance is required

TABLE 19 (*Continued*)

Type of seal	Description	Use of PTFE
	tiple elements and those used alone or with garter springs. They are most normally used at pressures up to 15 lb/in.^{2} but they can be designed to accommodate pressures up to 150 lb/in.^{2} at the lower speeds. Shaft speeds up to 2500 ft/min and 4000 ft/min can be handled without and with garter springs, respectively. They invariably have a thin film of lubricant between the shaft and never, therefore, run dry. Leakage is generally very low, varying from 0 to 0.002 gm/hr (one drop in 11 hr) in most instances	
Exclusion devices	These are used for separating two media, generally contamination from the working parts of a machine. While they do not have to seal against pressure, they may be similar in design to the positive contact seals, in which case they are known as "wipers." For more arduous duties, mainly in reciprocating applications, metal rings or lips, termed "scrapers," are used. Wipers are generally of leather or elastomers, and have relatively short lips; the most commonly used metals are copper alloyed with silicon or beryllium, brass, and aluminium, or manganese bronze, since low friction and non-abrasive properties are important. In this category are axial seals which are similar to me-	PTFE is not generally considered for these applications on the grounds of cost. However, PTFE is technically a very suitable material and should the cost situation change either by changes in raw material costs or design, then considerable quantities could be used

TABLE 19 (*Continued*)

Type of seal	Description	Use of PTFE
	chanical seals but do not have to cope with pressure, and "boots" or "garters," which are flexible covers rigidly attached two parts in relative reciprocating or oscillating motion (e.g., vehicle steering joints)	
Reciprocating Ring seals	These may be of the split or "solid-ring" type and are used extensively in compressors, pumps, internal combustion engines, hydraulic and pneumatic actuators. They are more rugged than lip seals and are used over a wide range of pressures and temperatures	Filled PTFE is already used extensively in hydraulic mechanisms and oil-free compressors. Split rings are used both with and without metallic expanders. Solid rings are used either alone or with elastomeric energizers. This latter type is often referred to as a "slipper seal"
Molded packings	This description covers a whole variety of packings in which the seals are primarily energized by the pressure being sealed. Conventional materials are leather and rubber both with and without fabric reinforcement. They take varied forms such as flange (or hat) type, cup, U-ring, V-ring, and O-ring as well as other cross-sectional shapes. The U-ring and V-ring are said to be balanced, since the seal is on both the OD and the ID and the pressure is balanced, whereas the flange and cup types are unbalanced	This is a growing field for PTFE and filled PTFE. While PTFE O-rings and molded U- and V-rings are well established, its use in flange and cup seals, particularly when formed from tape, has yet to be exploited. PTFE is extensively used as a spiral back-up (antiextrusion) ring for rubber O-rings
Diaphragm seals	Diaphragms are flexible dividing membranes spanning the gap between a moving and a sta-	Woven PTFE fabric can be used in place of cotton, etc., for temperatures up to 204° C

TABLE 19 (*Continued*)

Type of seal	Description	Use of PTFE
	tionary member. They may be seals or a transmitter of force. Design is generally arranged so that flexing, and not stretching, takes place. Materials used are fabrics (cotton, nylon, glass fibre) impregnated with elastomers	(400° F) and PTFE is used to coat woven glass fiber, to prevent abrasion between the filaments. The flex life of PTFE sheet is not generally considered adequate for it to be used
Clearance seals	These limit leakage by closely controlling the annular clearance between a rotating or reciprocating shaft and the relatively stationary housing. They are used where very high pressures and/or temperatures are involved and some leakage is tolerable. There are two major types, labyrinth and bushing (or ring) type. Because rubbing should not occur metals are invariably used	PTFE is not applicable
Simple compression packings	These are similar in some ways to the molded packings, but differ from them in that they are primarily energized by imposed compressive forces rather than the pressure being sealed. They are sold in coils or split rings rather than as continuous rings. They are generally round, square, or rectangular in section and are made from cotton or asbestos yarn which is twisted, braided, plaited, folded, or laminated, and impregnated with up to 30% of oil, graphite or PTFE as a lubricant	In addition to PTFE being extensively used for the impregnation of this type of packing, PTFE fiber is sometimes used as the main yarn. The stiffness of the packing can be varied by sintering the PTFE or leaving it unsintered

[a] Tech. Note F-13. ICI America Inc., Stamford, Conn.

sandwiches of TFE tape and stainless steel reduce stress relaxation and permit the use of high bolting pressures. Teflon TFE cord with an "O" or "D" cross-section provides a simple, easily applied and removed gasket for the faces of flanged joints.

Dynamic Seals

Table 19 describes various types of rotary and reciprocating seals and current uses of Teflon TFE in each type. In addition to the advantages of Teflon TFE previously cited (e.g., low friction, self-lubricating, chemical inertness, and thermal stability), other advantages include more uniform quality than with leather and other natural materials and good flexibility for conforming to sealing surfaces.

Ring seals are the type of dynamic seal in which Teflon TFE has made its major contribution to sealing. Their use for compressor rings has increased since the 1950's, and with the possibility for using them in internal combustion engines (both gasoline and diesel), these may become a major outlet for filled TFE. Teflon TFE piston rings permit compressors to operate dry, without lubricants that may be a contaminant or safety hazard. They are easier to fabricate than carbon rings, particularly in large sizes, and are satisfactory with dry gases (unlike carbon). Design procedures are given in the literature [15].

REFERENCES

1a. E. R. Braithwaite, Resin bonded PTFE as a bearing surface. *Engineering* (February 12, 1960).
1. K. R. Makinson and D. Tabor, The friction and transfer of polytetrafluoroethylene. *Proc. Roy. Soc. London Ser. A* **281**, 49–61 (1964).
2. D. G. Flom and N. T. Porile, Friction of Teflon sliding on Teflon. *J. Appl. Phys.* **26**, 1088–1092 (1955).
3. R. C. Bowers, W. C. Clinton, and W. A. Zisman, Effect of halogenation on frictional properties of plastics. *J. Appl. Phys.* **24**, 1066–1067 (1953).
4. R. E. Cunningham and W. J. Anderson, Evaluation of 40-millimeter-bore ball bearings operating in liquid nitrogen at DN values to 1.2 million. *NASA Tech. Note* NASA TN **D-2637** (1965).
5. W. A. Wilson, K. B. Martin, J. A. Brennan, and B. W. Birmingham, Evaluation of ball bearings separator materials operating submerged in liquid nitrogen. *Trans. ASLE* **4**, 50–58 (1961).
6. L. E. Scott, D. B. Chelton, and J. A. Brennan, Dry gas operation of ball bearings at cryogenic temperatures. *Advan. Cryog. Eng.* **7** (1962).

7. D. W. Wisander, W. F. Hady, and R. L. Johnson, Friction studies of various materials in liquid nitrogen. *NACA Tech. Note* NACA TN **4211** (1958).

8. D. W. Wisander, C. E. Maley, and R. L. Johnson, Wear and friction of filled polytetrafluoroethylene compositions in liquid nitrogen. *ASLE Conf., October* 1958; reprinted in *ASLE J.*

9. V. G. Fitzsimmons and W. A. Zisman, Thin films of polytetrafluoroethylene as lubricants and preservative coatings for metals. *Ind. Eng. Chem.* **50**, 781–784 (1958).

10. V. G. Fitzsimmons and W. A. Zisman, Thin films of polytetrafluoroethylene (Teflon) resin as lubricants and preservative coatings for metals, NRL Rep. 4753, Naval Res. Lab., Washington, D. C., June 1956.

11. E. Kay and E. D. Tingle, The use of polytetrafluoroethylene as a lubricant. *Brit. J. Appl. Phys.* **9**, 17–25 (1958).

12. P. West, Fluorocarbon coatings resist corrosion, heat and friction. *Mater. Des. Eng.* 112–115 (September 1965).

13. D. W. Wisander and R. L. Johnson, A solid film lubricant composition for use at high sliding velocities in liquid nitrogen. *Trans. ASLE* **3**, 225–231 (1960).

14. W. C. Barnes, Military and commercial airplane bearing field experience, Tech. Rep. AFFDL-TR-69-65. Air Force Flight Dynamics Lab., Wright-Patterson Air Force Base, Ohio, July 1969.

15. Anon., Filled TFE: properties and application design data, Tech. Note F-13, pp. 54–57. ICI America, Inc., Stamford, Connecticut.

Chapter 10

Miscellaneous Thermoplastics

While nylon and the fluorocarbon continue to be the major thermoplastic materials used in applications involving friction and wear, several other thermoplastics have been recently introduced that are finding increasing use. Table 1 lists typical properties of these materials.

A. POLYIMIDES

The aromatic polyimides are particularly suited for use at elevated temperatures. The one of most interest is produced chemically by a polycondensation reaction between pyromellitic dianhydride and an aromatic diamine. The imide linkage in polyimide resins is an unusually stable cyclic structure that confers excellent thermal stability. The polyimides are being used for gears, gear racks, ball bearing retainers, and other mechanical parts for service above 500° F.

Table 1 summarizes typical properties for two commercially available polyimides, Vespel* SP-1 and SP-2. SP-1 is the unmodified resin, whereas SP-2 contains 15% (by weight) of graphite powder in order to improve the friction and wear characteristics. SP-3 is a second modification that contains 15% MoS_2; its properties are similar to SP-2. Polyimides are also available with fiberglass reinforcements, metal fillers, and other specialty forms. Silver, copper, and other metal powders improve thermal conductivity, so that the frictional heat is carried away from the immediate contact surface. Such additions increase stiffness and reduce friction and wear substantially, but they also decrease tensile strength.

* Vespel is the trademark of the Du Pont Company. Polyimides are also produced by the Dixon Corp. under the tradename "Meldin."

TABLE 1. Properties of Miscellaneous Thermoplastics[a]

Property	Temp. (°F)	Polyimides		Acetals				Poly-carbonates Lexan	Ultrahigh molecular weight polyethylene, Hercules 1900
		Vespel SP-1	Vespel SP-2	Celcon M-90 Series	Celcon M-25 Series	Delrin 500 Series	Delrin 570X Series		
Ultimate tensile strength (psi)	−320	14,000	9,000						
	−40	10,500	7,000						
	+73			13,700	13,700	14,700	13,700	9,500	
	+160			8,800	8,800	10,000	8,500		
	+482	6,000	3,500	5,000	5,000	7,500	5,500		
	+600	5,000	2,500						
Tensile elongation (%)	−68					13	5		
	−30			25	35				
	+73	6.5	4.5	60	75	15	7	100	
	+140			230	280				
	+160					330	16		
	+482	6.5	4.5						
Compressive strength (psi)	+73	24,000	18,000					12,500	
	+302	16,000	15,000						
	+482	12,000	11,000						

Property	Temp (°F)								
Compressive stress (psi)									
at 1% deformation	+73			4,500	4,500	5,200	5,200		
at 10% deformation	+73			16,000	16,000	18,000	18,000		
Flexural strength (psi)	+73	13,000	14,000	13,000	13,000			13,500	
	+600	6,200	7,000						
Flexural modulus of elasticity (psi)	+73	610,000	460,000	375,000	375,000	410,000	880,000	340,000	
	+170			170,000	170,000	190,000	600,000		
	+250			80,000	80,000	90,000	440,000		
	+482	370,000	260,000						
	+600	330,000	230,000						
Notched Izod impact strength, ft-lb/in. of notch	−112								
	−40		0.8						
	+73	0.2	0.9	1.0	1.2	1.2	0.5	14	18
	+482	0.5	1.1	1.2	1.4	1.4	0.8		18
Specific gravity	+73	1.49	1.43	1.41	1.41	1.42	1.56	1.20	0.94
Hardness, Rockwell	+73	H78	H90	M80	M78	M94	M90	M70	R60
Poisson's ratio	+73		0.45					0.37	
Coefficient of thermal expansion (μin./in. °F)	−310–73		18–20						
	+73					45	20–45	39	
	73–392	21–30	26–30						
	392–752	24–46	33–39						

241

TABLE 1 (*Continued*)

Property	Temp. (°F)	Polyimides		Acetals				Poly-carbonates Lexan	Ultrahigh molecular weight polyethylene, Hercules 1900
		Vespel SP-1	Vespel SP-2	Celcon M-90 Series	Celcon M-25 Series	Delrin 500 Series	Delrin 570X Series		
Thermal conductivity (btu/hr-sq ft-°F-in.)	104	3.0	4.0						
Specific heat (btu/lb-°F)	+73	0.27						0.30	
Heat distortion temp. (°F)									
at 264 psi		680	470			255	315	270	
at 66 psi						338	345		183
Melting point (crystalline) (°F)								514	267
Water absorption (%)									
24 hr immersion	+73	0.32		0.22	0.22	0.25	0.25	0.15	
Equilibrium at 50% R. H.	+73	1.2		0.16	0.16	0.2	0.2		
Equilibrium, immersion	+73				0.80	0.90	1.00	0.35	
48 hr immersion	122	0.82							
Equilibrium, immersion	212							0.58	

	+73								
Tabor abrasion resistance (mg/1000 cycles) (1000-gm load, CS-17 wheel)	+73			14	14	20	33	9	
Kinetic coefficient of friction: dry, in air against									
itself	+73	0.20	0.18	0.35	0.35	0.35	0.2	0.24	0.35
steel	+73	0.20	0.18	0.15	0.15	0.15	0.08	0.73	
brass	+73			0.15	0.15	0.15	0.08		
aluminum	+73			0.15	0.15	0.15	0.08		
PV limit (psi-fpm)									
at 10 fpm	+73					4,800	7,500		
at 40 fpm	+73					3,600	6,500		
at 100 fpm	+73					3,000	5,500		3,000
at 400 fpm	+73					2,300	4,000		
at 800 fpm	+73								4,000
Wear constant (in.^{3}/min. ft-lb-hr)	+73						20×10^{-10}		

---

[a] Manufacturers' data.

Vespel SP-1 is one of the strongest plastics. It has a tensile strength of about 10,500 psi at room temperature, and it retains both a high strength and a high modulus even at 600° F. Its useful service range is from −400° F to +500° F for continuous service in air, to 600° F for continuous service in an inert atmosphere, and up to 900° F for short times. Its rate of thermal expansion is relatively low for plastics, being about twice that of aluminum and three to four times that of steels. It does not melt, but chars on heating in air. It has good dielectric properties, is stable in vacuum, is not degraded by nuclear radiation (up to doses of about 10^{11} rad), and resists most common chemicals and solvents. It is attacked by alkalis.

The coefficient of friction when run dry in air varies from 0.15 to 0.26. In nitrogen, the coefficients are significantly lower, being between 0.03 and 0.10. Wear rates in nitrogen are about three orders of magnitude lower than in air.

B. ACETALS

Commercially available acetal thermoplastic resins include Celcon[*] and Delrin.[†] Chemically, Celcon is a copolymer based on trioxane and Delrin is a polyoxymethylene. These plastics are notable for having a high elastic modulus, and they are therefore relatively stiff and rigid. They are also tough at both high and low temperatures. They are less expensive than other thermoplastic resins, such as the nylons and fluoro-carbons.

Table 1 gives typical properties for unfilled and Teflon TFE-filled acetals. The coefficient of friction of unmodified acetal resin against steel, brass, or aluminum is about 0.15 for dry operation in air. Against itself, the coefficient of acetal is about 0.35. The PV limit drops off as the sliding speed increases. Adding 22% Teflon TFE in the form of fine fibers, 0.008-in. diam by 0.02-in. long, cuts the coefficient of friction in half and almost doubles the PV limit. The wear constant for the Teflon TFE-filled composite is 20×10^{-10} in.³/min-ft-lb-hr.

Both acetal and the fluorocarbon filler are inert to many chemicals, especially organic solvents. However, strong acids and bases attack acetal.

---

[*] Celcon is the trademark of the Celanese Polymer Corp.
[†] Delrin is the trademark of the Du Pont Company.

The composite material can be used at 185° F in continuous service, and to higher temperatures for intermittent operation. Molded parts can be machined to final dimensions by conventional cutting tools.

C. POLYCARBONATES

Polycarbonates have exceptionally good impact strength and a high distortion temperature. The name "polycarbonate" is taken from the carbonate linkage which joins the organic units in the polymer. Table 1 summarizes properties of Lexan,* which is a commercially available polycarbonate resin.

The coefficient of friction increases from 0.24 at low speeds (~1 cm/sec) to about 2.0 at high speeds (~200 cm/sec) for Lexan sliding on Lexan in air without lubrication. For Lexan against steel, the friction coefficient varies between 0.35 and 0.82. Although it is not widely used as a self-lubricating material because of its high friction, Lexan has been successfully tested for balls for ball bearings on army tank gun turrets, where its toughness and ability to absorb impact are prime considerations.

D. ULTRAHIGH MOLECULAR WEIGHT POLYETHYLENE

Ultrahigh molecular weight polyethylene, with molecular weights between 2 and 5 million, combines excellent resistance to both abrasion and impact (cf. Figure 7, Chapter 7).

Table 1 lists typical mechanical properties for Hercules 1900,[†] an ultrahigh molecular weight polyethylene. Typical coefficients of friction for this material vary from 0.4 to 0.3 as the sliding velocity against steel increases from 100 to 800 fpm. Its *PV* value for designing journal bearings varies from 3000 to 4000 under the same conditions. These properties, plus its outstanding abrasion resistance, make it useful for bearings, gears, bushings, and many other equipment parts. When used for suction box covers in the pulp and paper industry, for example, polyethylene reportedly outwears more conventional materials such as end-of-grain maple, laminated phenolics, cast polyurethane, and even 304 stainless steel.

---

* Lexan is the trademark of the General Electric Company.
† Hercules 1900 is the trademark of Hercules, Inc.

Chapter 11

Phenolics

Phenolic laminates are the most widely used of the thermosetting laminates for mechanical applications such as gears and bearings. Typical laminating materials are paper, canvas, glass cloth, cellulose fibers and cloth, nylon cloth, and asbestos fiber, paper, and cloth. In addition, graphite or molybdenum disulfide powders can be dispersed in the base resin to improve the bearing properties further, although this causes a slight drop in mechanical properties. Laminates with other thermosetting resins, such as the epoxies, silicones, and melamines, are sometimes used to meet special conditions or requirements. For example, silicone resins laminated with glass cloth are useful at high temperatures (up to about 500° F); epoxy laminates have extremely low water absorption and high resistance to acids, alkalies, and solvents; melamine laminates have good resistance to electrical arcing.

Phenolic laminates have high load-carrying capabilities and provide gears with the highest horsepower ratings for an equivalent size of the thermosetting resins. They have PV ratings as high as 100,000. Thus, they are fitted for heavy-duty service, as in roll-neck bearings in steel mills and in propeller and rudder shaft bearings in ships. They are also used in various automotive applications, such as bearings for the steering suspension joints, brakes, and clutch pedals; in agricultural machinery for hay-baler slides and various bushings; in cranes for jib fulcrum bushings, main pinion bushings, king post bushings, and telescopic jib wear pads; and in railways for various bushings, liners, and rubbing strips. Heavy-duty applications are not the only ones for phenolic laminates, as they are also used in lightly loaded applications such as clock mechanisms and retainers for instrument ball bearings.

Phenolic laminates have high shock absorption without peening or taking a permanent set. They can be readily machined to close tolerances. They resist oils, greases, and mild chemicals. Exposed cotton fibers can absorb oil, so that the laminates can be made self-lubricating. They can be lubricated by water, which is a particular advantage for marine service.

Table 1 summarizes typical properties for cloth-base laminates meeting the standards of the National Electrical Manufacturers Association (NEMA). The canvas-base in NEMA Grade C is the coarsest fabric used in any of the cloth-base grades, and this grade provides maximum impact strength and toughness. Gears of NEMA Grade C are usually considered to have the power-transmitting capability of cast iron gears, and this grade is one of the most used for high horsepower gears. NEMA Grade CE has a cloth reinforcement that is somewhat finer than that of NEMA Grade C; it is therefore more machinable, so that finer and more accurate teeth can be produced. Grade L is a fine weave, cotton linen-base phenolic laminate with still better machinability, and NEMA Grade LE is an even finer grade. As machinability improves, toughness and impact strength generally are lowered.

Table 2 summarizes typical properties of specialty phenolic laminates designed especially for applications involving friction and wear. Data on coefficients of friction, limiting PV values, and wear rates are given in the table.

Mueller [1] has commented as follows on the design of gears made of laminated phenolics.

For maximum strength, gears should be designed in the 20-deg stub-tooth system. In calculating the horsepower of laminated gears and pinions, the standard Lewis formula, approved by the AGMA (American Gear Manufacturers Association), should be used:

$$HP = (0.000095 \times SWS \times FW \times Y \times PLV)/DP$$

where: SWS = safe working stress of the material in psi, which varies with speed. Static stress recommended by the AGMA for nonmetallic gears is 6000 psi. Values for SWS shown in Table 3 were calculated by the formula:

$$SWS = 6000 \times [150/(200 + PLV)] + 0.25$$

FW = face width in inches. Y = constant depending on number of teeth; see Table 4. PLV = pitch line velocity in fpm; this value is equal to $0.262 \times$ rpm $\times$ pitch diameter. DP = diametral pitch.

If a keyed drive system is used, the stress in the keyway of a laminated plastics gear should not exceed 3000 psi. The following two formulas can be used to calculate this stress:

$$S = (33,000 \times HP)/VA \qquad S = 63,000 \, HP/(rpm \times rA)$$

TABLE 1. Typical Properties of Cloth-Base Phenolic Laminates[a,b]

Mechanical properties	NEMA grade			
	C	CE	L	LE
Tensile strength (1000 psi)				
lengthwise	11	11	14	13.5
Crosswise	9	9	10	9.5
Flexural strength (1000 psi)				
Lengthwise	22	22	23	18
Crosswise	18	17	18	15
Compressive strength (flatwise) (1000 psi)	37	39	35	37
Modulus of elasticity in flexure (10^5 psi)				
Lengthwise	10	9	11	10
Crosswise	9	8	8	8
Edgewise impact strength (ft-lb/in.)				
Lengthwise	2.3	1.6	1.3	1.3
Crosswise	2.2	1.4	1.2	1.2
Rockwell hardness	M103	M105	M105	M105
Bond strength (lb/in.)	2000	2200	1700	1800

Physical properties	NEMA grade			
	C	CE	L	LE
Density gm/cm³	1.35	1.32	1.34	1.32
Thermal conductivity (btu/sq ft-hr-°F-ft)	0.17	0.17	0.17	0.17
Max recommended service temperature (°F)				
Short time	275	300	275	300
Continuous	225	250	225	250
Coeff. of thermal expansion (10^{-5}/°F)				
Lengthwise	0.58	0.58	0.43	0.58
Crosswise	0.69	0.68	0.58	0.80
Water absorption (24 hr) (%)				
$\frac{1}{16}$-in. thick	4.4	1.3	2.0	1.3
$\frac{1}{8}$-in. thick	2.5	0.9	1.4	0.8
$\frac{1}{2}$-in. thick	1.2	0.5	0.8	0.5

[a] G. J. Mueller, Laminated plastic gears. *Mater. Des. Eng.* **47**, 106–108 (September 1958).

[b] Properties given are average values and do not reflect NEMA limiting values.

TABLE 2. Properties of Wear-Resistant Phenolic Laminates[a]

ASTM test method	Property	Cellulose fabric[b]			Asbestos fiber[b]	Nylon[b]
		FM 3000	FM 3001	FM 3002	FM 3050	FM 1303
D792	Specific gravity	1.44–1.46	1.40–1.42	1.38–1.40	1.83–1.87	1.23–1.29
D955	Mold shrinkage (in./in.)	0.003–0.005	0.002–0.004	0.003–0.005	0.0005–0.001	0.014
D570	Water absorption (%)					
	24 hr at 74° F	0.5	0.6	0.6	0.5	0.3
	48 hr at 122° F	1.2	1.2	1.9	1.2	0.6
D638	Tensile strength (psi)	5,500	5,800	6,000	7,500	7,000
D695	Compressive strength (psi)	15,000	22,800	22,000	16,000	23,000
D790	Flexural strength (psi)	8,000	8,500	8,500	17,000	11,000
D256	Notch impact strength (ft-lb/in.)	0.50	0.60	0.70	4.5	0.55
D790	Flexural modulus (psi)	9.6×10^5	1.1×10^6	9.7×10^5	2.5×10^6	5×10^5
D785	Hardness, Rockwell M	114	113	115	112	111
D648	Heat distortion point (°F at 264 psi)	350	365	350	390	260
D696	Coef. of thermal expansion (in./in. °F) (78°–212° F)	26.0×10^{-6}	24.0×10^{-6}	26.0×10^{-6}	15.0×10^{-6}	53×10^{-6}
C177	Thermal conductivity (cal/sec-cm²-°C-cm)	8.0×10^{-4}	9.0×10^{-4}	7.0×10^{-4}	13.0×10^{-4}	—
[c]	Coefficient of friction					
	Static	0.10	0.18	0.12	0.23	0.48
	Dynamic	0.09	0.16	0.11	0.20	0.35
	PV rating	100,000	35,000	50,000	25,000	15,000
	Wear factor (in.³-min/ft-lb-hr)	35×10^{-10}	300×10^{-10}	120×10^{-10}	250×10^{-10}	300×10^{-10}
	Relative cost	2.3	1.0	1.4	3.5	1.0

[a] Data from Fiberite Corp., Winona, Minnesota.

[b] Filler.

[c] On thrust washer apparatus at 300 fpm against steel (18–22 Rockwell C hardness, 12–16 μin. finish), room temperature.

249

TABLE 3. Safe Working Stress for Cloth-Base Laminates[a]

Pitch line velocity (fpm)	SWS	Pitch line velocity (fpm)	SWS	Pitch line velocity (fpm)	SWS
100	4500	1200	2143	2700	1810
150	4071	1300	2100	2800	1800
200	3750	1400	2063	2900	1790
250	3500	1500	2029	3000	1781
300	3300	1600	2000	3100	1772
350	3136	1700	1974	3200	1765
400	3000	1800	1950	3300	1757
450	2885	1900	1929	3400	1750
500	2786	2000	1909	3500	1743
600	2625	2100	1891	3600	1737
700	2500	2200	1875	3700	1731
800	2400	2300	1860	3800	1725
900	2318	2400	1846	3900	1720
1000	2250	2500	1833	4000	1715
1100	2192	2600	1821		

[a] G. J. Mueller, Laminated plastic gears. *Mater. Des. Eng.* **47**, 106–108 (September 1958).

TABLE 4. Value of Y ($14\frac{1}{2}°$ or 20° Involute; Full Depth of Stub Tooth)[a]

No. of teeth	Y		No. of teeth	Y	
	$14\frac{1}{2}°$	20°		$14\frac{1}{2}°$	20°
12	0.067	0.078	27	0.100	0.111
13	0.070	0.083	30	0.102	0.114
14	0.072	0.088	34	0.104	0.118
15	0.075	0.092	38	0.107	0.122
16	0.077	0.094	43	0.110	0.126
17	0.080	0.096	50	0.112	0.130
18	0.083	0.098	60	0.114	0.134
19	0.087	0.100	75	0.116	0.138
20	0.090	0.102	100	0.118	0.142
21	0.092	0.104	150	0.120	0.146
23	0.094	0.106	300	0.122	0.150
25	0.097	0.108	Rack	0.124	0.154

[a] G. J. Mueller, Laminated plastic gears. *Mater. Des. Eng.* **47**, 106–108 (September 1958).

where: S = unit stress in psi. HP = horsepower transmitted. V = peripheral speed of shaft in fpm. A = square inch area of keyway in pinion (length × height). r = shaft radius in inches.

As an example, the horsepower rating of a canvas-base phenolic pinion having 21 teeth, a diametral pitch (DP) of 3, and a 4-inch face, and running at a speed of 850 rpm, would be determined as follows:

Pitch diameter = number of teeth/DP

$$= 21/3 = 7 \text{ in.}$$

$$PLV = 0.262 \times 850 \times 7 = 1559 \text{ fpm}$$

$$Y = 0.092 \text{ (for 21 teeth)}$$

$$SWS = 6000 \times 150/(200 + 1559) + 0.25 = 2012$$

$$HP = (0.000095 \times 2012 \times 4 \times 0.092 \times 1559)/3$$

$$= 36.55$$

REFERENCE

1. G. J. Mueller, Laminated plastic gears. *Mater. Des. Eng.* **47**, 106–108 (September 1958).

Index

A

Abrasion
distinguished from wear, 151
effects of impurities in molybdenum disulfide, 81
in wear of carbon-graphite, 62
by wear debris, 12
resistance, *see* Tabor abrasion resistance
Acetals, 244
properties, 240
PV limit, 188
Acrylic resins
for bonded fluorocarbon films, 220, 221
for bonded inorganic solid film lubricants, 27
Adhesion
factors, 7
of metals, 4, 6
theory of friction, 2
Adhesives, for bonded film lubricants, 26, 99, 122, 125, 220, 221
Alkyd resins
for bonded solid film lubricants, 27
temperature limit, 29
Alloying, effect on friction of metals, 8
Almen–Wieland tester, 40
Alpha LFW-1 tester, 38
Alpha LFW-3 tester, 40
Alpha LFW-4 press-fit tester, 40
Aluminum, pretreatment for bonding, 28
Area of contact
apparent, 2
equation for, 11
true, 2

B

Barium fluoride, 47, 67
Bearings
bronze, 107
carbon-graphite, 56, 61
fluorocarbon, 213, 229
high-temperature ceramic-bonded films of lead monoxide, 124
metal-graphite, 65
plastics, 146
Binders, *see also* Adhesives
for solid film lubricants, 26
Bonded films
binders, 26, 99, 122, 125, 220, 221
fluorides, 125
fluorocarbons, 220
general benefits of bonding, 24
graphite, 54
lead monoxide, 122
lead sulfide, 125
molybdenum disulfide, 97, 99
self-bonding, 25
techniques for applying, 30
Boron nitride, 128
coefficient of friction, 121, 128
Boundary lubrication, 13
Brushes
carbon brushes for electrical applications, 67
copper-graphite brushes, 67
silver-graphite brushes, 67
Buffing, molybdenum disulfide films, 103
Burnishing, for applying soft metal films, 131
Bushings, *see* Bearings

253

C

Cadmium plate, pretreatment for bonding, 28
Calcium fluoride, 125
  ceramic-bonded films, 125
  coefficient of friction, 125
Carbon, *see* Graphite
Carbon-graphite, 56
  bushings, 61, 65
  impregnated, 64
  mechanical applications, 56
  metal-impregnated, 64
  properties, 57, 60, 64
  PV value, 61, 65
  recommended grades, 58
  sintered metal-graphite composites, 66
Ceramics
  binders for fluoride films, 125
    for lead monoxide films, 122
    for lead sulfide films, 125
    for molybdenum disulfide films, 100, 101
Clearance
  carbon-graphite bushings, 62
  plastic journal bearings, 159
Coatings, fluorocarbons, 214
Coefficient of friction
  acetals, 153, 243
  boron nitride, 121
  calcium fluoride, 125
  carbon-graphite composites, 45
  definition, 1
  dichalcogenides, 116
  equation, 1, 11
  fluorocarbons, 153, 199, 201, 203, 204, 207, 209, 210, 222, 224, 225, 227
  graphite, 45
  hydrodynamic lubrication, 13
  inorganic solid lubricants, 20, 22, 121
  lead monoxide, 121, 122
  lead sulfide, 121, 125
  molybdenum diselenide, 116
  molybdenum disulfide, 78, 80, 83, 84, 97, 106, 115, 116,
  molybdenum ditelluride, 116
  niobium diselenide, 116
  niobium disulfide, 116

niobium ditelluride, 116
nylon, 153, 176, 177, 183, 193
phenolic laminates, 249
plastics, 153
polycarbonates, 243
polyethylene, 153, 243
polyimides, 243
silver, 121
soft metal films, 132
tantalum diselenide, 116
tantalum disulfide, 116
tantalum ditelluride, 116
tungsten diselenide, 116
tungsten disulfide, 116
tungsten ditelluride, 116
Coefficient of heat transfer, for plastic bearings, 155
Coefficient of wear
  acetals, 243
  definition, 149
  equation, 149
  filled fluorocarbons, 207, 208
  fluorocarbon-filled phenolics, 225
  phenolics, 225, 249
  plastics, 149
Cold welding, *see* Adhesion
Copper
  friction in vacuum, 5
  pretreatment for bonding, 28
Copper-graphite, for electrical brushes, 67
Crystal structure
  effects on adhesion and friction of metals, 8, 10
    of irradiation on graphite, 45
  graphite, 43
  inorganic solid lubricants, 18
  molybdenum diselenide, 114
  molybdenum disulfide, 78, 114
  molybdenum ditelluride, 114
  niobium diselenide, 114
  niobium disulfide, 114
  niobium ditelluride, 114
  tantalum diselenide, 114
  tantalum disulfide, 114
  tantalum ditelluride, 114
  tungsten diselenide, 114
  tungsten disulfide, 114
  tungsten ditelluride, 114

Curing bonded films
    of calcium fluoride, 126
    of lead monoxide, 122
    of molybdenum disulfide, 101

D

Design
    carbon-graphite parts, 61
    fluorocarbon structural bearing pads, 231
    gears of nylon, 174
        of phenolic laminates, 247
    metal-graphite parts, 65
    plastic bearings, 146
Dichalcogenides, 113
    coefficients of friction, 115
    crystal structure, 114
    electrical resistivity, 118
    oxidation, 115
    in powder metallurgy compacts, 119
    properties, 114
    radiation stability, 119
    vacuum stability, 118
    wear, 115
Dispersions
    graphite, 50
    molybdenum disulfide, 92

E

Epoxy resins
    as binders for fluorocarbon films, 221
        for inorganic solid film lubricants, 27
        for molybdenum disulfide films, 99, 101
    temperature limit, 29

F

Falex tester, 39
Fillers for fluorocarbons, 206
Films
    binders for, 26
    bonded films of molybdenum disulfide, 97
    chemically formed *in situ*, 105
    effect on metal-to-metal contact, 4
    fluorocarbons, 214
    integrity under load, 11
    oxide films on metals, 11

    removal in vacuum, 5
    soft metals, 130
Fluorocarbons, 195
    coatings, 214
    coefficient of friction, 153, 199, 201, 203, 204, 207, 209, 210, 222, 224, 225, 227
        of wear, 207, 225
    composites, 226
    filled, 206
    greases, 229
    hardness, 199, 207
    laminates, 213
    powder metallurgy composites, 227
    powders, 224
    properties, 196, 197, 207, 223
    PV limit, 188, 207, 208, 210
    radiation stability, 205
    reinforced, 206
    resin-bonded films, 220
    sheet, 213
    sintered films, 214
    tape, 213
    types, 196
    uses, 229
    vacuum stability, 205
    wear, 200, 209, 211, 224, 228
    woven, 222
Fluorides, *see* Calcium fluoride
Fluorinated ethylene propylene copolymer, *see* Fluorocarbons
Friction, *see also* Coefficient of friction
    adhesion theory of, 2
    characteristics, 1
    definition, 1
    laws of, 1
    mechanisms, 2
    metallurgical factors, 7
    stick-slip action, 3
Friction coefficient, *see* Coefficient of friction
Frictional heating, 3
    in plastics, 146

G

Gaskets, *see* Seals
Gears
    nylon, 175
    phenolic laminates, 247

Graphite, 42
  bonded films, 54
  brushes for electrical applications, 67
  carbon-graphite, 56
  coefficient of friction, 45
  condensable vapor effects, 47, 49
  crystal structure, 43
  dispersions, 50
  graphitization, 42
  impregnated carbon-graphite, 64
  lubricity mechanism, 46
  manufactured, 42
  metal-graphite composites, 65
  moisture effect, 23, 46
  natural, 42
  radiation effect, 45
  temperature effect, 48
  vacuum behavior, 46
Graphitization, 42
Grease
  fluorocarbon-based, 229
  with molybdenum disulfide, 108

H

Hardness
  effect on contact area, 10
    on friction and wear of molybdenum
      disulfide films, 98
  fluorocarbons, 199, 207
  nylon, 169, 181, 183, 184, 186, 191
  shafts for plastic journal bearings, 163
  soft metals, 130
  substrates for bonded films, 29
Heat dissipation from plastics, 141, 157
Hohman A-6 tester, 39
Humidity, *see* Moisture
Hydrodynamic lubrication, 12

L

Lead monoxide, 122
  ceramic-bonded films, 122
  coefficient of friction, 121, 122
Lead sulfide, 120
Load
  capacity of molybdenum disulfide, 83
  of nylon 187, 192

effect on bonded molybdenum disulfide
  films, 105
  on fluorocarbons, 202
Lubrication
  boundary, 13
  definition, 1
  hydrodynamics, 12
  solid, 13

M

Magnesium, pretreatment for bonding, 28
Melting points, of soft metals, 131
Metal(s)
  films as lubricants, 130
  friction of various combinations, 8
  hardness, 131
  melting points, 131
  oxidation, 130
  soft, 130
  vapor pressure, 134
Metal-graphite composites, 65
Metal matrix
  binder for inorganic solid film lubricants
    26
  for molybdenum disulfide films, 100
Metallurgical factors, 8
Metalworking, graphite dispersions for, 50
Moisture
  effect on graphite, 23, 46
    on molybdenum disulfide, 23, 88, 103
    on nylon, 174
    on various solids, 24
Molybdenite, 75
Molybdenum diselenide
  crystal structure, 114
  friction, 115
  properties, 114
Molybdenum disulfide, 75
  abrasive impurities, 81
  applications, 91
  binders for bonded films, 99
  bonded films, 97
  in carbon brushes, 67
  chemical analysis, 82
  coefficient of friction, 78, 80, 83, 84,
    97, 106, 115
  compared to other dichalcogenides, 114

crystal structure, 75, 114
dispersions, 92
effect of moisture, 88, 103
  of particle size, 90
  of sliding speed, 104
  of substrate hardness, 98
  of surface pretreatment, 99
  of surface roughness, 99
  of temperature, 84
  of vacuum, 89
film thickness, 102
in fluorocarbons, 206
load-carrying capability 83, 105
in nylon, 179
occurrence, 75
in oils and greases, 108
oxidation, 85, 118
particle size, 82, 90
phosphate pretreatment of surfaces, 95
in plastics, 107, 179, 206, 239
in polyimides, 239
in powder metallurgy compacts, 107
powders, 82, 90
properties, 76
purity, 81
radiation stability, 90
wear life, 97
Molybdenum ditelluride
  crystal structure, 114
  friction, 115
  properties, 114

N

Nickel, friction against tungsten in vacuum, 5
Niobium diselenide
  crystal structure, 114
  friction, 115
  properties, 114
Niobium disulfide
  crystal structure, 114
  friction, 115
  properties, 114
Niobium ditelluride
  crystal structure, 114
  friction, 115
  properties, 114

Nylon, 164
  coefficient of friction, 153, 176, 177, 183
  filled, 179
  gear design, 175
  hardness, 169, 181, 183, 184, 186, 191
  load-bearing capacity, 187
  properties, 165, 180, 183, 184, 186, 190
  PV limits, 178, 188
  reinforced, 179
  sintered, 189
  Tabor abrasion resistance, 170, 181, 185
  types, 164
  wear, 193, 209

O

Oils, with molybdenum disulfide, 108
Oxidation
  dichalcogenides, 115
  metals, 130
  molybdenum disulfide, 85, 118
  tungsten disulfide, 118

P

Particle size, molybdenum disulfide powders, 82, 90
Phenolic laminates, 246
Phenolic resins
  as binders for fluorocarbon films, 220, 221
  for inorganic solid film lubricants, 27
  for molybdenum disulfide films, 99, 101
  temperature limit, 29
Phosphate, surface pretreatment for film lubricants, 27–29, 95, 215, 221
Piston rings
  carbon-graphite, 56
  fluorocarbons, 237
Plastics, 139, *see also* specific plastics and classes
  advantages, 139
  bearing design, 146
  classes, 143
  disadvantages, 141
  testing, 146
  uses, 143

Plating, soft metal films, 131
Polyamides, *see* Nylon
Polycarbonates, 245
   properties, 240
   PV limit, 188
Polychlorotrifluoroethylene, *see* Fluorocarbons
Polyethylene, 245
   effect of molecular weight on wear, 152
   properties, 240
Polyimides, 239
   properties, 240
Polypropylene, PV limit, 188
Polytetrafluoroethylene, *see* Fluorocarbons
Polyvinylidene fluoride, *see* Fluorocarbons
Powder metallurgy composites
   dichalcogenides in, 119
   fluorides in, 128
   fluorocarbons in, 227
   molybdenum disulfide in, 107
Pretreatment of metal surfaces for solid
   film lubricants, 27, 28, 95, 99, 221
PV limit, 146
   acetals, 188, 243
   carbon-graphite, 61
   definition, 61, 146
   fluorocarbons, 188, 207, 208
   metal-impregnated graphite, 65
   nylon, 178, 188
   phenolic laminates, 249
   polycarbonates, 188
   polyethylene, 243
   polypropylene, 188
   reinforced thermoplastics, 188
   testing, 146

R

Radiation stability
   dichalcogenides, 119
   fluorocarbons, 205
   graphite, 45
   molybdenum disulfide, 90, 105
Reichert tester, 40
Run-in
   molybdenum disulfide films, 103
   molybdenum disulfide-filled greases for, 110

S

Sealing rings, *see* Seals
Seals
   carbon-graphite, 56
   fluorocarbon, 232
Self-bonding, 25
Shell four-ball tester, 30
   results with greases, 109
Silicone resins
   for bonded solid film lubricants, 27
   temperature limit, 29
Silver
   coefficient of friction, 121
   electrical brushes of silver-graphite, 73
   film lubricants, 130
   hardness, 131
   vapor pressure, 134
Silver-graphite, for electrical brushes, 73
Sintering, 9
Sodium silicate as binder for MoS_2 films, 100, 101
Soft metals, 130
   film lubricants, 130
   uses, 135
   vapor pressures, 134
Solid lubricants, definition, 15
Speed of sliding, *see also* PV limit
   effect on fluorocarbons, 203, 208
      on molybdenum disulfide films, 104
Steels, pretreatment for bonding, 28
Stick-slip, 3
Structural bearing pads, 231
Surface films, *see* Films
Surface pretreatment, *see* Pretreatment
Surface temperature, due to frictional heating, 3

T

Tabor abrasion resistance
   acetals, 243
   fluorocarbons, 199
   nylon, 170, 181, 185
   polycarbonates, 243
Tantalum diselenide
   crystal structure, 114
   friction, 115

oxidation, 117
properties, 114
Tantalum disulfide
 crystal structure, 114
 friction, 115
 oxidation, 117
 properties, 114
Tantalum ditelluride
 crystal structure, 114
 friction, 115
 properties, 114
Teflon, *see* Fluorocarbons
Temperature
 adhesion and sintering of metals, 9
 at interface of plastic bearings, 154
 of rubbing solids, 3
 due to frictional heating, 3
 effect on molybdenum disulfide, 84, 104
  on plastics, 156
  on various inorganic solid lubricants, 23
 high-temperature ceramic-bonded films
  of calcium fluoride, 125
  of lead monoxide, 122
  of lead sulfide, 125
  of molybdenum disulfide, 100
Testing
 Almen-Wieland tester, 40
 Alpha LFW-1 tester, 38
  LFW-3 tester, 40
  LFW-4 press-fit tester, 40
 Falex tester, 39
 Hohman A-6 tester, 39
 methods for solid film lubricants, 30
  for plastics, 146
 pressure-stepping test for plastics, 146
 Reichert tester, 40
 Shell four-ball tester, 30
 Timken tester, 38
 in vacuum, 4
Thermoplastic resins as binders for solid
 film lubricants, 26
Thermoplastics
 acetals, 244
 binders for solid film lubricants, 26
 fluorocarbons, 195
 polyamides, 164

polycarbonates, 245
polyethylene, 245
polyimides, 239
Nylon, 164
Teflon, 195
Thermosetting resins as binders for solid
 film lubricants, 26
Thickness
 bonded solid film lubricants, 29, 102, 122, 126
 molybdenum disulfide platelets, 80
 soft metal films, 132
 wall thickness of plastic bearings, 158
Timken tester, 38
Titanium, pretreatment for bonding, 28
Tungsten, friction against nickel in vacuum, 5
Tungsten diselenide
 crystal structure, 114
 friction, 115
 oxidation, 117
 properties, 114
Tungsten disulfide
 crystal structure, 114
 friction, 115
 oxidation, 115
 properties, 114
Tungsten ditelluride
 crystal structure, 114
 friction, 115
 properties, 114

V

Vacuum deposition of soft metal films, 131
Vapor pressure, metals, 134
Vacuum
 effect on dichalcogenides, 118
  on fluorocarbons, 205
  on graphite, 47
  on molybdenum disulfide, 89, 105
 experiments in, 4
Velocity, effects on friction and wear, 2, 29

W

Wear
 dichalcogenides, 115
 distinguished from abrasion, 151

fluorocarbons, 200, 209, 211, 224
inorganic solid lubricants, 121
plastics, 209
molded plastics with fluorocarbon fillers, 224
nylon, 193, 209
Wear coefficient, *see* Coefficient of wear

Wear life, molybdenum disulfide, 97, 100
Welding, frictional, 2, 8

Z

Zinc plate, pretreatment for bonding, 28
Zytel, *see* Nylon